ANIMAL EVOLUTION

TEXT-BOOKS OF ANIMAL BIOLOGY

*

Edited by JULIAN S. HUXLEY, F.R.S.

A General Zoology of the Invertebrates
by G. S. Carter

Vertebrate Zoology
by G. R. de Beer

Comparative Physiology
by L. T. Hogben

Animal Ecology
by Charles Elton

Life in Inland Waters
by Kathleen Carpenter

The Development of Sex in Vertebrates
by F. W. Brambell Rogers

*

Edited by H. MUNRO FOX, F.R.S.

Animal Evolution
by G. S. Carter

Zoogeography of the Land and Inland Waters
by L. F. de Beaufort

Parasitism and Symbiosis
by M. Caullery

ANIMAL EVOLUTION

A STUDY OF RECENT VIEWS OF ITS CAUSES

BY

G. S. CARTER

*Fellow of Corpus Christi College
and Lecturer in Zoology
in the University of Cambridge*

Nunquam aliud natura, aliud sapientia dicit.—Juvenal

SIDGWICK AND JACKSON LIMITED
LONDON

FIRST PUBLISHED 1951

PRINTED AND BOUND IN GREAT BRITAIN BY
WILLIAM CLOWES AND SONS, LIMITED, LONDON AND BECCLES

PREFACE

THIRTY or forty years ago interest in the study of evolution was decreasing, and it seemed likely that it would decrease further as time went on. The opinions of palæontologists and geneticists were opposed, and investigation of evolutionary problems on the lines followed since the middle of the nineteenth century seemed to have reached a dead end. The result of this unsatisfactory state of affairs was that many zoologists, having lost interest in the problems of evolution, hastily concluded that it was questionable whether the Darwinian theory was at all generally true. Since that time there has been a surprising revival of interest in the study of evolution, a revival made evident by the large number of books and papers published on evolutionary problems, especially in America. The deadlock was broken by a general broadening of outlook in many branches of zoology, not least in the study of evolution itself, and by consequent opening of new lines of investigation. It is now possible to frame a theory of evolution which, though its details may not be accepted by all, is at least not in obvious contradiction with the results of any branch of zoology. Accompanying this success there has been a general revival of belief in Darwin's theory, though the form of it now held is very different from the forms held before these advances.

In the present book I have tried to state this modern theory. To some extent it must still be personal; it cannot be said that full agreement has been reached. I have stated it in the form that seems to me to bring together most successfully all the facts that must be taken into account. I cannot hope that all zoologists will agree with me everywhere.

An understanding of evolution, so far as we can reach it, is fundamental to any real knowledge of zoology, and some account of its theory is a necessary part of every university course in zoology. In writing the book I have chiefly had in mind the student reading zoology at a university, but I hope

v

that the book may also be of use, as a summary of the subject, to zoologists whose main interests lie in other directions. With these readers in view, I have tried to avoid overloading the text with excessive weight of evidence, but I have in many places given references to sources in which more detailed discussion can be found.

I have advisedly restricted myself to *animal* evolution, in spite of the fact that the evolution of animals and plants is treated as a single subject in most of the recent books. My chief reason for doing so is that it seems to me that the mechanism of evolution and its results, for instance in the nature of the species, are so different in animals and plants that the subject is better treated separately in the two groups of organisms. Other branches of botany and zoology are not normally discussed together, and I cannot see why the theory of botanical and zoological evolution should be. Also, to have dealt with the evolution of plants, if I had been competent to discuss it, would have increased the length of the book considerably.

The background of fact on which a modern theory of animal evolution should be based is very wide; indeed, it should include the whole of animal biology. A summary of the more important ranges of fact was clearly needed before discussion of the theory was possible, and this summary forms the first part of the book. In these chapters I was forced to select some from the many possible subjects for discussion. In making the selection, I have chosen subjects the discussion of which seemed to me most likely to be useful as an introduction to the second half of the book, but I have not been able to cover by any means all the necessary background. In one respect the selection may need explanation. I have included a chapter on the recent results of genetics although there are several recent and excellent books on that subject. Recent books on genetics do not lay much emphasis on a part of the subject that was of special interest for my purpose, physiological genetics. Also, a knowledge of present-day genetics is quite essential before a modern theory of evolution can be discussed, and I have found that students of zoology often have little knowledge of its recent advances. This is especially true of physiological genetics. It seemed better to provide the necessary facts here, rather than to trust to the reader getting them from other books. I think it will not be disputed that the other chapters of the first part of the book are necessary.

In the views of evolutionary theory that I have expressed I have not, so far as I know, gone in general much further than many zoologists who are working on the problems of evolution are willing to go. In treating the deme as the unit of natural history and of evolutionary divergence, I have taken a standpoint not previously common, but this view seems to me a direct and necessary inference from the recent work of the naturalists. I have also, perhaps, laid more emphasis on preadaptation than many would be willing to lay, and at some other points the views I have expressed may not be general today. It is always difficult to define the exact contemporary position of opinion in a progressive subject, especially where, as in discussions of evolution, individual opinions differ widely. In any case, it is certain that many statements I have made, and many views I have expressed, will need to be modified as the result of future work.

In a book intended to summarise recent views, it is inevitable that quotation from other authors should be frequent and detailed. There have been numerous books in recent years covering parts of the ground I have tried to cover, such as Waddington's *Modern Genetics*, Goldschmidt's *Physiological Genetics* and *The Material basis of Evolution*, Dobzhansky's *Genetics and the Origin of Species*, Fisher's *Genetical Theory of Natural Selection*, Mayr's *Systematics and the Origin of Species*, de Beer's *Embryos and Ancestors*, Simpson's *Tempo and Mode in Evolution*, and others. To these my debt has been great, and will be obvious. I should like especially to acknowledge my debt to the last of these books. I am also greatly indebted to the only recent book known to me that covers the greater part of the field, Huxley's *Evolution, the Modern Synthesis*, and to the articles by various authors published in *The New Systematics* edited by Huxley. Most of these books are written for the zoologist rather than for the student, and therefore in greater detail than the book I had in mind should be. From them the reader can derive a modern theory of evolution, but the student seldom has the time necessary for doing so, and this is often true also of the zoologist whose chief interests are in other fields.

I should like to thank several friends who have read parts of the book and saved me many errors. Among these are Dr. J. E. Smith (ch. I, II), Mr. J. Smart (ch. III, IV), Dr. T. C. Carter (ch. II), Dr. D. S. Falconer and Dr. A. C. Crombie (ch. V).

November, 1949.

CONTENTS

LIST OF ILLUSTRATIONS

ACKNOWLEDGMENTS

I AM indebted to the following authors and publishers for permission to reproduce figures, and wish to express my thanks to them.

To the Chicago University Press for Figs. 1–3 from Dr. A. S. Romer's *Man and the Vertebrates*, 1941, Appendix 2 and p. 17; to the Wagner Free Institute of Science for Figs. 5–7 and 58 from Prof. C. L. Fenton's *Studies in the Evolution of the Genus Spirifer*, 1931, pp. 52, 53, 57, 61, 141; to the Council of the Geological Society of London for Fig. 11 from the article by J. H. Davies and A. E. Trueman in vol. *83* of the Quart. J. geol. Soc., pp. 212, 216; to the Editor of the Geological Magazine for Figs. 9 and 10 from the article by Prof. A. E. Trueman in vol. *59*, pp. 259, 263; to the United States Dept. of the Interior, Geological Survey for Figs. 12 and 13 from the U.S. Geological Survey Monograph No. 55 on *The Titanotheres of Ancient Wyoming, Dakota and Nebraska* by H. F. Osborn, vol. *2*, pp. 724, 769; to the Cambridge University Press and the Cambridge Philosophical Society for Fig. 14 from the article by W. K. Gregory in vol. *11*, 1936, p. 335; to the MacMillan Company for Figs. 15 and 57 from *A History of the Land Mammals of the Western Hemisphere* by W. B. Scott, copyright 1937 by the American Philosophical Society, Fig. 58a and c being after Cope; to the Cambridge University Press and the Editor of the Journ. of Genetics for data of Fig. 16 from an article by R. C. Robb in vol. *31*, 1935, pp. 42–3, and to the Editor of Nature for data of the same figure from an article by E. C. R. Reeve and P. D. F. Murray, vol. *150*, 1942, pp. 402–3; to the Editor of the American Naturalist for Fig. 17 from an article by Prof. A. E. Hersh in vol. *68*, 1934, p. 547, and for fig. 19 from an article by H. F. Osborn in vol. *68*, 1934, p. 224; to the Columbia University Press for Figs. 18, 20, 56, 60, 62, 63 from *Tempo and Mode in Evolution* by Dr. G. G. Simpson, 1944, pp. 10, 92, 107, 128, 132, 175; to Mr. N. V. Martinus Nijhoff for Fig. 22 from an article by T. H. Morgan, A. H. Sturtevant and C. B. Bridges in Bibliographia Genetica, vol. 2, 1925, p. 92; to the American Genetic Association for Fig. 23 from an article by T. S. Painter and H. J. Muller in the Journal of Heredity, vol. 20, 1929, p. 289, for Fig. 25 from an article by C. B. Bridges in vol. 29, 1938, p. 12, and for Fig. 29 from an article by C. W. Metz and M. S. Moses in vol. 14, 1923, p. 197; to the Editor of Nature for Fig. 26 from an article by H. J. Muller et al. in vol. 135, 1935, p. 254; to the Council of the Brooklyn Botanic Gardens for Fig. 27 from an article by O. L. Mohr in the Proc. 6th Intern. Congr. Gen. vol. 1, 1932, p. 196; to the Editor of Science for Fig. 28 from an article by C. B. Bridges in vol. 83, 1936, p. 210; to the Wistar Institute and the Editor of the Journ. exp. Zool. for Fig. 30 from the article by W. E. Castle in vol. 53, 1929, p. 428; to the University of California Press for Figs. 31 and 32 from an article by Prof. R. B. Goldschmidt in Univ. Calif. Publns. Zool., vol. 41, 1935, Fig. 2 and Pl. 16; to the Editor of Nature for Fig. 33 from the article by Prof. R. B. Goldschmidt in vol. 107, 1921, p. 782; to the Weidmannsche Verlagsbuchhandlung for Fig. 34 from the article by A. Kühne and K. Henke in the Abhandl. Ges. Wiss. Göttingen, Maths.-phys. kl., vol. 15, 1936, pp. 241–2; to Herr J. F. Bergmann of Munich for Fig. 35 from the article by E. L. Balkaschina in Arch. f. Entwickl.mech., vol. 115, 1928, pp. 450–1; to Messrs. Allen and Unwin for Fig. 37 from An Introduction to Modern Genetics by Prof. C. H. Waddington, 1939, p. 60; to the Columbia Univ. Press for Fig. 38 from Genetics and the Origin of Species by Prof. Th. Dobzhanski, 2nd edn., 1941, p. 146; to the Gebrüder Borntraeger for Fig. 39 from the article by Prof. R. B. Goldschmidt in vol. 25, 1920, pl. 6, of the Z. ind. Abst. Vererb.1.; to the Editor of the American Naturalist for Figs. 40, 43, 45 from the article by Dr. E. Mayr in vol. 74, 1940, pp. 262, 264, 273; to the Cambridge Univ. Press for Fig. 42 from Darwin's Finches by D. Lack, 1947, pp. 19, 102; to the Oxford Univ. Press for Fig. 41 from the article by H. J. Muller in The New Systematics edtd. J. S. Huxley, 1940, p. 235, for Fig. 49 from the article by Prof. S. Wright in the same volume, p. 167, and for Fig. 53 from the article by N. W. Timoféeff-Ressovsky in the same volume, p. 99; to the Columbia Univ. Press for Fig. 44 from Systematics and the Origin of Species by Dr. E. Mayr, 1944, p. 183; to Messrs.

Williams and Wilkins for Figs. 46 and 47 from *The Struggle for Existence*, 1934, by G. F. Gause, pp. 101, 106; to the Cambridge Univ. Press and the Company of Biologists, Ltd., for Fig. 48 from the article by G. F. Gause in vol. *12*, 1935, p. 47, and for Fig. 55 from the article by E. N. Willmer in vol. *11* of the Journ. exp. Biol., 1934, pp. 287, 289, 291; to the Editor of the Proc. Nat. Acad. Washington for Fig. 50 from the article by Prof. S. Wright in vol. *23*, 1937, p. 308; to the Editor of the American Naturalist for Figs. 51 and 52 from the article by Prof. S. Wright in vol. *74*, 1940, pp. 241, 246; to the Wistar Institute and the Editor of the Journ. Morph. for Fig. 54 from the article by G. K. Noble and M. E. Jaeckle in vol. *45*, 1928, p. 285; and to the Oxford Univ. Press for Fig. 61 from *Embryos and Ancestors* by Prof. G. R. de Beer, 1940, p. 49, after L. Bolk, Probleme der Menschwerdung.

Introduction

PART I

The Basis of Biological Fact

Chapter I

THE PALÆONTOLOGICAL DATA
pp. 9–48

Chapter II

THE GENETIC BACKGROUND
pp. 49–110

1

PART I

Chapter III

THE SPECIES IN ZOOLOGY
pp. 111–139

Chapter IV

INFRASPECIFIC CATEGORIES
pp. 140–163

Chapter V

COMPETITION, ISOLATION, NATURAL SELECTION
pp. 164–201

INTRODUCTION

THE aim of zoology is to study and interpret the life of animals, and an important place in the science must be given to study of the means by which the animal world is able not only to persist through long periods of time but also continually to give rise to new and more efficient forms of animal life, that is to say, to the study of animal evolution. Interpretation of the progress of evolution is essential to the science if it claims to cover at all broadly the facts of animal life.

Evolution is a many-sided subject, and it is not possible to discuss all aspects of it in a single book. It is therefore necessary to state clearly at the beginning the parts of the subject that it is intended to discuss, so that the range of the discussions may be defined and parts of the subject outside the range may be excluded.

Study of the problems of evolution falls at once into two immediately distinguishable parts. The first of these is collection and elaboration of the evidence on which belief in evolution as a fact of nature—belief that animals have in fact descended from forms unlike themselves—is founded; the second is development of a theory that will account for the progress of evolution. One may believe in evolution as a fact of nature without accepting any of the theories that have been proposed to account for it. Many zoologists believed that evolution has occurred before Darwin published *The Origin of Species* (1859) and therein founded the theory which was accepted by the majority and which, in a modified form, most hold today. Buffon, Erasmus Darwin and to some extent von Baer accepted "descent with modification" in the eighteenth and early nineteenth centuries,[261] but its acceptance was then by no means general. Among those who rejected it was Cuvier, perhaps the greatest name in the zoology of the early nineteenth century, and he was not alone. It was a part of Darwin's great contribution to the science that he convinced the large majority of

3

zoologists that evolution has taken place. This he did mainly by his success in the second part of his contribution, that of proposing a *theory* of evolutionary change, which, though it was not immediately accepted by all, was at least founded upon observation and arguable. When a theory had been proposed in which many could believe, the evidence that evolution has taken place was more readily accepted. By the end of the century, forty years after the publication of *The Origin of Species*, the fact of evolution was accepted by almost all zoologists. It remains so today.

It is not the object of this book to discuss the evidence that evolution has occurred. That has been done many times (e.g. [185, 200, 273]). Also, it may be doubted whether the evidence is of a kind to be satisfactorily summarised in a single book. The surest way to reach conviction of this truth is by a general study of biology. The great body of evidence that in any such study accumulates from all branches of the science is enough to convince almost everyone.

The object of the book is to discuss whether a theory can be put forward at the present time that will explain the means by which evolutionary change has been brought about, and especially to discuss this in the light of the more recent results of biology. Here there is much more room for disagreement, though in the last thirty years, as investigation has gone on in many directions, progress towards a generally accepted theory has been marked and rapid.

In discussing modern views of evolution only two theories, both proposed in the earlier part of the nineteenth century, need be considered. These are the theories of Lamarck and Darwin. That of Lamarck will be almost wholly disregarded in our discussions, and some reasons for not considering it more fully are perhaps needed at the outset. Lamarck's theory was set out in his *Philosophie Zoologique* (1809), fifty years before Darwin's. Since then it has been variously interpreted and modified, but in essence it remains the same. This theory and all those related to it assume that influences affecting the body in the course of its life-history—the use and disuse of parts, habits, and even, in some forms of the theory, injuries—produce effects that are inherited and will reappear in later generations. If it could be shown that inheritance of such "acquired characters" really occurs, these theories would provide an explanation of many types of evolutionary change more direct, and subject to fewer difficulties, than Darwin's theory can provide; adaptation would be a direct result of the experience of the animal. However, although many zoologists have tried to demonstrate Lamarckian inheritance, some in recent years, no instance of it has been experimentally proved to general satisfaction. Also, it is very difficult to conceive any means by which action on the body during its life-history could modify the animal's hereditary mechanism and be inherited. This could be so only if our present views of inheritance are entirely incorrect or incomplete—and most zoologists think this unlikely. These arguments do not prove the impossibility of Lamarckian inheritance. It would be rash to deny that it occurs because we cannot imagine its mechanism; nature is often able to surprise us. And the fact that we are not able to demonstrate it may be due to the short period of our experiments. Lamarckian inheritance has not been disproved, and some zoologists believe that a complete explanation of evolution is impossible without it; but until we have sound evidence of its reality it should not be used as the basis of our interpretation of evolution. We must found our theory on effects that can be shown to be real, and follow out their consequences as far as they will go towards a complete interpretation. Moreover, the Lamarckian theory, even if it be true in some sense, will certainly not account for the whole of evolution (p. 192). We must leave it to the future to decide whether it plays some part, or none.

The theory of evolution in which the great majority of contemporary zoologists believe is derived from that of Darwin. His theory was based on the following propositions:

1. He accepted from Malthus the fact that the reproductive powers of animals are much greater than is needed to maintain their numbers. Only if a very large proportion of the offspring are destroyed will the numbers remain constant.

2. As a result of this, there will be an active "struggle for existence" between the individuals of a species and, since many species often live in the same habitat and make the same demands on the resources of the habitat for food and

other needs, between the species. The struggle for existence will be inter- as well as intra-specific.

3. Animals vary, and, so he assumed, their variations are inherited.

4. In the struggle for existence favourable variations will be preserved and unfavourable exterminated. This he called "natural selection". By accumulation of favourable variations this selection will lead to a gradual change in the characters of the animal towards better adaptation, and thus to evolution.

Not all zoologists accepted Darwin's theory immediately. Those who rejected it did so on various grounds, of which perhaps the most widely held was that it is impossible to attribute the co-ordinated and directional changes of evolution to unco-ordinated variation (v. Baer, Owen, Kölliker). Those who held this view pointed out that Darwin had suggested no principle guiding the course of evolution; he had merely shown how the ill-adapted would be removed. They thought that more than this is needed to account for the astonishingly precise co-ordination of the parts of organisms, and for the directional character of much of evolutionary change, the fact that animals evolve not in random directions but often in the same direction for long periods. It may be remarked that the difficulty behind this objection is one of the greatest that evolutionary theory still has to face (ch. IX). But as time went on this opposition decreased. By the end of the century opposition of most kinds was much less, and indeed almost insignificant.

Darwin had collected a large body of evidence in favour of his theory, and to those of his contemporaries who accepted his views it seemed that the explanation of evolution given by him was, if not complete, at any rate as nearly complete as was possible at the time. There was little stimulus to further work on the theory; the more immediate task seemed to be to work out its implications in general zoology. One kind of zoology more than any other was followed. From 1860 to the end of the century zoological effort was concentrated on comparative morphology, comparative embryology, and palæontology; and on building from the results of these studies a reliable account of the phylogeny of the animal kingdom. Not only evolutionary theory suffered neglect; other branches of zoology, such as comparative physiology and ecology, were also neglected. Some by-ways of evolutionary theory, as they may perhaps be called —for instance, mimicry and sexual selection—were actively studied, and there was much elaboration of the evidence that Darwin had collected in support of his theory. Only one large theoretical advance was made. This was Weismann's establishment of the independence of the germ-plasm, which gives rise to the genital products, from the rest of the body surrounding it, the soma. From the time of his demonstration of this truth dated the clear distinction between inheritable variations and non-inheritable "fluctuations", the latter due to action on the body during its life-history, and the disbelief of most zoologists in any form of Lamarckian inheritance (in which Darwin had not entirely disbelieved).

It is strange that the publication of *The Origin of Species* should have resulted in concentration of zoological effort on morphology and related branches of zoology, for Darwin himself was a naturalist and general biologist, and by no means primarily a morphologist. Almost all his work shows this, but especially his later books on the biology of earthworms, orchids and other organisms; his only large piece of morphological work was his account of the Cirripedia, published (1851) before *The Origin of Species*. Nevertheless, it was fortunate that zoology went in that direction, for, as later history has shown, progress in evolutionary theory required a more accurate knowledge of the laws of inheritance than was then available. Little advance in the theory was probable before the rediscovery of Mendel's work in 1900, and the development of genetics that followed it.

During the first twenty years of this century the results of the geneticists seemed to many zoologists to have little bearing on the theory of evolution. Palæontological evidence showed that evolutionary change is gradual and often directional, leading towards the development of new adaptational structure, whereas the mutations with which the geneticists were then working were large changes of structure, random in direction, and very often degenerative. The two types of change seemed entirely distinct. It appeared obvious that evolution did not proceed by "saltations" such as genetic mutations seemed necessarily to produce, and that its chief feature is formation of new structure, not loss of that already present. It has been one of the most striking advances in the zoology of the last thirty years that recent modifications of genetic theory have brought the outlook of the geneticists so much closer to that of the palæontologists and morphologists that it is now possible to discuss a theory of evolution in accord with them all.

It is our object to discuss this theory. But, if we are to do so to any purpose, it must be realised that a theory of evolution cannot be based on genetics, morphology and palæontology alone. A satisfactory theory must be in agreement with the results of all the other branches of biology, and in the present century many of these other branches have given results of great importance to our enquiry. Systematics has given us a clearer view of the differences between animal groups; mathematical study of populations has shown us some of the conditions under which change can spread in a population, and one population replace another; and study of the living animal and its ecology, return to which has been so characteristic of recent zoology, has enabled us to understand in more detail the conditions under which animals live, and even sometimes to observe the initiation of evolutionary change in living animals. We shall have to discuss all these subjects, and others.

CHAPTER I

THE PALÆONTOLOGICAL DATA

In approaching the problems of evolution, the first facts to be considered are those of palæontology. Our experience is so short that we can observe only the smallest evolutionary changes in living animals; palæontology alone gives us direct evidence of the course of evolution on a large scale, and shows us what types of change have been effective in it. We need the palæontological evidence as a background to which to refer the less direct evidence of other branches of biology.

Palæontology can give us this direct evidence, but it must not be thought that it can do much more. A theory of evolution can never be deduced from palæontological fact alone. Fossils may show us the changes by which one animal has evolved from another, but they tell us very little of the means by which these changes were brought about. The palæontologist may be able to exclude some theories of evolution on the ground that they demand change not in accord with his facts; he claimed to be able to do so for Mendelian theories in their earliest forms at the start of this century. But to build a theory of evolution is much more the concern of the biologists who deal with the nature of the animal organism and with the changes that can take place in it—geneticists, students of animal life-histories, ecologists and others. The part of palæontology in the study of evolutionary theory resembles that of natural selection in the process of evolution; it serves to remove the inefficient but cannot itself initiate.

As soon as we begin to consider the data of palæontology, we are confronted with the undeniable truth that the fossil record is very far from being complete, and it may be doubted whether so incomplete a record can give any reliable information of the course of evolution. To answer this question it is necessary to

9

consider the nature of the evidence on which palæontological conclusions are based.

The most direct palæontological evidence is derived from the rare instances in which it is possible to trace a changing fauna through a considerable period of geological time, and to observe the evolution of the fauna directly. This can only be done where a series of strata are laid down continuously upon each other, without intermissions. Even in these series there is always the possibility that animals have migrated into the fauna from outside, so that some at least of the later forms may not be derived from the earlier. But detailed examination of the structure of the forms may leave little doubt of their succession from each other, and in several instances has done so. The series then gives us a reliable record of the fauna over the whole period, and we can observe the evolutionary changes that took place in it. Even where breaks occur in the series of strata, if they are not too great or numerous, accurate and detailed examination of the animals may establish the succession. We may still be able to conclude that we have before us a single changing fauna.

In these series we can see evolution at work over periods of many thousands of years, much longer periods than any we can give to observation of living animals, but still short periods on the time-scales of both geology and evolution. Only small evolutionary differences can be evolved in them; new subspecies and species may be formed, but not new genera, families and classes. For all the major changes of evolution they provide no evidence.

Except when dealing with these series, the palæontologist has to rely on remains of animals preserved at long intervals of time, often in different parts of the world, and in very different strata. He has no direct knowledge of the many forms that were intermediate between these; he can only deduce the relationships of the forms he finds by study of their structure. Further, the record is incomplete not only in the small proportion of forms that are preserved, but also in preservation of only part of the structure of the body, usually only the hard bones or shell. Nevertheless, in some groups of animals, especially in the vertebrates, intensive study of the morphology of the fossil forms has given us a clear account of the general course of evolution. Phylogenetic trees of the evolution of these groups have been built up, and there can be no doubt that these trees are correct, at least in their broad features.

Palæontology may be able to tell us of some other characters of the animals of the past. Young animals are sometimes preserved and from these the course of the later stages of development may be worked out. The habitat in which an animal lived may be deduced from the nature of the stratum in which it is preserved. Often the assemblage of forms found in the same stratum will tell us something of the biological conditions under which the animal lived. These and other data may be of value in discussions of the general problems of evolution.

Such is the nature of the evidence to be got from palæontology. However fragmentary, it is direct, or at least much more direct than any other evidence we have. It gives a sound, if fragmentary, account of the course of evolution. Our theories must never be allowed to conflict with it.

There is one further question we should ask before we try to extrapolate to the whole of evolution from the small sample of evolutionary change shown us by fossils. Is the sample displayed by the fossil evidence likely to be representative of evolution as a whole? There can be no doubt that in one respect the palæontological sample is not representative. Common and dominant forms will be much more generally preserved than the rarer ones; and, certainly, the forms that the palæontologist uses for his detailed studies will be only the common species, for others cannot be found in sufficient numbers ([178], p. 32). This may be important to us, for, as we shall see later (p. 253), the process of evolution differs significantly according as the species is rare or abundant. And a rare species is not necessarily unimportant in the evolution of its group. Some change in its constitution, or in the conditions of its environment, may at any time lead to its becoming abundant and, perhaps, the ancestor of many later forms.

This point must be kept in mind. It means that changes of kinds other than those we find in fossils may have played a part in evolution. But it must not be allowed to discountenance the evidence of palæontology as a whole. We know that changes of the types observed in fossils have played their part, and almost certainly a very large part, in evolution.

With this introduction we may pass to a summary of the facts of evolution as they are displayed by the palæontological evidence. We are mainly interested in defining the *types* of change that have taken place in animal organisation. We are interested in the details of the actual course the changes have followed only in so far as it shows us what types of change have occurred. Even so, the field is wide and the summary must be rapid. If we may, it will be convenient to concentrate attention on the group of animals of which we have the most detailed knowledge. This group is undoubtedly the vertebrates. For several reasons we know their evolution much better than that of any invertebrate group—they have evolved within the period of the fossiliferous rocks, so that we have evidence of their evolution throughout its course; their structure, owing to the presence of internal and often external hard parts, is better preserved than that of most invertebrates; and the interest of palæontologists has been concentrated on them more than on other animals.

To assume that the vertebrates will give us an accurate view of the general nature of the process of evolution implies, first, that we believe that the process is similar in all animals. It is unlikely that this is true of the details of the process, or of all its features, but we have no evidence that the process differs significantly in the various groups of animals in its broad out-lines, and it is with these broad outlines that we are concerned.

Use of vertebrate evolution as a type of animal evolution implies, secondly, belief that the group is a suitable one for this purpose. It will not be so if vertebrate evolution has many peculiar features. There is no doubt that the vertebrates are in some ways exceptional animals. They have been the most successful of all animals—extending their dominance more widely than any others—and their evolution has been abnormally rapid. But these are quantitative, rather than qualitative, differences and allowance can be made for them. It seems that we may without much danger take vertebrate evolution as illustrating the evolutionary process in the animal kingdom, so long as we remember that the parallel between their evolution and that of other animals is not likely to be exact.

Fig. 1 shows a phylogenetic tree of the vertebrates according to recent views of the palæontologists, and in Fig. 2 outlines of

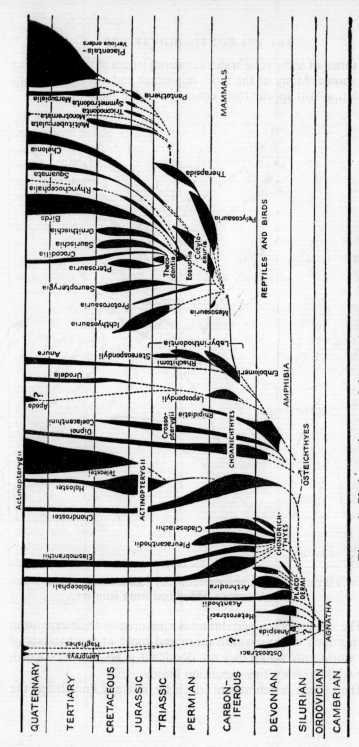

Figure 1. Phylogenetic tree of the vertebrates. (After Romer)

the forms of a few vertebrates at various stages of their evolution are shown. Many of the more important features of vertebrate evolution will appear from consideration of these figures.

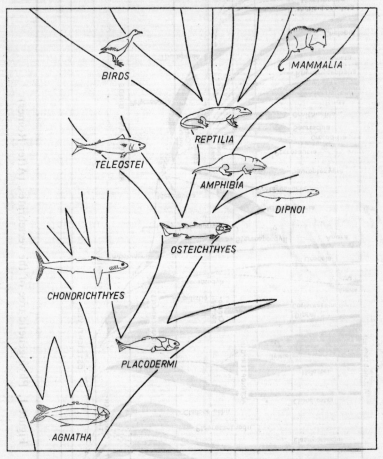

Figure 2. Forms and evolutionary relationships of the vertebrate groups. (Modified from Romer)

The success of the vertebrates is measured by their expansion during their evolution into more and more of the habitats of the world until today they are dominant in all. It will be worth our while to trace this expansion briefly.

The earliest vertebrates of which we have any knowledge, the early Agnatha, lived, as did almost all the primitive vertebrates, in fresh waters and probably in shallow and stagnant fresh waters. They were heavily armoured fishes living on the bottom of their habitat. Behind this stage we have no fossil evidence, but it is possible that a still earlier manner of vertebrate life was that represented today by *Amphioxus* and the ammocœte larva of the lamprey. This was a sluggish and semi-sedentary existence in which the animal, half-buried in mud or sand, filtered its food by means of mucus from a current of water passed through its mouth and gill-slits. From this habit, if the ancestral vertebrate possessed it, the Agnatha had escaped to a free but slow-moving life, searching for their food, which was probably invertebrates and decaying animal matter, on the muddy bottom on which they lived. All the Agnatha we know were clearly specialised animals, but they almost all agree in living this type of life, which we may conclude to have been characteristic of the vertebrate stock at this stage of its evolution. A few exceptional forms (*Birkenia*) lived a more active, free-swimming life.

The Placodermi ("Aphetohyoidea") were descendants of the Agnatha and were the first group composed as a whole of strong-swimming, pelagic fish. They also were fresh-water animals. They chased their prey in the open water. From them all the higher fishes are believed to have been derived. The first group of these, the Chondrichthyes, which includes our modern sharks and rays, early colonised the sea and have ever since been mainly marine. They gave rise to no later vertebrate groups and need not further concern us. All the remaining fishes belong to the Osteichthyes, the "bony fishes". The more primitive of these remained in the fresh waters and showed many adaptations to fresh-water life not, so far as we know, present in their predecessors, the Placodermi. Examples of these characters were their development, very similar to that of the Amphibia, and their lungs by which they breathed air when the stagnant waters in which they lived lacked oxygen.* They soon divided into two groups: (1) the Actinopterygii, from which by a long course of evolution were derived the modern bony fishes, the Teleostei, another mainly marine group which specialised in many directions but did not evolve further; and (2) the

* Our knowledge of these characters is deduced from study of the primitive living forms, not from fossil evidence.

Choanichthyes, from one group of which the first vertebrates to leave the water, the Amphibia (newts, frogs and toads), were descended. The latter, though living at least partly on land, are only half adapted to terrestrial life. They possess typical pentadactyl limbs fitted for terrestrial locomotion, but their development is still aquatic and their skin is permeable to water. Complete adaptation to terrestrial life was reached by the evolution from Amphibia of the reptiles, in which the skin became impervious and the development terrestrial, in an enclosed egg. From the reptiles, the birds and mammals were independently evolved, the former adapted to flying, the latter to a fast-moving life on the ground or in the trees. Though the structure of birds and mammals is very different, being differently altered from reptile structure, some of their adaptations are parallel. In both, the circulation is improved by complete division of the heart, and both evolved greater isolation from the conditions of the environment by becoming warm-blooded. Both groups, in these and other characters, show advance on the reptile type of organisation.

This short summary of vertebrate evolution will give us some idea of how evolution takes place in a successful group of animals.

(1) In the first place, we may note that throughout the evolution there was repeated change of habitat and habit as well as of structure. Changes of habitat and habit were indeed much more numerous than we have outlined. Repeatedly some of the members of a group left the habitat of the majority and adopted a different habit; pterodactyls and bats as well as birds became aerial. Some too have gone back to the manner of life of earlier groups; many turtles and other reptiles became aquatic and so did the whales, sea-cows and seals among the mammals. Thus we reach our first conclusion. In their evolution animals have changed frequently in habit and habitat. It seems clear that we may regard structural evolution as being in large part adaptation to the new conditions to which the animal became exposed during or after changes in habitat and habit of life (cf. [250]).

If this is so, the study of evolution demands much more than a knowledge of the morphology of the evolving animals; it requires also, and most importantly, knowledge of their whole life and especially of their natural history and ecology. It is this insistence on evolution as a phenomenon in natural history that distinguishes most clearly the modern outlook on its problems from the earlier, mainly morphological, outlook. Morphological studies may suffice for working out the phylogeny of animals, for phylogenetic conclusions are largely based on structure. When we try to explain the means by which evolutionary changes came about, we must discuss them in relation to the changing life of the animals.

(2) As each of the main groups of the vertebrates became successful, it formed the dominant group of animals in its habitat, and the earlier groups, if they survived, did so as only a relatively small part of the fauna. In the waters the successive fish types replaced each other—the Agnatha, Placodermi and Osteichthyes in the fresh waters and the Chondrichthyes and Teleostei in the sea. The land was first dominated by the Amphibia, then by the reptiles, and last by the mammals.

Each group, as it became dominant, underwent a type of evolution which, so far as we can see, was similar in all. Any large environment contains a number of smaller habitats which differ in the conditions they offer to animal life. In the waters the conditions on the bottom, in the open water and at the surface, on the shore and in the greater depths, are all different; on land conditions differ on the ground, in the trees, underground, in the deserts and forests and so on. Each of these habitats may be subdivided until we reach the small but distinguishable "niches" in which the species live.

The members of each successful vertebrate group, soon after the group became dominant, distributed themselves among these smaller habitats within the wider range of the group, and became adapted to the different habits of life that were appropriate to these habitats. This process of subdivision of a successful group of animals is known as *adaptive radiation*. Its course for the placental mammals is shown diagrammatically in Fig. 3. But this figure is over-simplified. Adaptive radiation is not, as appears in the diagram, confined to the initial splitting of the major group at the beginning of its period of dominance; it continues so long as the group maintains its dominance. The early subdivisions of the mammals are represented today by the mammalian orders. They have each given rise throughout the Tertiary to smaller groups adapted to smaller habitats and more

A.E.—2

specialised habits. Of these branches the modern species are the latest twigs. A more detailed, but still simplified, tree of the phylogeny of the titanotheres is given in Fig. 12 (p. 33).

Birds and mammals started to radiate in this way at the beginning of the Tertiary epoch, or in the late Cretaceous; reptiles started their radiation in the late Carboniferous; Amphibia in the late Devonian. There were several earlier

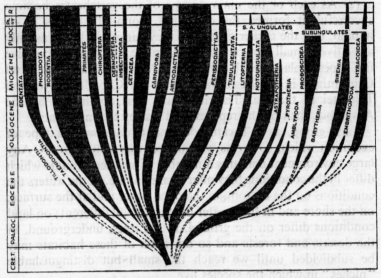

Figure 3. Adaptive radiation in the placental mammals.
(After Romer)

radiations of the fishes. In vertebrate evolution there has been a succession of these radiations.

Adaptive radiation is, then, the means by which a successful group of animals fills all the parts of its range by giving rise to forms adapted to the many and various habits of life possible within the range.

(3) Between each of these radiations a new type of vertebrate organisation was evolved, the mammal or the bird from the reptile, the reptile from the amphibian, the amphibian from the osteichthyan fish, and the later types of fishes from the earlier. In this process the whole organisation of the body is altered; every organ is modified and many new organs are evolved—

hair, a placenta and many other organs in the mammals; an enclosed egg, and an impervious skin in the reptiles. These changes are much more complex and fundamental than those of adaptive radiation, which, as we shall see (pp. 34 ff.), consist largely (though not wholly) in alterations in the relative sizes of the parts of the body and much less in formation of new organs.

In each instance of the evolution of a new vertebrate type, it was the last-evolved dominant group that gave rise to the new type. One of the radiating lines of the earlier group gradually developed the new organisation in the course of its adaptive radiation. In the origin of the mammals the branch that took on mammalian structure was the group of the synapsid reptiles, which became more and more mammal-like throughout late Carboniferous and Permian times. Birds evolved during the Triassic and Jurassic from another reptilian stock, one of the groups of the dinosaurs. Each of these evolutionary processes took some 40–60 million years. It is not surprising that this type of evolution should be slow, since the changes involved in it are complex and deep-seated, and must be co-ordinated throughout the whole process, in order that the animal may remain viable.

From this account of the general course of vertebrate evolution, it is clear that the bifurcating tree that has been so generally used as a diagram of the course of this, as of other, examples of evolution does not accurately represent it. The phylogeny does not normally bifurcate. The diagram should rather consist of a series of many-branched divisions, each branch repeatedly dividing after its origin, and one of the branches leading to the next radiation.

(4) By no means all the changes of vertebrate evolution have so far been discussed. We have considered only the adaptive changes of evolution, but we shall find later (pp. 183, 212) that non-adaptive change plays a significant part in evolution. We may leave the subject to be discussed there. There is still another type of change that has undoubtedly been continuous throughout vertebrate evolution and has had important results. This is a gradual improvement of the body as a living mechanism.* Every animal that survives is shown by its survival to be

* For a discussion of the concept of progress in evolution, see [178], pp. 556 ff.

efficient to the standard required by the conditions of its life, but this is not to say that all animals are equally efficient organisms. As the organisation of its body improves, the animal is able to lead a wider life, less at the mercy of the conditions of its environment. In a real sense it becomes more efficient. Changes of many kinds in the body, both structural and physiological, play a part in this increase in efficiency, but there is one improvement that is perhaps more effective in it than any other. This is better isolation of the conditions within the body (those of the internal medium) from changes in the external environment, so that the animal may lead its life in greater independence of changes around it.

The evidence that the vertebrate body has become more efficient during its evolution necessarily comes rather from study of living animals than of fossils, for many of the changes are physiological. But there can be no doubt that the improvement has been real and great, and some changes of this type may be seen in fossils. Two examples taken at random from those for which we have fossil evidence are: the improvement in the organisation of the brain and the central nervous system allowing better control of the body and more complex behaviour; and the modifications of the limb structure in the evolution of the mammals which made possible a more efficient locomotion. Examples of the very numerous physiological improvements that occurred in vertebrate evolution are: a controlled body temperature; a more rapid circulation, so that the same volume of blood can be responsible for a greater amount of transport; and more accurate control of the chemical conditions in the internal medium, as, for instance, its pH.[15] If there is any truth in the effectiveness of natural selection in evolution, it is to be expected that the later animal should be more efficient. It is certainly true that the vertebrate became more efficient as it evolved.

(5) We have considered vertebrate evolution solely as a progress from the more primitive to the higher types, but it must not be forgotten that only a small proportion of the members of the phylum have taken part in that progress. The vast majority of each group, both individuals and species, died out without giving rise to any higher forms. The larger evolutionary changes are rare events.

It may be that every animal population is always evolving, but if so it is clear that the evolution is often very slow and that its rate varies greatly. The progress of the vertebrates has been rapid as compared with that of most other animals, but rapid evolution is certainly not characteristic of all vertebrates. We have alive today examples of many of the more primitive groups, which have not altered in their fundamental organisation since their groups were dominant. The lampreys and hag-fishes (Agnatha), the lung-fishes, sturgeons and Polypterus (primitive osteichthyans), are examples of these surviving forms. They have clearly undergone at most very slow evolution, since the periods at which their groups first evolved. That the rate of evolution is highly variable is as true of the invertebrates as of the vertebrates. We find some invertebrates in Palaeozoic rocks generically the same as forms living today (e.g. the brachiopod, *Lingula*), whereas other invertebrates, such as the insects, have evolved rapidly. This is a subject that we shall have to discuss in more detail later (ch. XI). Here we need only note the variability of the rate of evolution.

As evidence that the evolution of the successful groups of invertebrates has not been different in its general features from that of the vertebrates, it may be noted that the phylogenetic tree of the insects shows a succession of radiations similar to those of the vertebrates, with the evolution of new insect types between them. Our knowledge of evolution in other groups is less detailed, but so far as it goes it seems to indicate a similar process. There are some indications of earlier radiations in the background of invertebrate phylogeny ([37,] ch. XXIII).

It must also be remembered that not all animal groups have been successful in the sense that we have used the term of the vertebrates. Besides those in which evolution has been very slow or has not advanced at all, there are others, for instance many parasitic groups, that have become adapted to specialised habitats and have degenerated so far as the structural complexity of their bodies is concerned. Many of these are very abundant animals, but they are far removed from the main course of animal evolution and have not given rise to later types that became dominant in other environments.

In this discussion we have found in the process of the evolution of a group of animals three stages or levels that are, at least to some extent, distinct. There is, first, the origin of the smallest evolutionary differences as seen in continuous series of strata; secondly, there is the differentiation of the members of a group in adaptive radiation; and thirdly, the evolution of a new type of animal organisation from its predecessor. Our discussions of the last of these forms of evolution have been confined to its largest examples in the vertebrates, the origins of the classes, but it should be taken to include the origin of any of the higher systematic categories, orders and even families as well as classes. Since these categories originate during the course of adaptive radiation, it is clear that no hard line can be drawn between the evolutionary process that gives rise to them and that of adaptive radiation.

The three levels of evolution have been called *micro-*, *macro-* and *mega-evolution*. We will next consider in more detail the conclusions of the palæontologist concerning evolution at each of these levels.

1. MICRO-EVOLUTION

We have today several instances in which sequences of fossils have been traced through series of strata. Invertebrates have been used in all these studies; this is inevitable since vertebrates are never preserved in sufficient numbers to make them suitable material for this type of work. Invertebrates of several groups have been used—graptolites, corals, lamellibranch molluscs, ammonites, brachiopods, sea-urchins. Not all these investigations can be discussed here.

In the earlier work of this kind, changes in the form and structure of the organisms were observed, but not further analysed. Rowe [259] studied the irregular sea-urchins of the genus *Micraster* in the Chalk. He was able to distinguish more than one line of descent. In one of these lines he found a gradual and continuous change from the form of *M. cor-bovis* to that of *M. cor-anguinum* (Fig. 4). Many characters changed—the shape of the test, the structure of the oral opening, the forms of the ambulacra, and so on. These changes took place to a large extent independently, though simultaneously. Also, they occurred in an environment that was, so far as could be determined, unchanging.

One other character of the changes in these sea-urchins was

very marked, as it is in all evolution in fossil forms. This is that the changes were *directional*; changes of the same kind continued through a considerable course of evolution, becoming gradually more exaggerated as the evolution continued. Thus in *Micraster* the test became continually more pointed, and the mouth less round, throughout the evolution. The *directions* of the changes were the same throughout. Such a directional change may be called an *evolutionary trend*. We shall find the general occurrence of these trends important when we try to interpret evolution (ch. IX).

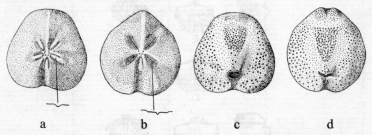

a   b   c   d

Figure 4. An evolutionary line in the sea-urchin, *Micraster*. a, c—aboral and oral views of *M. cor-bovis*, the earlier member of the line; b, d—similar views of *M. cor-anguinum*, the later member. Below a, b—sections of the ambulacrum in the two species. Note changes in shape, in position of the aboral centre, in the structure of the ambulacrum and the pores of its tube-feet, in the shape of the mouth, and in the arrangements of the bosses of the spines. (After Rowe)

An extremely elaborate and detailed investigation was carried out by Fenton [98] on the brachiopod genus *Spirifer* from a long series of Devonian strata in Iowa. Here the environment was not entirely constant; that it varied rhythmically was shown by repeated changes from more to less calcareous deposits and *vice versa*. But the evolutionary changes showed no correlation with these variations of the environment, which may be disregarded in discussing the evolution. We see in both these first examples of micro-evolution that evolutionary change may take place without significant change in the environment. This is not to say that the change is entirely without adaptational value. It may still be adaptive to the unchanging conditions.

Fenton was able to distinguish many lines of descent, and

found direct evidence of evolution in all of them. Examples of such evolution are given in Figs. 5 and 6, in which marked alterations in the shape of the shell are evident. He was able to deduce phylogenetic trees and these showed repeated division of a stock to give rise to numerous smaller groups (Fig. 7). His work also had bearings on several evolutionary problems

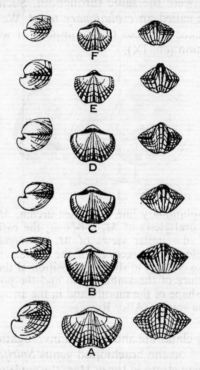

Figure 5. Evolution of a line of brachiopods (*Spirifer venatus*). Ascending stratigraphical order from A to F. (After Fenton)

with which we are not at the moment concerned—evolution of non-adaptive characters, orthogenesis, the ageing and degeneration of races. We shall return to discuss these questions later (chs. VII–XI).

Carruthers [34] studied the evolution of a coral genus, *Zaphrentis*, in Carboniferous strata. His specimens were collected at exposures in different localities, and therefore were not so clearly derived from a single changing fauna as those of

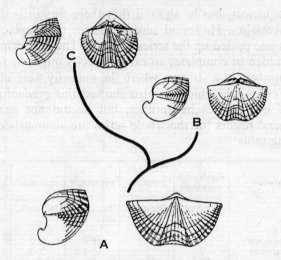

Figure 6. Divergent evolutionary lines in brachiopods
(*Spirifer varians*). (After Fenton)

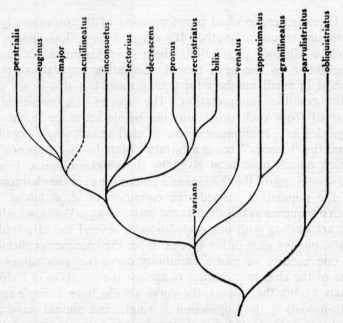

perstrialis euginus major acutilineatus inconsuetus tectorius decrescens pronus rectostriatus bilix venalus approximatus granilineatus parvulistriatus obliquistriatus

varians

Figure 7. Radiation in brachiopods (*Spirifer orestes* group).
(After Fenton)

2*

other sequences, but he showed that there was little doubt of their succession. He found several species that replaced each other as one passed up the series of strata. The replacement was never sudden or complete; an earlier species might be found in small numbers in a stratum where the majority were of a later form. Fenton's brachiopods also showed this *gradual* replacement of one species by another, but he did not analyse it. Carruthers' results for the whole series are summarised in the following table:

Stratum	*Zaphrentis delanouei*	*parallela*	*constricta*	*disjuncta*	No. of Specimens
	Per cent.	Per cent.	Per cent.	Per cent.	
Upper					
Millstone grit .	0	0	5	95	20
Upper limestone .	0	0·3	16·2	83·5	315
Lower limestone .	0·8	3·3	69·8	26·2	679
Cementstone group	69·1	30	0·9	0	110
Lower					

There is here gradual transformation of the prevalent type from one species to another. If we regard the various species as each a distinct population, there is replacement of each population by the next, though the earlier populations may persist in small numbers for a long time. But this is not the only possible interpretation. The species are presumably derived from each other and the whole sequence might be regarded as a continuous course of change in a single population, the "species" being arbitrary points in this sequence to which names have been given by the palæontologists. If so, we should regard the changes as a gradual shift in the characters of the population towards the condition of *Z. disjuncta*. In such a sequence as this there is one certain way to decide whether we are dealing with one population or several mixed populations, one for each of the species. If for the specimens collected at one horizon we plot a variability curve (i.e. plot values of one of the changing characters against the numbers of individuals having the values), the curve should have a single apex (uni-modal) if the population is single, but should have an apex for each of the mixed populations (pluri-modal) if the population consists of distinct but mixed elements (Fig. 8).[274]

Carruthers' data are not enough to allow us to determine which alternative is true of *Zaphrentis*.

Trueman [308, 309, 310] discussed these questions in the course of his investigation of the origin of the coiled lamellibranch *Gryphæa* from oysters of the genus *Ostrea* (Fig. 9) in the Lias (cf. also Swinnerton [295, 296, 297]). Evolution of forms to which the name *Gryphæa* is given occurred independently several times in these strata. This repeated parallel evolution may have been in all cases a response to the same need; it may have been an adaptation to life on a muddy substratum on which attachment was difficult. In these conditions it was an advantage for the

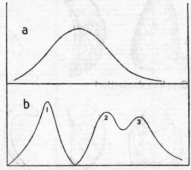

Figure 8. Curves of variation in single (a) and mixed (b) populations

mouth of the shell to be raised above the mud. Even so, it shows that the same directional trends may arise more than once in evolution—a polyphyletic origin of a group is not impossible. Trueman studied one instance of the evolution of *Gryphæa* in which the strata were continuous throughout.

As in all such examples, numerous characters altered in the course of the evolution—the shape of the shell, its angle of coil, its breadth as compared with its length, the area of attachment, and so on. In general, each of these characters (which have been called *bio-characters* by the palæontologists) showed a definite trend during the evolution, but their changes were largely independent in speed and amount.

Trueman found that, if a population at a single stratigraphical horizon is taken and the variability of any one of the characters is plotted for it, a uni-modal curve is obtained. This is seen in each of the curves of Fig. 10. We may therefore say without doubt that the population at each horizon is single. Fig. 10 also shows that the mean value of the character (in this case the number of whorls that the shell forms) alters continuously

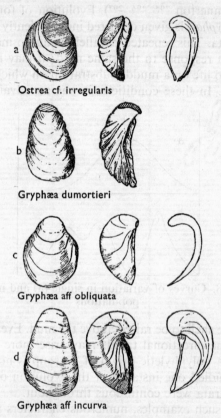

a

Ostrea cf. irregularis

b

Gryphæa dumortieri

c

Gryphæa aff obliquata

d

Gryphæa aff incurva

Figure 9. Four stages of an evolving line of *Gryphæa*, to show the change of form in the shell. (After Trueman)

throughout the sequence. The figure gives the values at only a few widely spaced horizons, but if the horizons were closer, the change between each would have been less. There can be no doubt that, in this and very many other examples of micro-evolution, the changes of form are continuous and gradual; if they take place by sudden steps, the steps are extremely small.

This absence of large sudden changes (saltations) in palæontological micro-evolution is one of its most striking features, and
is important from the point of view of the theory of evolution.

In such evolution as this, the curve given by a later population
may not be entirely outside the range of that of an earlier

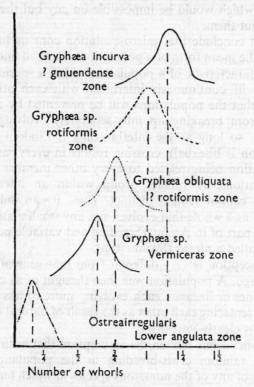

Gryphæa incurva
? gmuendense
zone

Gryphæa sp.
rotiformis
zone

Gryphæa obliquata
!? rotiformis zone

Gryphæa sp.
Vermiceras zone

Ostreairregularis
Lower angulata zone

Number of whorls

Figure 10. Curves of variation in the number of whorls of the shell
in successive populations of an evolving line of *Gryphæa*. (After
Trueman)

population. It is then possible that the change from the one
curve to the other was due to selection from among the members
of the earlier population, and descent of the whole of the later
population from the selected individuals. If that were so, there
would have been no true evolution in structure: the whole
change would be due to the selection. But this can hardly be
true of the whole sequence of Fig. 10, and would presumably have

been still more obviously untrue if the sequence had been longer. Even in Fig. 10, the curve of *G. incurva* is outside the range of *O. irregularis*; characters not known to be present in *O. irregularis* seem clearly to have arisen in the course of the evolution. We have no reason for surprise at this. New characters must arise in evolution, which would be impossible on any but the smallest scale without them.

We must conclude that micro-evolution consists in gradual change of the mean form of a population. We shall find (p. 142) that it is characteristic of a population within a species that its members will continuously interbreed with each other. It is also clear that the populations will be prevented by the inter-breeding from breaking up into separately evolving smaller groups for, so long as the interbreeding is random (and the reproduction is bisexual), crossing results in every member of the population being related to every other member within a few generations. A smaller group within an interbreeding population cannot remain distinct. Thus, it can only be the population as a whole that evolves, not any smaller assemblage that forms part of it. An interbreeding and variable population has been called a *plexus* (Swinnerton).

This conception is very different from that generally held a few years ago. A population was then thought of as consisting of many lines or lineages, each evolving more or less independently and replacing each other as the result of natural selection. That view is clearly unrealistic.

These conclusions rely on the assumption that nothing inter-feres with random cross-breeding in the population. In a population of any of the numerous species in which fertilisation is external, random crossing is almost certain, provided the population does not extend over too large an area. In other animals it may be less certain, though in most, so long as the population is single, it is probable that crossing is more or less general. (We shall return to discuss these questions more fully later, pp. 142,185–9.) But as soon as two populations are isolated from each other in any way, so that they are prevented from interbreeding, we should expect them to evolve in different directions (pp. 146 ff.). For this reason populations of the same species collected from distant localities might be expected to differ in small characters, although the localities were at the same stratigraphical horizon. Clift and Trueman ([45], cf. also [68]) found this to be true in lamellibranchs of the genus *Carbonicola* from different exposures of the same coal seam (Fig. 11). In at least one character (Fig. 11c) the two populations here compared are distinctly different. We are considering here

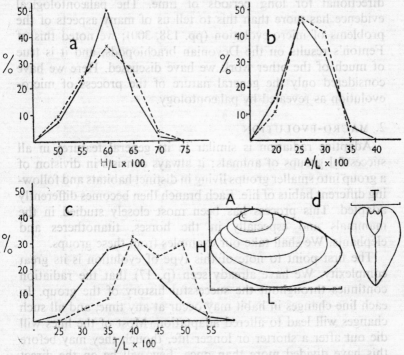

Figure 11. Variation in two populations of *Carbonicola* from different exposures of a coal seam. a–c: Variation in three characters, the two populations being distinguished by full and broken lines. d: Side and end views of the shell for the definition of the characters. (Redrawn from Clift and Trueman)

another and different type of evolutionary change, that between two isolated populations and not the change of a single population with time, but in this type also it is the interbreeding population that evolves. We have no palæontological evidence of the manner in which evolutionary divergence in isolated populations is brought about, but we shall discuss it again on the evidence of the biology of living animals (p. 185).

Palæontology, then, shows us micro-evolution as a process of gradual change in interbreeding populations. These changes may accumulate to form large differences of structure though the steps of which they are composed are always very small. The change is simultaneous in many characters and often directional for long periods of time. The palæontological evidence has more than this to tell us of many aspects of the problems of micro-evolution (pp. 138, 300); we noted this of Fenton's results on the Devonian brachiopods, and it is true of much of the other work we have discussed. Here we have considered only the general nature of the process of micro-evolution as revealed by palæontology.

2. MACRO-EVOLUTION

Adaptive radiation is similar in its general features in all successful groups of animals; it always consists in division of a group into smaller groups living in distinct habitats and following different habits of life. Each branch then becomes differently adapted. This process has been most closely studied in the mammals and especially in the horses, titanotheres and elephants. We shall take our examples from these groups.

The first point to note of this type of evolution is its great complexity. We have already seen (p. 17) that the radiation continues throughout the successful history of the group. In each line changes in habit may occur at any time, and all such changes will lead to altered adaptation. Most of the lines will die out after a shorter or longer life, though they may before this have divided more than once. Few will be on the direct line of descent to later forms.

The majority of the fossils we find will belong to these collateral and unsuccessful branches. In any general study of the group all these must be sorted out and distinguished. Their specialisations must be discounted in studying the evolution of the group as a whole. Adaptive radiation is therefore a complex subject, and by no means easy to interpret. The complexity of the process is illustrated in Fig. 12 in which a summarised phylogeny of the titanotheres between the Eocene and the Lower Oligocene, when they died out, is given ([234,] vol. II, p. 724). This figure still gives a greatly simplified diagram of the evolution.

Secondly, we should note that the changes of body form in adaptive radiation are often very large. Outlines of typical titanotheres during the course of their evolution are shown in

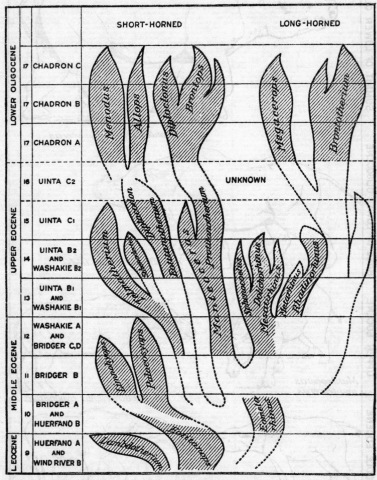

Figure 12. Simplified phylogeny of the titanotheres. (After Osborn)

Fig. 13 ([234], vol. II, p. 769), but the changes of form may be much greater than these. Fig. 14 gives recent conclusions on the phylogeny of the modern rays ([144], cf. also [145]), and illustrates the large changes of form that may take place. The evidence on which this figure is based derives mainly from the

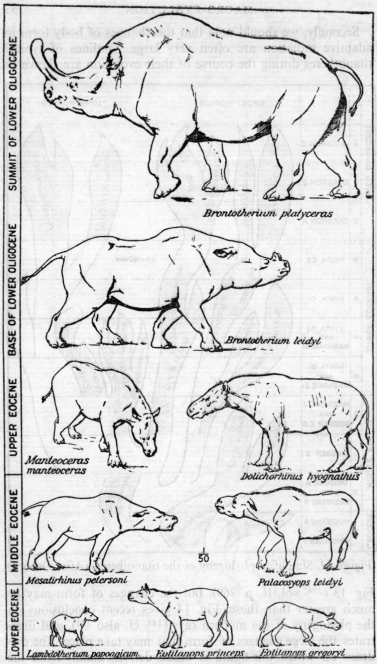

Figure 13. Change of body form in the evolution of the
titanotheres. (After Osborn)

comparative morphology of recent rather than fossil forms, but there can be no doubt that we have here another example of adaptive radiation.

Another noteworthy feature of adaptive radiation is that there is often marked increase in size of the individual as the

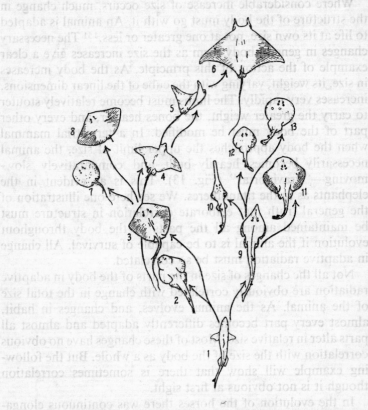

Figure 14. Adaptive radiation in rays. (After Gregory)

evolution proceeds. This appears for the titanotheres in Fig. 13. In the horses the increase is from the size of the ancestral Eocene *Eohippus* (=*Hyracotherium*), which was about the size of a cat, to that of our modern horses. In both these groups the increase in linear dimensions was about six times, or in weight 200 times. There was a similar increase of size in the elephants.

This increase of size is true of many groups, especially among terrestrial animals,* but not all groups show it. Some animals in most groups have remained small, or even become smaller with the progress of evolution. Nevertheless, more often than not, at any rate in terrestrial animals, the average size increases as the adaptive radiation of its group proceeds.

Where considerable increase of size occurs, much change in the structure of the body must go with it. An animal is adapted to life at its own size, not at one greater or less.[151] The necessary changes in general body form as the size increases give a clear example of the action of this principle. As the body increases in size, its weight, varying with the cube of the linear dimensions, increases very rapidly. The limbs must become relatively stouter to carry the greater weight, the bones heavier, and every other part of the body must be modified. In a terrestrial mammal when the body approaches the upper limit of size, the animal necessarily becomes heavily built and comparatively slow-moving—"graviportal" (Fig. 13). This is as evident in the elephants as in the titanotheres. We see here one illustration of the general truth that elaborate correlation in structure must be maintained among all the parts of the body throughout evolution if the animal is to be capable of survival. All change in adaptive radiation must be so correlated.

Not all the changes of size in the parts of the body in adaptive radiation are obviously correlated with change in the total size of the animal. As the animal evolves, and changes in habit, almost every part becomes differently adapted and almost all parts alter in relative size. Most of these changes have no obvious correlation with the size of the body as a whole. But the following example will show that there is sometimes correlation though it is not obvious at first sight.

In the evolution of the horses there was continuous elongation of the facial region of the skull and shortening of the cranial region. Four stages in the course of this evolution are shown in Fig. 15, where change in the shape of the skull is made more obvious by the deformation of the grid placed over it (cf. [300,] pp. 1051 ff.). These four types are not on a single direct line of equine descent, but they are close enough to the direct course of the evolution to represent for our purpose the change in the shape of the skull.

* The adaptational reason for increase in size is discussed at p. 293.

In Fig. 16 [255, 251] the lengths of the facial and cranial regions
of the skull in a much longer sequence of horses between

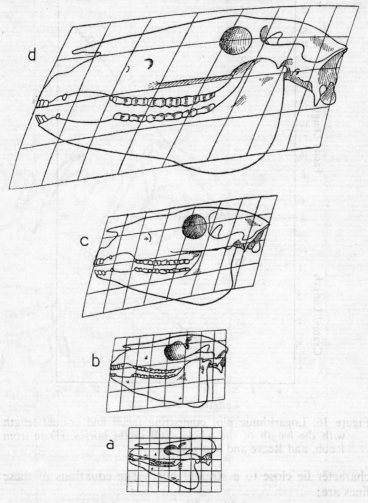

Figure 15. Evolution of the shape of the skull in the horses.
(Redrawn after W. B. Scott)

Eohippus and *Equus* are plotted on a double logarithmic plot
against the length of the skull as a whole. Skull-length may be
taken as a measure of the size of the body, since the relative

size of the whole head did not greatly alter in this evolutionary series. It will be seen that on this plot all the points for each

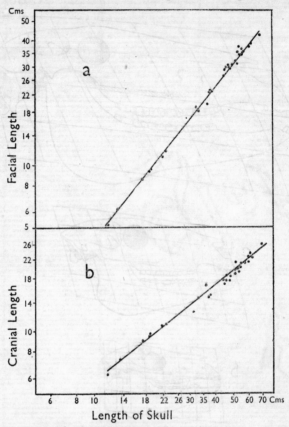

Figure 16. Logarithmic plot comparing facial and cranial length with the length of the whole skull in the horses. (Data from Robb, and Reeve and Murray)

character lie close to a straight line.* The equations of these lines are:

$$\log y = 0 \cdot 29 + 1 \cdot 2 \log x, \text{ or } y = 0 \cdot 29 x^{1 \cdot 2},$$

where y is face length and x skull length, and

$$\log \dot{y} = 1 \cdot 13 + 0 \cdot 725 \log x, \text{ or } y = 1 \cdot 13 x^{0 \cdot 725},$$

where y is cranial length and x skull length.

* Reeve and Murray [251] suggest that the lines should be double, with a bend near *Pliohippus* at a skull length of about 40 cm.

The meaning of the straightness of these lines [176] on the logarithmic plot is that, throughout the evolution, face and cranial length are increasing at rates that bear constant, though different, proportions to the increase in the length of the skull. It is the advantage of the logarithmic plot that it gives direct comparison between the proportional increase in the sizes of the two organs that are plotted against each other. Wherever the logarithmic plot is a straight line, implying a relation between X and Y of the form $Y=bX^k$, k (i.e. the slope of the line on the logarithmic plot) gives this comparison. According as k is greater or less than 1, the organ represented by X is growing more or less rapidly than that represented by Y, and the difference between the value of k and unity gives a measure of the inequality. Such changes are called *allometric*, positive if k is greater than 1, negative if it is less. When k is equal to 1, the organs are not altering in relative size and the evolution is called *isometric*. In contrast to k, b has no clear biological meaning; it varies numerically with the units chosen. [201] The value of b varies also in related animals and presumably in evolution ([229], quoted by de Beer [69]). The constant k is called the *relative growth constant* of the evolution.

Much more markedly allometric change than that in the horse's skull may occur. In Fig. 17 the length of the horns in a series of titanotheres is plotted against skull length. [164] Here the points again fall reasonably close to a straight line, and thus k is constant. Its value is very large, about 9.

Allometric change has some other features that should be noted:

1. Change in the relative sizes of organs is not restricted to evolutionary lines in which size is increasing. It plays a large part in all adaptive radiation, as much where the body size is constant or decreasing as where it is increasing. The sizes of any two organs can be plotted against each other, and the changes in relative size may be, and usually are, allometric whenever an organ becomes larger or smaller. Where change of size of an organ is not correlated with change of size in the body as a whole, it is due to differences between the growth rates of the organs. We shall discuss this immediately.

2. Results such as those of Fig. 16 show the changes in this

type of evolution to be gradual; large saltations play as little part in macro- as in micro-evolution. The fossil series are never close enough to allow us to decide whether the change is strictly continuous, or takes place by series of *small* sudden jumps. But the fossils give no evidence for sudden changes of any kind.

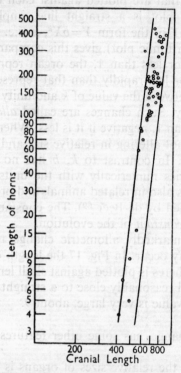

Figure 17. Logarithmic plot of cranial length against length of the horns in titanotheres. (After Hersh)

3. Allometric changes are as clearly directional as those of micro-evolution. Continuous response to a long-continued adaptational need may account for some at least of the directional character of these changes (p. 295).

4. Though the values of the relative growth constants often remain unaltered through long evolutionary series, as in the horses' skulls (Fig. 16), changes in them during evolution sometimes occur. Such change is almost always sudden, from

one value that remains constant for long periods to another that again remains constant for long. Fig. 18 ([275,] p. 10) gives an instance of such a change, also from the horses. Here the height of the paracone, one of the cusps of the molar teeth, is plotted against the length of the ectoloph, the ridge on the outer border of the crown of the same tooth. The latter is taken as a measure of the size of the whole tooth, and the comparison between these two characters gives a measure of the height of the crown, between the low-crowned, brachyodont, condition of the early horses and high-crowned, hypsodont, teeth of their

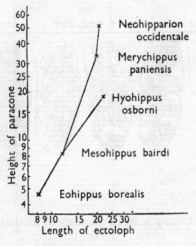

Figure 18. Evolution of the molars in horses. (After Simpson)

modern descendants. In the line *Eohippus–Mesohippus–Hypohippus* the crown was increasing slightly in height, though the teeth remained brachyodont. The increase was almost exactly allometric, i.e. the value of k was nearly constant. But in the origin of *Merychippus* the growth of the height of the crown became much more rapid, k being much greater. This rapid growth was continued in the evolution of *Neohipparion*. *Merychippus* was one of the earliest horses with clearly hypsodont teeth.

It is noteworthy that in this example the sudden change in the relative growth constant occurred at the time of an important change in the life of the animals. From *Eohippus* to *Mesohippus* the horses were browsing animals, forest-living, and feeding on soft vegetation such as leaves; *Hypohippus* retained this habit. Crushing, brachyodont, teeth were suitable to the soft diet. *Merychippus* and *Neohipparion* were the first of the more modern grazing horses, and hypsodont, grinding, teeth were evolved in adaptation to this new habit. The change in the relative growth constant seems to be correlated with the change of habit (cf. pp. 270–1).

We see here that not all the evolution of adaptive radiation is the result of allometric change. Change in the value of a relative growth constant is clearly not such a change; it is a *new* feature

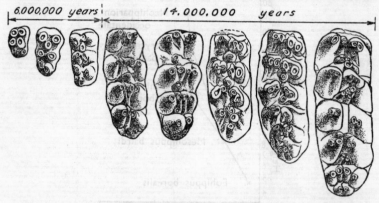

Figure 19. Aristogenesis in the teeth of mastodonts. (After Osborn)

in the organisation of the body. New structures and organisation occur frequently in macro-evolution. Let us take another example. Fig. 19 shows some stages in the evolution of the crown of one molar in a line of proboscidean descent, that of certain mastodonts.[235] In the ancestral (Eocene) *Mœritherium* the molar was a fairly typical mammalian tooth with four large cusps and a line of smaller cusps on its hinder border. In the course of the evolution its cusps increased greatly in number and became united in transverse ridges, which in turn became more numerous. In parallel lines, leading to the mammoths and elephants, the evolution was carried much further; the ridges became still more numerous, grew greatly in height and the spaces between them became filled with cement. Thus the complexity of the elephant's tooth was reached, the most complex grinding tooth that has been evolved in the mammals.

There is here allometric change—for instance, in the increase of the height of the cusps and ridges—but there is equally clearly formation of new structure in the origin of new cusps, their combination into ridges, the use of cement, and so on.

We have, then, a second type of change in adaptive radiation distinct from allometric change in relative size. Osborn ([234, vol. II, p. 811 ff.]) distinguished these two types of change. He called an allometric change correlated with change in body size an *allometron*, and the formation of a new structure or character a *rectigradation* or, later, an *aristogene*,* in allusion to the improvement in adaptation that normally results from this type of change when it is successful.

We cannot say very much of the nature of aristogenes. They are clearly changes in the heredity of the animal.† They are certainly of more than one kind. Many are due to changes in the relative growth constants of the parts, as we have seen in the development of hypsodontism in the horses. It is indeed possible that most new structures and organs arise by changes of this kind. Differentiations arising in the growth-rates of parts of a tissue, where there was no differentiation before, will give rise to new characters. Thus, for example, a new cusp in the mastodont's molar might be initiated by a new differentiation giving an increased growth-rate in the small part of the tooth where the new cusp is to arise. If the scale of the new differentiations were small enough, most types of new structure could be so formed. But not all. One other type of aristogenesis is alteration of the histology of the tissues, a change of structure within the cells. The origin of a new tissue is clearly not caused by a change in relative growth constants. Nor are some other types of aristogenesis.

It is not necessary for our purpose to analyse the structural details of the aristogenes that have arisen in evolution. That

---

* Cf. [235], p. 210. "Aristogenes are new adaptive units originating directly in the gene-plasm and slowly evolving into important functional service." The term is here used for *any new* element of pattern in the organisation of the body. This is a somewhat wider use but seems justified since the essential point is the novelty of the aristogene. Osborn associated with the term theoretical views that are not implied here.

† But see p. 94.

is of interest in phylogeny rather than in the study of the process of evolution.*

3. MEGA-EVOLUTION

We defined mega-evolution as the origin of a new system of animal organisation (p. 22), and saw that it occurred in the formation of new classes, orders, etc. We found it to take place by evolution of new organisation in one of the radiating lines of the preceding group during its adaptive radiation.

Since macro- and mega-evolution occur simultaneously in a single line of descent (p. 22), it is obviously unsound to look for large differences of kind in the processes that cause them. Indeed, it is hardly possible that the processes should be different in kind, since we have, in the origin of classes, orders, families and so on, a series in which the structural change and new organisation become progressively less until we reach the specific and subspecific differences of the smallest changes of typical adaptive radiation. There are no clear breaks in the series.

Yet there can be no doubt that there are differences between the larger and smaller differentiations of evolution. These differences are quantitative rather than qualitative. The greater the structural differentiation evolved, the larger the part that aristogenesis, as contrasted with allometric change, plays in the evolution. Formation of new characters is more evident in the origin of the mammals than in that of the orders within the mammals, and more evident there than in the origin of the smaller systematic groups within the orders. Allometric change occurs in all forms of evolution, in the larger differentiations as well as in the smaller; it is more clearly dominant in the latter. The reverse is true of aristogenesis.

It may be suggested that even these quantitative differences are more apparent than real, that their apparent existence is due to the fact that we know less of the details of mega- than of macro-evolution, and that much of the allometric change in mega-evolution has been lost in subsequent re-adaptation. There may be some truth in this suggestion, though it is unlikely that re-adaptation would be as complete as the suggestion implies. In so far as it is true, mega-evolution is merely a summarised and condensed form of macro-evolution in which it is

* For a recent general discussion of this subject see W. K. Gregory.[144]

mostly the formation of new structure that has been preserved. But it must not be assumed without further evidence that the two processes differ in no other way than this.

We know less of mega-evolution for more than one reason. One reason is that the fossil evidence very rarely allows us to trace a group to its exact point of origin in a preceding group ([275], p. 107). Often our fossil series extends nearly to the origin of the group, but the actual origin is missing; and it is at this point that the most interesting changes of mega-evolution took place. In Fig. 20 the stages missing in our evidence of the

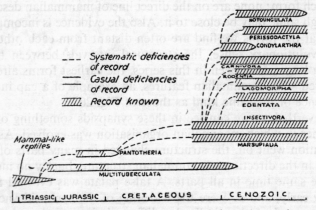

Figure 20. Deficiencies in the record of the palæontology of the mammalian orders. (After Simpson)

evolution of some of the mammalian orders are shown. There are similar gaps in our knowledge of the phylogeny of many other large vertebrate groups. We shall see later (p. 338) that the probable reason for these gaps is that the earliest stages in the differentiation of a group were comparatively rapid, and, perhaps also, that they took place in geographically restricted habitats.

Though the early stages of an example of mega-evolution may be rapidly passed through, it is certain that mega-evolution may often be continued in a group for long periods. The structural changes in the origin of the mammalian orders were relatively small, and the period of their evolution may have been short, but where the change was greater, the evolution must necessarily have occupied a long time. We noted that this was true of the evolution of both mammals and birds from reptiles; both took some 40–60 million years.

Let us examine in more detail the process of mega-evolution as it occurs in its larger examples. We do not know much of the mega-evolution of the birds, for they are rarely preserved as fossils—*Archæopteryx* and *Archæornis* are our only fossils truly intermediate between birds and reptiles. But we have a long series of synapsid reptiles from which we can deduce the process of the evolution of the mammals.[31] Here the evidence is to some extent confused by close and elaborate specialisation in each form; none are on the direct line of mammalian descent, though some may be close to it. Also the evidence is incomplete in that the forms we find are often distant from each other in an evolutionary sense, the structural intervals between them being large. And, even in this series, the earliest forms already showed some mammalian features, an example of a gap in our evidence of the same kind as those of Fig. 20.

Nevertheless, we can see in these synapsids something of the manner in which mammalian organisation was evolved. As the evolution went on, the structure changed in many parts of the body in the direction of mammalian structure, but by no means at the same time in all parts. A false palate was evolved relatively early, and so were the widening of the synapsid vacuity in the roof of the skull, the differentiation of the teeth to resemble incisors, canines and molars, and the modifications of the limbs by which the elbows and knees were brought under the body. All these were present in forms that are still without question classed as reptiles. On the other hand, the teeth did not become rooted, and the quadrate and articular were not included in the chain of small bones in the middle ear until much later. The presence of these characters is usually taken as diagnostic of a mammal.

The history of the quadrate and articular illustrates another point. Growth of the squamosal towards the articulation of the jaw and reduction of the smaller bones at the hind end of the jaw started early and was continuous throughout synapsid evolution. But until this process had proceeded so far that the squamosal and dentary had taken over the articulation from the quadrate and articular, the latter bones remained in the positions that they had always occupied in the reptiles, though they were much reduced. It was only when the change in the articulation had taken place that they were free to pass into the ear and take over their new function.

These two changes—alteration in the articulation of the jaw and elaboration of the structure of the ear—were distinct in origin. There can be no doubt of this if we consider the needs they served. The first was probably a response to need for strengthening the jaw. It answered this need by simplifying the jaw's skeletal support, which in the process was reduced to a single bone. The second was clearly an adaptation to improve the functioning of the ear. These are, without doubt, unrelated needs. But the second change was impossible, at least in the form in which it occurred, until the quadrate and articular had been set free.

Thus, we have in the modification of the ear an example of an adaptive change which could only take place because the organism possessed at the time a character the origin of which was unconnected with its use in the new adaptation. This is one type of *pre-adaptation*, a phenomenon which we shall discuss in more detail later (ch. VIII). The reptile was pre-adapted to forming a chain of bones in the middle ear by having free quadrates and articulars which had lost their earlier functions and could be used for the purpose. If they had not been available, the chain of bones could not have been formed, unless in some quite different way.

Two other features of mega-evolution deserve mention. First, it is certain that there is no more evidence for large and sudden evolutionary changes here than in micro- and macro-evolution. Secondly, it seems to be true that most of the changes of mega-evolution are in response to the adaptational needs of the organism. We have in our argument assumed this to be so. In this, mega-evolution differs markedly from the smaller evolutionary changes and especially from those of micro-evolution. Much of the differentiation between species, both in fossils [98, 99] and at the present day ([80], pp. 29, 136; [256], pp. 274 ff.; [10]), is, so far as can be seen, non-adaptive. This is still more true of the differences between the categories lower than species— subspecies, races, etc.

It should also be noted that the changes of mega-evolution

are as clearly directional as those of micro- and macro-evolution. This is indeed a character that is general throughout all palæontological evolution. It is one of the most obvious characters of the fossil evidence, and one which any satisfactory theory of evolution must account for.

This short survey gives us the following conceptions of the process of evolutionary change as displayed in the facts of palæontology:

Evolution takes place by gradual, continuous and directional change in the mean structure of variable and interbreeding populations. Large saltations are at least rare in the process in general. Evolutionary change is slow, but its speed may greatly vary. On the level of micro-evolution, much of the change is non-adaptive, but at higher levels adaptation is responsible for at least the greater part of the change; evolution becomes more clearly adaptational the larger the evolutionary changes we consider. The populations are continually undergoing adaptive radiation, spreading into new habitats and adopting new habits. It seems that in the evolution of adaptive characters it is especially the assumption of new habit, acting together with changes in the external environment, that determines change in adaptation, though other needs, such as that for greater efficiency in the organisation of the animal, are also effective. Evolution is largely a response to the changing natural history of the animal.

The changes of organisation that occur in evolution are of several kinds. In all types of evolution allometric change plays a large part, but aristogenesis, the formation of new organisation, has also an essential part to play. It is relatively more important in the larger changes of evolution, and especially in the evolution of new systems of animal organisation (mega-evolution). It, also, is of more than one kind. Change in the relative growth constants of the body—change in the systems of allometry—is one of the most widespread and important kinds of aristogenesis, but there are others. Evolution, except on the smallest scale, is impossible without aristogenesis.

CHAPTER II

THE GENETIC BACKGROUND

IT is not necessary for us to discuss the whole of the recent results of genetics. What we need in our attempt to interpret evolution in animals is a clear conception of the general features of the hereditary mechanism in the individual. This must include, besides knowledge of the organisation of the hereditary material, an understanding of the manner in which it expresses itself in the body of the organism, of the changes that are likely to occur in the mechanism, and of the effects to which these changes will give rise. This is a wide enough field, but there are considerable parts of genetics outside it. We can omit genetic processes peculiar, or almost entirely peculiar, to plants, for we are considering only animal evolution. We can omit variations of the genetic mechanism that occur in only a few animals—they will not be important in evolution—and a great deal of the detail of unusual types of chromosome behaviour. Besides the normal bisexual reproduction, there is among animals, less common but widely distributed, a second type of reproduction, which may have important effects on the evolution of the animals that make use of it. This is non-sexual —or, better, non-syngamic—reproduction, in which union of gametes at fertilisation does not occur. It includes the various forms of parthenogenesis, bud-formation, fission, etc. We must consider its evolutionary significance.

THE EARLY RESULTS OF GENETICS

The history of genetics since the rediscovery of Mendel's work in 1900 is best divided into the periods before and after T. H. Morgan started (1909) the intensive investigations of the genetics of *Drosophila* on which a large part of present-day views of the hereditary mechanism are founded. It will be well to summarise the views held in 1909 before we go on to discuss how these views have been altered by the results of later work.

In the period before 1909 the foundations of genetic theory were laid down.[246] First, Mendel's conclusions were confirmed. It was shown that characters of the kinds used in his experiments are inherited independently, and remain distinct ("pure") through an indefinite number of generations, i.e. "blending inheritance" does not occur in them. The first filial generation (F1) may be intermediate between the parents, but this is not blending inheritance, since the characters separate in the second filial generation, and there appear in the same pure form in which they were present in the parents. Mendel's proportions of the individuals of each form in this generation—the well-known 1:2:1 proportions for a single pair of characters—were confirmed. Inheritance of two or more pairs of characters in the same cross was observed, and the proportions obtained in the F2 generation agreed with expectation. Dominance in the F1 generation was studied and found to be either complete, when the hybrid was indistinguishable from one (the dominant) of the two forms that were crossed to produce it; or incomplete, when the cross was intermediate between the parents. The fact of linkage was noted, that is to say it was found that certain characters remained associated in heredity and did not separate in the F2 generation as the majority of characters did. It was also found that linkage might be incomplete, when the "forbidden" combinations of characters occurred, but in smaller proportions than in the absence of linkage.

Mendel had concluded that his results would be explained if each gamete could carry only one member of a pair of contrasting characters (*allelomorphs*), whereas the zygote and adult might carry both, i.e. if the characters of a pair separate (segregate) in the process of the formation of the gametes. On this assumption a zygote which carried both members of a pair of allelomorphs (Xx) was called a *heterozygote*, and one with only one member, but two examples of it (XX or xx), a *homozygote*. The behaviour of the characters in heredity was very early compared with that of the chromosomes at meiosis and fertilisation, which was already known from cytological studies. If the characters were carried in the chromosomes, their segregation in the gametes would be explained by the reduction of the chromosome number from $2n$ to n at meiosis; the purity of the characters in inheritance would be the result of the persistence of the individuality of the chromosomes through both division and meiosis; and the fact that a zygote can carry both allelomorphs would be in accord with the return to the double number of chromosomes ($2n$) at fertilisation. The observed proportions between the numbers of individuals of different types in F2 required that on the average half the gametes of a heterozygote carried each of any two allelomorphic characters, and this was in accord with the facts of meiosis in which chance seemed to determine which of a pair of chromosomes passed into a gamete. Finally, linkage was to be expected if more than one character was carried in a chromosome, for characters carried in the same chromosome should not separate. Incomplete linkage, however, was not explained; its explanation came later.

Thus, by the end of this period, the view that the characters were carried in the chromosomes was supported by a large body of circumstantial evidence. It was accepted by the majority of geneticists, but rather as a very probable hypothesis than as proved fact. The elements believed to carry the hereditary characters in the chromosomes were called "genes". The whole hereditary material of an individual, the whole aggregate of its genes, was called a "genotype", and the form of the body that such a genotype produces was called a "phenotype".

Johannsen during this period established the possibility of separating from mixed populations of self-fertilising beans "pure lines" (each descended from a single plant), and observed that variation within each of these lines was less than that between the lines.[184] This was in agreement with the purity of the hereditary characters and with the theory that they were carried in the chromosomes. For, if the chromosome theory was true, no alteration of the hereditary material should occur in self-fertilisation, unless the individuals were heterozygotic (i.e. the two chromosomes of a pair carried different allelomorphs). This was unlikely in natural races. Even if some lines were heterozygotic, variation should be much less in self-fertilisation than in crossing between different individuals. The variation that did occur in a pure line was shown not to be inherited and was attributed to action of the environment on the phenotype during its life-history.

The origin of inherited variations was observed in the early

work in genetics, though it was found that they originate comparatively rarely. A change that gave rise to an inherited variation, i.e. a change in the hereditary material of an animal, was called a "mutation",* or, at first, a "sport". It was found always to occur suddenly. At the time, all these mutations were thought to be due to chemical or physical change in individual genes. Those studied by the early geneticists almost always had large effects in the phenotype—large modifications of colour distribution, of structure in organs such as the wings of insects, the comb in fowl, the hair in mammals, and so on. They were also very often degenerative. It was natural that these large mutations should be used in the early experiments, for they were the most easily found and investigated.

One other phenomenon in genetics was first observed at this time. This was the genetical determination of sex. The sex chromosomes were discovered, and their peculiar behaviour at meiosis noted. Mammals and Diptera were found to be homozygotic (XX) in the female sex; birds and Lepidoptera in the male. Sex chromosomes were observed in several other groups of animals,[90] with various levels of differentiation between the X and the Y. Simultaneously, physiological control of secondary sexual characters was demonstrated in various animals, [276, 198] and for a time the results of these two lines of work seemed to be in opposition. They were later reconciled, when it was shown that the secondary sexual characters in most vertebrates are physiologically controlled by secretions of the gonads, themselves genetically determined in sex.

Thus, a basic understanding of the hereditary mechanism of the body, the means by which parent and offspring come to resemble each other, was reached. That the resemblance is not perfect has always been evident and admitted. Its imperfection is not entirely due to genetic differences between the generations. The characters of the phenotype are in part determined by the environmental conditions it meets during its life, not only by accidents that happen to it but also in many animals by the

* This term has had a complex history. It was first used by Waagen [317] for any recognisably distinct stage in a population of fossil animals undergoing micro-evolution. It is still used in this sense by palæontologists. De Vries [71] first used it in the genetical sense, an inheritable change in the genotype of an animal. Such changes were all at first regarded as due to chemical changes in the genes. For the later distinction between "gene-" and "chromosome-mutations", see pp. 57–58.

nature of the environment in which it is living ([37], ch. VII)—the phenotype is determined by a balance between hereditary and environmental conditions.

RECENT VIEWS OF THE ORGANISATION OF THE GENOTYPE

Morgan's choice of *Drosophila* as a subject for genetic investigation was an extremely wise one. The ease with which this fly can be bred in the laboratory, and its short life-history, made it easy to obtain a large supply of genetic material from it. Its small haploid number of chromosomes (4 in *D. melanogaster*, Fig. 21) made the analysis of its genotype relatively easy. And the much later, entirely unexpected, discovery of the

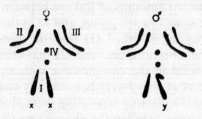

Figure 21. The chromosomes of male and female *Drosophila melanogaster*

expanded chromosomes in the salivary glands of *Drosophila* (and other Diptera) added greatly to these advantages. They have been exploited in the very extensive and varied investigations of Morgan's school in America. So extensive has their work been, and so valuable their results, that the criticism is often made that use of a single genus for so much recent genetical work is dangerous. This criticism has little weight. All the main features of our modern conceptions of genetics have been confirmed in other animals and may be taken to be generally true, at least in the Metazoa. We may safely use conceptions based on study of *Drosophila* as the background for our discussions of the process of evolution.

1. THE ORGANISATION OF THE GENES IN THE CHROMOSOMES

Morgan early suggested [215] that the belief that the genes were carried in the chromosomes and the facts of incomplete linkage (p. 51), if considered together, required that parts of the chromosomes were sometimes exchanged at meiosis, so that separation of linked genes could occur although they were carried in the same chromosome. This exchange of material between the chromosomes was called *crossing-over*. Acceptance of its reality was at first a deduction from the facts of linkage, but the chromosomes were known to associate alongside each other in pairs at meiosis, and to coil round each other. Breakages and exchanges between the pairs seemed not improbable.

Cytological demonstration of crossing-over was obtained later,[285] when crossing-over was directly observed, at points called *chiasmata*. But the theory of its occurrence was supported much earlier by a large body of evidence derived from study of the proportional amounts of linkage between different pairs of genes in the same linkage group, and so in the same chromosome. If it may be assumed (1) that the genes are linearly arranged in the chromosomes, and (2) that crossing-over may occur at any point in the chromosome with equal likelihood, the percentage of crossing-over between any two genes will be proportional to the distance separating them along the chromosome. The distances between the different pairs of genes could therefore be compared by determining the percentage of crossing-over for each pair. Also, the values for the distances so found should be additive. Thus, if crossing-overs between genes A, B and B, C are in the proportion of $1:k$ (and therefore the distances along the chromosome are in this proportion), then crossing-overs between A and C should be either as $1:1+k$ or as $1:1-k$ according as C lies in the chromosome outside or inside the length $A-B$. From these results the arrangement of the genes A, B and C can be deduced, and the deductions can be confirmed by taking another gene D of the same linkage group, for the percentages of crossing-overs between this gene and A, B, C should be concordant with the arrangement of these genes already deduced. If a large number of genes are taken, the results for all should be concordant with each other, and, if it is so, a large body of evidence for linear arrangement of the genes in the chromosome will have been gained. This evidence can be extended until all the genes in each of the linkage groups of the animal's genotype have been used. In *Drosophila* more than 1000 genes are known, arranged in four linkage groups corresponding in size and number to the haploid chromosomes, and the percentages of crossing-over have been determined for most of them, and found to be in general additive. Analysis showed that in *Drosophila* crossing-over occurs in the female (homozygous) sex only. Restriction of crossing-over to one sex is not general in animals.

This extensive agreement between theory and observation strongly supported the theory—namely, that the genes are carried in linear arrangement in the chromosomes and that partial linkage is the result of crossing-over.

Exceptionally, analyses of the distances between the genes in the chromosomes are not entirely in agreement with the simple theory just given; in particular the relative distances between the genes are not always strictly additive. Some of these divergences from theory can be explained. For instance, it was found that, if two genes are separated from each other by a long distance along the chromosome, the crossing-over value between them is often smaller than the sum of the values for several intermediate genes. But this is not surprising, for in a considerable length of the chromosome it is to be expected that *two* crossing-overs might sometimes occur at the same meiosis, and when this happens the two distant genes will not be separated. Thus, the crossing-over value between these genes will be less than represents the distance between them; it will be less by the proportion of the gametes in which the crossing-over is double. Analysis in such cases of the variation from the additive value given by closer genes showed that the differences were usually in approximate agreement with those expected.

In other respects the results are not entirely in accordance with the theory, but they are at least good enough to allow maps of the positions of the genes in the chromosomes of *Drosophila* to be drawn (Fig. 22). Similar but less complete maps have been drawn for some other organisms—mouse, fowl, locust, some plants, etc. Though the genes are linearly arranged along the chromosome, it was found that they are not evenly spaced along it. In some parts of the chromosomes there are distances in which no known genes occur; in others they are more crowded.

It must be realised that these maps, based as they are on

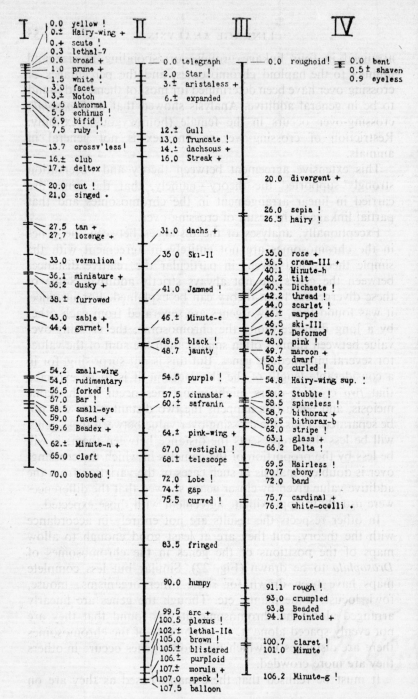

Figure 22.—Map of the chromosomes of *Drosophila melanogaster* as deduced from linkage analysis. (After Morgan, Sturtevant and Bridges)

the results of linkage analysis, will only give an accurate picture of the arrangement of the genes in the chromosome if the assumptions inherent in the method of making the analysis are correct. These assumptions were mentioned at the beginning of our discussion. The first is that the genes are linearly arranged in the chromosomes. There can be no doubt of the truth of this; it would be impossible to make any map unless it were true. Secondly, it was assumed that crossing-over is equally likely at all points in the chromosome. This is much more doubtful, and indeed we shall find reason for believing that it is not entirely true (p. 61). But even if it is untrue the map will still have a meaning; it will still show the linear arrangement of the genes. It will differ from the true picture in that parts of the chromosome where the crossing-over frequency is less than the average will be compressed in the map, and those where it is more than the average will be expanded.

From the results of linkage analysis the frequency of crossing-over at meiosis can be deduced. On the average, there must be, in *Drosophila*, at least one crossing-over between each pair of chromosomes at meiosis. In some organisms there may be many more than this—up to an average of ten.

We have noted (p. 52) that it was assumed in the early years of modern genetics that the only possible type of change in the genotype was a physical or chemical change in the gene itself (p. 52). It was soon found that alteration could also occur in the arrangement of the chromosomes and of the genes within them. Whole chromosomes might be lost or reduplicated, and even whole sets of *n* chromosomes might be added. This gave individuals with abnormal chromosome numbers—*polysomics* or *aneuploids* when only some of the chromosomes were abnormal in number, *polyploids* when whole sets of chromosomes were added. We will consider these conditions later (p. 74); for the present we will discuss only re-arrangements within the chromosomes. Several different kinds of these were found. Parts of a chromosome might become detached from the rest and joined to another chromosome (translocation), or lost (deletion); parts could be reversed in the chromosome (inversion), or doubled (duplication). All these changes require that chromosomes may be broken at meiosis and their parts

3*

reunited in a different arrangement. This in fact occurs. Breakages are not uncommon, and union of broken ends occurs;
unbroken ends of chromosomes never unite*. Many of these
abnormalities, especially the deletions, were found to be lethal
(i.e. they caused the death of the organism at some stage of
its life-history before maturity) in the homozygous condition
unless they were very small, but heterozygotes were often
viable. The effects in the phenotype of these re-arrangements are
similar to those of the mutations due to changes in the chemical
nature of the genes. The two types of mutation were distinguished as "gene" and "chromosome mutation".

Re-arrangements within the chromosomes were first recognised by the occurrence of abnormal crossing-over values
between the genes involved in a re-arrangement and others
outside it. The distance between two genes was altered by the
re-arrangement, and therefore the percentage of crossing-over
between them was altered; or, when the re-arrangement was
a translocation, the results appeared in transference of the
genes in the affected region from one linkage group to another.
Thus, belief in the reality of the re-arrangements was at first
founded on deduction from linkage analysis—they were
hypothetical—but occasionally a large translocation could be
seen in cytological preparations. An example is given in
Fig. 23.[236]

Full confirmation that the re-arrangements are real followed
the discovery of the very extraordinary chromosomes of the
salivary glands of the Diptera and, among them, of *Drosophila*.[162] The nuclei of the cells of these glands are large, and
the chromosomes within them are enormously expanded. The
chromosomes are paired and therefore of the haploid number.
They are permanently in a condition similar to that of the
meiotic prophase. Their length is as much as 150 times that of a
normal mitotic chromosome. Each chromosome is cylindrical,
and within the cylinder can be seen a large number (about 64
in *Drosophila* and more in some other forms) of threads
(*chromonemata*) which run along the whole length of the
chromosome. It is doubtful how the chromonemata are

* In Fig. 23 the union of the translocation is in all probability not to the end
of chromosome II but to a break near the end, and a small piece of II may have
been translocated to the broken end of III (Muller *in litt.*).

arranged. They may be restricted to the surface of the cylinder
or spread throughout its thickness. [237], [238] Across the chromonemata can be seen alternating dark- (*euchromatic*) and lightly-
staining (*heterochromatic*) bands. The arrrangement of these
bands is irregular—they are at unequal distances and of unequal
thicknesses—but their arrangement is the same in all the
chromonemata of a chromosome and, so long as the two paired

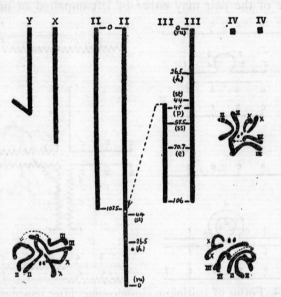

Figure 23. Evidence of a translocation in *Drosophila melanogaster*.
Above and to the left, linkage maps of the abnormal (heterozygous) fly. Below and to the right, metaphases from similar
flies showing the abnormally long II and short III chromosomes.
(After Painter and Muller)

chromosomes are genetically identical, in the two chromosomes. Each band is in contact with the same band in all the
other chromonemata, so that the bands appear to cross the
whole thickness of the chromosomes. Where the paired chromosomes are homologous, pairing of the bands in the two chromosomes is accurate and, to all appearances, perfect. It implies
that pairing of the chromosomes is an exact pairing of their
parts as well as a pairing of the chromosomes as wholes.

At first sight it would seem that abnormal arrangement of

the bands within one of the chromosomes of a pair (owing to the presence of a chromosome mutation in the heterozygous condition) must prevent exact pairing of the bands, and one might expect that meiosis would then be unsuccessful. In fact, pairing is modified in these conditions but, very often, meiosis succeeds. In parts where the chromosomes are homologous, pairing is normal; parts without homologues in the other chromosome of the pair may either be left unpaired or may pair

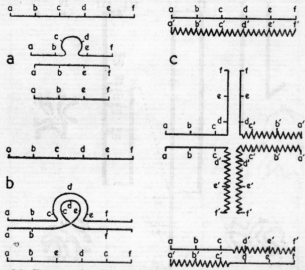

Figure 24. Forms of pairing in chromosomes after re-arrangements due to chromosome mutation. a—Deletion; b—inversion; c—translocation. In each figure the unmodified chromosomes are shown above and the modified below; in the centre the forms taken by the chromosomes in pairing are shown

with homologous parts in a different chromosome, if these are present. Even where there is an inversion, the inverted parts often succeed in pairing accurately with their non-inverted homologues in the other chromosome. This is brought about by the formation of loops of various kinds at the positions where the chromosomes are re-arranged (Fig. 24). Many individuals with heterozygous abnormalities of these kinds are able to produce viable gametes. Crossing-over is, however, in general reduced by the presence of structural differences in the chromosomes.

A drawing of one of the salivary-gland chromosomes of *Drosophila* is given in Fig. 25.[28, 29]

When the chromosomes were examined in the salivary glands of a *Drosophila* in which the presence of a chromosome mutation had been deduced from the results of linkage analysis, it was found that the abnormality could be *seen* in the arrangement of the bands of the chromonemata. The details of the observed re-arrangement were then found to correspond with the deductions that had been drawn from linkage analysis. Abnormalities of every size and kind were confirmed by direct observation in this way, minute inversions and duplications as well as large re-arrangements. Even small irregularities in the formation of the bands could be seen. Some small re-arrangements are shown in Fig. 26.[222]

From these observations it was possible to identify the position of many of the genes in the chromosomes; for the position of an abnormality that is known to affect a certain gene must be the position of that gene. We have thus a second method of mapping the chromosomes. So far as the linear arrangement of the genes is concerned, this method gives results in complete agreement with those of linkage analysis, but the two methods do not always agree in the relative distances they give between pairs of genes—a distance between two genes may be a shorter or longer proportion of the whole length of the chromosome in the salivary-gland chromosome than in the map based on linkage analysis. Comparison between maps of the same chromosome made by the two methods is given in Fig. 25.

In discussing the maps founded on linkage analysis (p. 57) we noted that variations in the frequency of crossing-over in different parts of the chromosome would result in the distances between the genes in these maps being distorted. There is no doubt that this is the reason for the differences between these lengths in the salivary-gland chromosomes and in the maps deduced from linkage analysis. Since observation of the salivary-gland chromosome is a much more direct method than linkage analysis, its results must be accepted.

The evidence of the salivary-gland chromosomes finally removed any doubt of the truth of the linear arrangement of the genes and of their location at definite points in the chromosome. The maps derived from observation of the salivary-gland

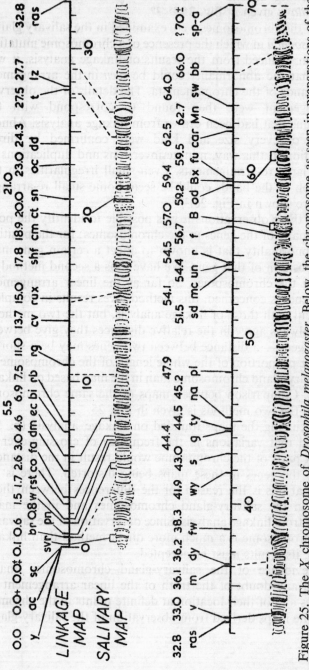

Figure 25. The X chromosome of *Drosophila melanogaster*. Below, the chromosome as seen in preparations of the salivary gland; above, the map deduced from linkage analysis. Corresponding positions are connected by lines. (After Bridges, redrawn)

chromosomes must be accepted as giving accurately the arrangement of the genes in the chromosomes.

Other features of the organisation of the genes in the
chromosomes are much less certainly known. Normal mitotic
and meiotic chromosomes contain, in place of the numerous
chromonemata of the salivary-gland chromosomes, one to four

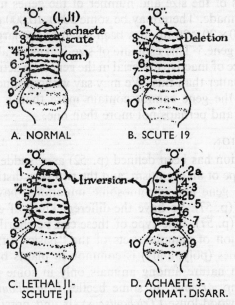

A. NORMAL   B. SCUTE 19

C. LETHAL JI-   D. ACHAETE 3-
   SCHUTE JI   OMMAT. DISARR.

Figure 26. The left end of the *X* chromosome in *Drosophila melano-*
    gaster with small re-arrangements corresponding to certain
    mutations. (After Muller, Profokieva and Raffel)*

longitudinal threads, the *chromatids*. The visible structure of
the euchromatic regions is simpler in the normal chromosome
than in that of the salivary gland. The staining property of the
euchromatic regions is due to the presence of nucleic acid,
which is thought to be associated with the active hereditary

* Prof. Muller wishes to correct this figure as follows. In "A" the line of
apparent optical separation within ring 2 does not necessarily separate the loci of
ac and sc, and is not necessarily identical with the break within ring 2 shown in
"D". In "C" the upper break may have been within or just below ring 1, and the
lower break correspondingly higher and within ring 2; hence the numbering
given represents only the longest inversion here possible. In "D" the brace
indicating the inversion should end just below 2a.

material. They are therefore believed to contain the genes.* But each band is certainly not the site of a single gene; there is no doubt that the genes are much smaller than the bands, smaller even than the finest divisions into which the bands, which are often complex (Fig. 26), can be seen to be divided. The fact that in *Drosophila* some bands have been clearly shown to contain more than one gene proves the truth of this. Rough estimations of the size and number of the genes in *Drosophila* have been made. There may be some 5000–10,000 genes in this fly, and $100 \times 20 \times 20$ mμ has been given as the largest possible size of the gene.† This estimate of size makes no allowance for the presence of inactive material in the gene; the active gene may be even smaller than this. We may say without much danger of error that the gene cannot contain more than a few protein molecules, and perhaps not more than one.

2. MUTATION

A mutation has been defined (p. 52) as a sudden change in the genotype of an organism, and the two very distinct kinds of mutations, gene and chromosome mutations, have been distinguished (p. 57). So have the different kinds of chromosome mutations (p. 57). One type of these can be shortly discussed. Reduplication of complete sets of the "basic" (*n*) number of chromosomes (polyploidy) is common in plants but is known to occur in nature among animals only in some races of the brine-shrimp *Artemia*, in some beetles (*Curculionidæ*),[294] perhaps in a wood-louse (*Trichoniscus*),[312] and possibly in a few other animals. Viable polyploids have been experimentally produced in a few animals, e.g. *Drosophila* and some Amphibia.[97] Polyploidy has been of little importance in animal evolution. On the other hand, we shall find (p. 74) that changes in the chromosome number within a set have certainly been important in animal evolution. Re-arrangement within a chromosome is of very great importance.

(a) *Gene mutations*

The mutations that were used in early genetical experiments were supposed each to result from a change in the chemical or

* See C. D. Darlington,[65] for evidence that the heterochromatic regions are not genetically functionless.
† $1\mu = 1/10^3$ mm., $1m\mu = 1/10^6$ mm.

physical nature of a single gene. This gene was looked upon as controlling the character in the phenotype that was changed by the mutation, and the phenotype was thus regarded as a mosaic of characters each under the control of a gene. The recessive condition was regarded as due to the loss of a gene that was present in the dominant—the "presence-and-absence" theory. We have now to follow the changes in the conception of the gene and of its action in the body that have been caused by later work.

Very soon it was found that more than one gene might act on a single character. For instance, the form of the comb in fowls was found to be controlled by at least two genes, those responsible for the "rose" and "pea" shapes. But this did not greatly modify the general conception; the body was still looked upon as a mosaic, with each part under the control of its own genes.

The presence-and-absence theory was soon found to be too simple to account for the facts. First, it was found that new mutations might be dominant as well as recessive, and reversal of a mutation was found to be possible—a recessive mutation sometimes mutated back to the original dominant condition. It was easy to imagine the sudden loss of a gene but not so easy to understand how one could be suddenly formed or regained.

Secondly, the discovery of multiple allelomorphs showed that mutation might take several forms in a single gene. These multiple allelomorphs are series of recognisably distinct mutations all taking place in the same locus in the chromosome. That they are all mutations of a single gene is shown by the fact that the phenotypic effects of all members of the series are of the same general nature, varying only in the extent of their differences from the normal (non-mutated) type—varying, that is to say, only in the "intensity" of their action. Many of the allelomorphs may mutate to each other and back to the non-mutated, normal condition (p. 97).

Numerous such series occur in *Drosophila*; some of the best known are the allelomorphs of "white" eye-colour, of which there are more than a dozen, of "vestigial" wing, and of "bobbed", a gene affecting the formation of bristles. The "white" series all weaken the colour of the eyes, giving a gradation of colours from the deep-red eye of the wild type to full white. The "vestigial" series gives a range of phenotypes from the full size of the normal wing to a minute rudiment (Fig. 27).[213]

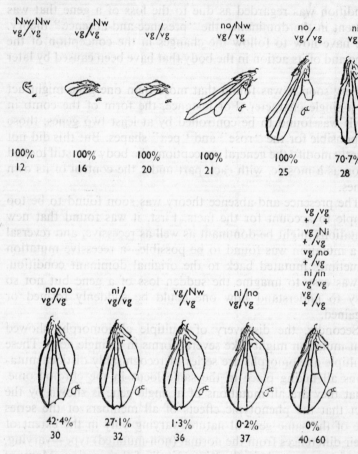

Figure 27. A series of phenotypes of the wing and haltère in *Drosophila melanogaster* produced by combinations of the allelomorphs of "vestigial". The figures below the diagrams are explained on p. 102. Symbols above the figures define the combinations in the paired chromosomes; vg+ is the unmutated (normal) form. (After Mohr)

Since each of these series shows a succession of forms in which the phenotype is altered more and more from the normal until the condition of the fully mutated gene is reached, it is clear that, whatever the nature of the change that we call mutation, it must be able to take place in a series of steps. Mutation is certainly not complete loss of a gene; rather, in these cases, it appears to be an alteration in the gene's efficiency, and one that is quantitatively variable. This is probably true of mutation in general, but the alteration, even of recessive mutation, is not always negative in effect, weakening some positive character in the phenotype. For instance, "full-black" in mice is recessive to the wild type; the stronger colour is recessive. We shall return to this point later (p. 103). Similarly, dominant mutation is quantitative increase of a gene's efficiency, not addition of a new gene not previously present.

Though several allelomorphic mutations may occur in a single gene, it is certain that a gene cannot mutate in an indefinite number of ways. Only a certain number of allelomorphs occur in each series, and, apart from these series of allelomorphs (which must be regarded not as each a different type of change in the gene but as more or less extreme forms of the same change), multiple mutations in single genes are not common. A few examples of two distinct mutations in the same gene are known. "Ultra-bar" is a second mutation at the locus of the well-known "bar" gene of *Drosophila* (p. 72).

The truth that the possible directions of mutation in a gene are restricted is supported by much other evidence. If the gene could mutate with equal readiness in an indefinite number of ways, we should not expect that reversal of a mutation should be common—as it is—or that allellomorphs should mutate to each other. A second mutation in a gene that had already mutated should in the majority of cases be different from the first and unrelated to it. This is not so.

The directions in which mutation can occur are undoubtedly determined by the chemical and physical organisation of the genes; only some changes in this organisation are possible. Further evidence for this is given by the fact that the same mutations may occur in several related species ([80], pp. 108 ff.). Here the gene appears to carry its structure beyond the species, and similar changes in its structure can occur in different species. Even in different species only very few different mutations can occur in a gene.

It must be concluded, first, that mutation is not complete loss of a gene, and, secondly, that mutation is a change in the gene's physical organisation, which may take several quantitatively different forms; but at most only a few qualitatively different changes may occur in a gene.

The original conceptions of the gene and its action were next shown to be inadequate in that not merely two or three, but a large number of genes may control a single character. In *Drosophila* there are at least thirty distinct genes controlling eye-colour. These are all at different loci in the chromosomes and therefore not allelomorphs of each other. The body is certainly not a mosaic of parts each under the control of one or a few genes.

This was further emphasised when it was found that a single gene may affect many parts of the body. The genes are generally known by their most obvious, "primary", effects, but when their action is studied more carefully it is found that most of them act also, though less obviously, on other parts of the body. Dobzhansky [77] showed that the gene of "white" eye-colour in *Drosophila* alters the form and colour of the testis and spermatheca. He also investigated [78] the multiple effects in *Drosophila* of two allelomorphs, "stubble" and "stubbloid", the primary action of which is to shorten the bristles. He found that they alter the shape of the wing, the length of the legs, and the number of branches of the antenna. Many other examples of these multiple (*pleiotropic*) effects could be given.* When we speak of a gene by its name, we should remember that the name merely recalls the primary effect and that the gene may have much more general action. There is no reason for surprise that genes have these widely distributed effects, for every cell in the body contains the whole genotype, and must be altered to some extent by mutation in any gene. It is perhaps more surprising that many mutations have recognisable effects on only a few tissues or organs; other parts of the body may be affected but the changes in them are too small to be recognised. We should think of a mutation as, potentially at least, altering the whole organisation of the body.

It follows from this that we may expect the phenotypic effect

---

* E.g. O. L. Mohr,[213] for multiple effects of "vestigial" in Drosophila .The pleiotropic effects of "minute" genes are referred to below (p. 70).

of any mutation to be altered by changes in many other genes of the genotype. This is found to be so; whatever mutation we choose, we find that there are many other genes that recognisably alter its expression when they mutate. Further, it is believed by many that there are a very large number of genes of which the only recognisable action is to alter the effects of mutation in other genes; these are called *modifying genes*.* Frequently the effect of each modification is slight, but the modifications are numerous and together they may have large effects. They are the usual cause of variability of the expression of a mutation in a natural population, in so far as such variation is inherited, and of increase or decrease of the expression under selection.†

It must not be thought that the modifying action of genes is always slight. Genes are known that will completely suppress the expression of some other gene. When such genes have no other recognisable effect, they are known as *suppressors*.

A somewhat different phenomenon is that known as *epistasis*. Two mutated genes act primarily on the same character but in different ways. When both are present the expression of one is suppressed and the phenotype is indistinguishable from that produced by the other ("epistatic") gene alone. Thus in some rodents a mutated gene E^d gives black coloration and entirely suppresses the expression of a gene A^w, which in the absence of E^d gives a light-bellied grey. E^d is epistatic to A^w. In these cases of epistasis, the one gene is dominant over the other, but the "dominance" is different in kind from that between allelomorphs, the usual genetical use of the term.‡

Between complete suppression and the small effects of typical modifying genes all intermediates are known. Thus, Hersh [163] has observed the modifying action of several well-known genes on the expression of the mutation "bar" in *Drosophila*. Bar

* Few modifying genes have been localised in the chromosomes, or have been isolated and shown to be inherited in the Mendelian manner. Eight modifiers of "eosin" eye-colour in *Drosophila* are exceptional in this respect. They were shown by C. B. Bridges [26] to be typical genes, showing normal Mendelian heredity and occupying definite loci in the chromosomes. For the great majority of modifiers the belief that they are of the same nature as normal genes is hypothetical, though the hypothesis may be regarded as very probably true. They are undoubtedly hereditary factors that can be passed on from one generation to another.

† See K. Mather [204, 205] for discussion of *polygenic* combinations of modifying genes and their part in producing change under selection. See also discussion in *Nature*, vols. 149–151, 1942–3, and pp. 135, 211 below.

‡ Cf. p. 83.

is a mutation of which the primary effect is to reduce the number of facets in the eye—the normal eye has about 750 facets; in the presence of heterozygous bar there are about 350, and with homozygous bar about 70. Hersh used a stock with homozygous bar (and also another mutation, "forked"—f), and observed the number of facets when still other mutations were also present. Some of his results are given in the following Table. It will be seen that each of the other mutations (Scute, sc; Echinus, ec; etc.) increases or decreases the number of facets, and thus modifies the action of the "bar" gene. Some of these effects are considerable in size. The other genes all have their own primary effects, which are unrelated to that of "bar". They are therefore not typical modifying genes but the results illustrate the points that the action of a mutation may be modified by any of a large number of other mutations, and that the modification is variable in extent. It is these points that are important for us in our attempt to interpret the organisation of genotype.

Genotype								Difference in facet number from pure fB
sc	—	—	—	—	—	f	B	0·26
—	ec	—	—	—	—	f	B	4·87
—	—	cv	—	—	—	f	B	23·94
—	—	—	ct	—	—	f	B	−15·28
—	—	—	—	v	—	f	B	18·51
—	—	—	—	—	g	f	B	−24·32
—	—	—	—	—	—	f	B	0·00
sc	ec	cv	ct	v	g	f	B	2·73

(From Hersh, simplified.)

Another type of interaction between genes, which can hardly be regarded as modification or suppression, is that in which two genes with identical effects have together no more effect than each has separately. The "minute" genes of *Drosophila* give an example of this.[267] These are a numerous class of genes at different loci all of which have very similar or identical effects which are widely pleiotropic. They alter the form of many organs, decrease the size, the speed of development, viability and so on—they give in fact one of the best examples of the pleiotropic action of genes. They are lethal when homozygous, but many are not so when heterozygous. When two are present, both as heterozygotes, their effects are not greater than those of a single heterozygous gene of this type.

Alteration of the quantitative extent of the expression of a gene is not the only form of modification. The structural form of the expression may be altered (its *specificity*). Also, some mutations are expressed not in all the individuals of a population that possess them but only in some percentage of the individuals. This percentage is known as the *penetrance* of the mutation. It, also, can be modified by the presence of other mutations.

Most of the mutations we have considered alter structure or colour pattern, but almost every other character of the phenotype is under the control of genes. Physiological characters such as the length of life—almost every mutation, not only those of the "minute" genes, alters the life-span to a greater or less extent—or the range of viable temperatures; some characters of behaviour such as waltzing in mice; pathological conditions such as hæmophilia and night-blindness in man, are all controlled by genes. A most important class of mutations that has only incidentally been mentioned is that of the numerous "lethals" which cause the death of the organism at some stage in its life-history. Also, nothing has been said of sex-linkage, in which the gene is carried in the X chromosome and can only appear as a homozygote in the sex bearing two X chromosomes. Genes in the Y chromosome are rare, but a few are known in *Drosophila*. Effects of mutation in the Y chromosome genes can only appear in the heterozygous sex, in which alone the Y chromosome is present. Mutations of all these types are subject to modification.

(b) *Chromosome mutations*

We will first consider re-arrangements within the chromosomes, returning later to mutations in which the number of the chromosomes is altered.

At first sight it would seem that those chromosome-mutations that consist only in re-arrangement of the position of the genes, and not in loss of them or increase in their number, should have no effect on the phenotype, for in such changes no alteration would be made in the genes present or in their number. If this were so, the only chromosome mutations to have any phenotypic effect would be the deletions and duplications. It is, however, found that inversions and translocations may also alter the phenotype. They do so because the action of a gene is to some extent dependent on the characters of the genes near it in the chromosome. An inversion or translocation separates genes near the end of the re-arranged segment from some of their original neighbours and brings them close to other genes. Their action will therefore be somewhat different before and after

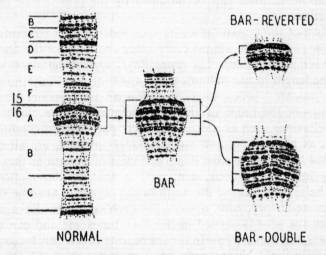

Figure 28. Reduplications in the "bar" locus of *Drosophila melanogaster*. (After Bridges)

the re-arrangement. Modification of the action of a gene by its neighbours in the chromosome is known as the *position effect*.

The first proof of the existence of a position effect was obtained from the behaviour of the bar mutation (*B*) in *Drosophila*. Observation of the salivary-gland chromosomes showed that this mutation is not, as was at first thought, a gene mutation; the bar mutant differs from the normal by a small duplication in the position of the gene (Fig. 28). A second duplication may occur in the same position and results in this gene being present in triplicate. This is known as "double-bar" (*BB*).* Reversal of the bar mutation may also occur ("reversed-

* We are not concerned with the second, distinct, mutation at this locus, "ultra-bar", mentioned earlier (p. 67).

bar") when the segment is, so far as can be seen, in the normal (non-mutated) condition—i.e. with no duplication.[27]

In the absence of any position effect, it would be expected that heterozygous double-bar $(BB/+)$ * would give the same phenotypic effect as homozygous bar (B/B),* for in both the mutated gene is present twice. But this is not so; the heterozygous double-bar always shows a greater effect than the homozygous bar. This difference can only be due to the different arrangement of the genes in the chromosomes, i.e. to a position effect. That there is no permanent change in the physical or chemical nature of the gene, as a result of the duplications, is shown by the fact that the behaviour of reversed-bar is indistinguishable from that of the normal, non-mutated fly.

Other examples of position effects have been studied.[79] Their reality must be accepted as established, and we shall find that they have probably been of great importance in evolution (pp. 211–212).

One other point in the work on the bar gene is of great interest. For many years bar had been regarded as a gene mutation, and it was only when the salivary-gland chromosomes were examined that it was realised that it is in truth a small chromosome mutation. Some other mutations have been shown to be re-arrangements after they had been thought for long to be gene mutations.[223] This suggests the possibility that many and even, possibly, all the mutations that we have called gene mutations may really be re-arrangements, many probably too small to be seen. How far this is true is in dispute, but it may be said that there is no sufficient evidence at present for the conclusion that *all* gene mutations are re-arrangements. Indeed, there is some evidence (from the action of ultra-violet light) that gene mutations in general are different in nature from re-arrangements.[203] We may, however, note that, if it were shown in the future that all gene mutations are of this nature, it might lead to a conception of the genotype similar to that proposed by Goldschmidt.[140] He thinks that we should give up the conception of the genes as separate entities in the chromosome and think of them rather as parts of the whole chromosome, which he would consider as a *unit*, modifiable in its parts (by what we

* These symbols represent the condition of the paired chromosomes of the zygote. The + sign is used for the normal, wild, condition.*

have called mutations), and expressing its action in the body as the result of its constitution in all its parts. Whether this view will be held in the future cannot at present be said.

Even if all mutations were found to be re-arrangements, this would not account for all the re-arrangements that occur in the chromosomes of animals in nature. Larger changes, especially large translocations, certainly occur in evolution (p. 132), though in experiments they are often lethal. It is also found that the chromosome number varies in closely related species—see

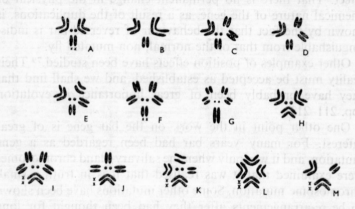

Figure 29. Forms and numbers of the chromosomes in some species of *Drosophila*. (After Metz and Moses)

Fig. 29, in which are shown the forms of the chromosomes on the equatorial plate of certain species of *Drosophila*.* For these forms to be evolved from each other it is necessary that chromosomes must have been both added to and removed from the genotype in evolution.

The means by which these changes in the chromosome number are brought about in evolution is not very clearly understood.[323] To understand the difficulties involved it is necessary to consider the nature and functions of the centromere, the organ in the chromosome responsible for its movements to the pole of the spindle at mitosis and meiosis. The centromere is a body contained in the substance of the chromo-

* As noted above (p. 64), experimental polyploids are viable in *Drosophila* and some other animals.

some at some point of its length. It passes in front of the rest of the chromosome to the pole, so that when it is near the centre of the chromosome (*metacentric*) the latter appears V-shaped on its path to the pole, and when it is near the end (*acrocentric*) the chromosome appears straight. All chromosomes, if they are to behave normally, must contain a centromere, for without it they cannot pass to the poles. In *Drosophila* and most other organisms a chromosome cannot contain more than one,* for if two centromeres are present they will often be attracted to opposite poles and the chromosome will be broken as they separate. Centromeres are believed never to originate *de novo*, but there is evidence that two in contact may sometimes fuse into one, and that, at least in plants, a centromere may divide transversely when the chromosome breaks across it. When this happens both halves of such a chromosome may possess a centromere.

These facts enable us to discuss how the chromosome number of an animal may be altered. Direct loss of a whole chromosome is usually lethal in experiments and duplication of a whole chromosome is at least harmful. It is possible that duplication of one of the original chromosomes might in some circumstances not be sufficiently injurious to cause extinction of the individual that carried it. If so, such a chromosome might later be altered from its identity with the chromosome of which it was originally a duplication—by translocation and other re-arrangements, which need not individually be large. It would then be impossible to see that it had arisen as a duplication and the chromosome number would have been increased by one. Unless a new chromosome can arise in this way, it would seem that the number could only be increased by breakage of a chromosome at the centromere, which itself divided, so that each part possessed a centromere. This would have to be accompanied by union of each half of the chromosome at this point with parts of other chromosomes by translocation, for centromeres are never exactly terminal. This process seems too complicated a course of events to be likely.

Loss of a chromosome is perhaps easier to understand. Two

---

* In *Ascaris megalocephala* each chromosome is known to have several centromeres (*polycentric*). This may also be so in some insects (Heteroptera). The behaviour of such chromosomes differs from that of the more common monocentric type.

chromosomes might perhaps break very close to the centromeres and the parts containing the centromeres might unite with fusion of the centromeres. The parts without centromeres might then be translocated to other chromosomes. This is possible but unlikely, for it too requires a very complicated group of events. It is more likely that a series of translocations might transfer the substance of a chromosome to others until the first chromosome was reduced to a size at which its loss would not be lethal.* If it were then lost, the chromosome number would have been reduced. This is the most probable way in which loss of a chromosome could happen.†

Whatever the method by which they are brought about, comparison of the chromosomes in nearly related species shows that large scale re-arrangements undoubtedly occur commonly in evolution, and that, among these re-arrangements, alteration of the chromosome number is frequent. These are certainly ways in which the genotype is altered in the evolution of animals, but we must admit that our present knowledge is not enough to tell us clearly how they are brought about.‡

3. THE EXPRESSION OF THE GENES IN THE PHENOTYPE

We have next to ask what are the underlying changes in the living process that result from mutation and give rise to the various visible changes in the body that follow mutation.

First, the wide range of mutation must be emphasised again. Most mutations are normally recognised by the changes in adult structure that they cause, and it is these structural mutations that have been most closely investigated. We therefore cannot avoid paying most attention to mutations of this type, but it must not be forgotten that, for our purpose of interpreting animal evolution, the many mutations that control the physiology and behaviour of the animal may be as important as structural mutations. Survival of an animal species may be

* The centromere is usually situated in a small region of the chromosome without genes. This might make the required reduction of the chromosome easier. But *Drosophila pallidipennis* is an exception to the rule that there is a vacant region near the centromere,[87] and the presence of a vacant region must not be assumed to be general.

† An artificial reduction of the *n* number from 4 to 3 by means similar to these has been accomplished in *Drosophila melanogaster* ([91], quoted by Waddington, *Modern Genetics*).

‡ H. V. Crouse [57] gives some evidence that the position of the centromere in the chromosome may be altered in evolution (*Sciara*, Diptera).

determined by many characters besides its adult structure. The physiology both of the adult and of the developing young, the length of the animal's life and its powers of reproduction, and many other features of the biology may influence the animal's chance of survival.

Even when we are considering mutations that are expressed in characters of the adult structure, we cannot confine our discussion to the adult stage of the life-history. It is a fundamental truth of animal biology that the adult form is a product of its development, and that almost every change in the adult is caused by some alteration in the processes of development (p. 314). Though we normally recognise mutations by their effects in the adult, their immediate action is in fact very often on the processes of development.

There are some features of development that are not usually emphasised by the embryologists but are very important for an understanding of the action of change in the genotype. This is especially true of the part played by the emergence of pattern in development, and we must therefore shortly discuss this subject before we pass on to the effects of mutation. We will consider only the development of the fertilised or parthenogenetic egg, disregarding the various other processes by which animals attain their specific forms—bud-formation, regeneration, etc. ([37], ch. XX)—for these have not been of any considerable importance in evolution.

The emergence of pattern is one of the most universal features of development. Pattern expresses itself in all differentiation of parts within the body. This can be said without expressing any opinion about the means by which the patterns come to emerge. By whatever means the development of pattern is brought about, it is clear that specific form, as such and distinct from other properties of the species, is determined by the pattern of the tissues and organs that form the body. Other kinds of change, such as growth and increasing complexity of behaviour, accompany the emergence of pattern, which is only one of the features of development, though a universal and characteristic feature.

Some pattern may be present in the egg before development starts. The first indication of pattern is usually the polarity axis which is often determined in the unfertilised egg, and some other indications of pattern may also be determined at that time—for instance, in snails, the left- or right-handedness of segmentation which determines in later development the direction of the spiral of the shell. [267, 215, 47] The remaining axes of symmetry are determined during segmentation shortly after fertilisation.

Soon after fertilisation, and still during the segmentation of the egg, other types of pattern begin to appear in the differentiation of the organs and tissues. One of the earliest is the distribution of the differences that distinguish the two primary tissues, the ectoderm and the endoderm. Throughout the rest of development these patterns continually become more intricate. In part the differentiations take the form of histological and structural differences between the cells. Some are produced under the influence of neighbouring tissues by the process known as evocation. [318, 225] Differential growth takes a large place in the differentiation. [176] It follows in general the laws that we found to control allometric change of form during evolution (p. 37), but we know very little of how the different growth-rates of the tissues are determined and controlled. All these changes take a determined course which is different in each species.

However complex the course of development, it leads in the end to the emergence in each species of the peculiar pattern of the adult specific form, with an exactness that is always surprising but never perfect. Individual animals always differ in small details of structure.

We have now to ask how genetic change modifies these processes so as to produce the changes in adult structure that we recognise as the effects of mutation. There are at least three ways in which it might do so: (1) The *rate* of some developmental process might be altered so that the change of pattern as development proceeds is faster or slower than the normal; for example, the allometric growth of a part might be brought nearer to or farther from isometry. (2) The *period in development* at which some change occurs might be altered in either direction. Such action will alter not only the form of the developmental stages, but also that of the adult, for it will allow a longer or shorter time than the normal for differential growth before the adult condition is reached. (3) Both these types of change will alter the relative sizes of parts of the body and so alter its patterns, but they will not originate new structure. A third type of alteration that might result from genetic change is that *new differentiations*, new patterns, might be caused to arise either in developmental stages or in the adult.

We must discuss whether genetic change is able to produce alterations of each of these types in the structure of the body.

(a) *Rate genes*

We will first consider the evidence that genes may control the *rates* of developmental processes in the body.

Many of the processes that occur during development are at base chemical. In the chemistry of non-living matter the rates of reactions are controlled by the physical conditions under which they take place, and especially by the temperature. If genes, and the changes in them, control the rates of chemical processes in the body, and if, as is true, abnormal environmental conditions may, like mutations, modify the course of development, it is to be expected that there should be similarity between the action of mutation and of these abnormal conditions in the environment. In fact, this is found to be so. It is found that abnormalities similar to those that result from mutation may often be produced by unusual environmental conditions of many kinds, and especially by exposure to temperatures outside the normal range. Individuals which possess abnormalities simulating the effects of genetic change but produced by action of the environment have been called *phenocopies* (Goldschmidt [138]). As an example of these similarities, those that Goldschmidt [137] produced by treating larvæ of *Drosophila* with high temperatures may be quoted. The larvæ were exposed to temperatures between 35 and 37 deg. C. for short periods at definite stages of their development. They showed modifications of the wings and other organs very like certain well-known mutations. The table on p. 74 summarises his results. The similarity between the actions of genes and temperature gives strong evidence that the genes act by altering the *rates* of processes in the body.

In the production of phenocopies it is necessary to treat the larvæ at a defined short period in the development, and, as is shown in the table, this period differs for each effect. It is therefore clear that it is not the chemical development as a whole that is altered by the abnormal conditions but rather some process that occurs at the time at which the treatment is effective. And since the process must be similarly altered by the experimental conditions and by the mutations, it appears that the action of the mutations must also be restricted to processes at these short stages of the development. We shall later find (pp. 84 ff.) other evidence that genes exert their action on short and well-defined periods in the development of an animal.

Phenotype simulated	Conditions of Treatment			Phenocopies
	Age of Larva	Temperature	Exposure	
	Days	deg. C.	Hours	Per cent.
Scalloped . . .	4½–5½	35	12–24	70
Curly	6 –7	35–37	18–24	76
Ski	6 –6½	36–37	12	43
Spread . . .	5½	35	18–24	91
Curved . . .	5 –7	36	18	23
Dumpy . . .	5	36	12	34
Lancet . . .	7	36–37	18	22
Miniature . .	5½–7	36–37	12–18	40
Blistered . . .	5 –6	36	18	10
Rolled . . .	7	35–37	18–24	40
Trident . . .	7	35–37	6–24	82
Eye-size . . .	5½–6	37	18	100
Horns . . .	7	35	24	4
Benign . . .	4½	35	18–24	75

(From Goldschmidt.)

It is not only in phenocopies that genes can be shown to control the rates of change in the animal body. The allometric growth-rates of tissues are a second example of quantitative processes of change in the body; they are often under the control of genes. One of the best-known and clearest instances of this control is that of the differences between the sexes of insects and vertebrates in secondary sexual characters. The ultimate control is here the genetic differences of the sex chromosomes, whether this difference is one of a single gene or of many closely linked genes (as has been shown to be true in *Drosophila*,[58] and is probable in the vertebrates). This ultimate genetic control is exerted over the form of the secondary sexual characters by means which are not the same in all animals. In vertebrates it is well known that the form of the secondary sexual characters is under the control of hormones secreted by the gonads, the differentiation of the gonads in the male or female direction being determined in general by the genetic constitution *; in insects the form of the organs is more often (and perhaps always) determined directly by the genetic constitution of the tissue cells themselves. But in both groups the differences in the form of the organs are due to unequal allometric growth in the two sexes—all the organs are present in both sexes but grow at different rates in the male and female. We thus have here a clear example of ultimate control of allometric rates of growth by the genetic constitution.

Another example of control of allometric growth by genes has been thoroughly investigated in the interaction between bar and other mutations in the eye of *Drosophila*. We have already discussed interaction between these mutations from another point of view (p. 69). The point of interest here is that the eye has two parts, the dorsal and ventral lobes, and it was found that, when the development of these was compared, their relative changes in size could be expressed as an allometric equation of the form $Y=bx^k$ (p. 38). The values of b and k were altered (modified—p. 69) by the presence of other mutations,[163] i.e. the constants of the allometric growth were controlled by the genotype.

Quantitative processes in the body of many other kinds are under the control of the genotype. Any process from the growth of the body as a whole to the production of a single chemical constituent may be so controlled. Quantitative control of the growth of the whole body is shown in the work of Castle and Gregory ([42], cf. also [40]) on large and small races of rabbits (Fig. 30). Here the genetic difference is multiple, but the effect is clear. The difference in growth-rate is due to quicker or slower growth during development; the eggs are equal in size.

Genetic control of the concentration of a single constituent is shown in the early work of Onslow,[233] who found that in the rabbit some genetic differences in pigmentation are caused by variations in the concentration in the tissues of an oxidase, the enzyme that causes oxidation of tyrosine to give the black

---

* But see for a recent discussion of the determination of sex in the vertebrate gonad, W. S. Bullough, *Nature*, **160**, 9, 1947.

pigment, melanin. He concluded that the immediate action of the gene is to control the *rate* at which the oxidase is produced. A somewhat similar case is that of the deposition of pigment in the eye of *Gammarus*.[114] In the normal form of this animal the eye is red in young embryos, but gradually darkens during embryonic life and is fully black at hatching. The darkening

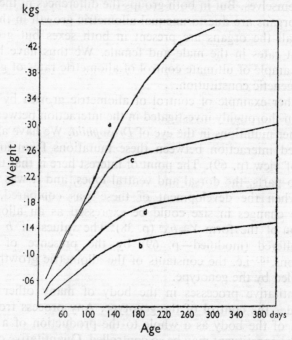

Figure 30. Growth rates of males in large and small races of rabbits. a—Large race; b—small race; c—F_1 between these; d—backcross of this F_1 with the small race. (After Castle)

is due to melanin formed in the eye during the later stages of embryonic development. There is a red-eyed mutant, in which the eyes of the early embryo are indistinguishable from those of the normal form, but darkening starts later and is much slower; the eye never becomes fully black. The mutation here alters not only the rate at which the pigment is produced, but also the time of its production (p. 84).

In biochemistry one of the most frequent mechanisms of chemical change is that a substance in the body is produced not by a single reaction but by a chain of reactions each controlled by an enzyme. In each reaction a product of the earlier reactions is used as the substrate. In more than one recent investigation, genes have been found to control these linked reactions, the reactions being each under the control of a different gene. An example is the work of Beadle and Ephrussi (cf. [20], for a review) on the red pigment of the eye of *Drosophila*. The pigment is formed by a series of reactions in which at least two genes, and almost certainly more, are concerned. If one of these genes —"vermilion" (*v*)—is inactive, as the result of a mutation, the colour of the eye is vermilion; a vermilion precursor of the normal pigment is formed but is not elaborated further; the chain is broken at this point. But the step from vermilion to the normal red is not wholly controlled by the vermilion gene; there is another gene—cinnabar (*cn*)—needed for full elaboration of the pigment. If *v* is active and *cn* inactive, the eye has a brownish-red, cinnabar, colour, but, if *v* is inactive, *cn* has no effect—the eye is vermilion whether *cn* is active or not. Thus *v* is epistatic (p. 69) to *cn*. These results may be explained if we assume that *v* controls an earlier member of the chain of reactions than that on which *cn* acts, and that the product of the reaction controlled by *v* is required for the reaction controlled by *cn*, which changes a cinnabar eye to the normal red. Epistasis may often be due to some such background as this.

We meet here the conception that genes act in the body by controlling the rates of enzymic reactions, and this view is becoming accepted of the action of very many genes. The genes probably exert their control over the enzymes by controlling their formation. There is much evidence for these views. A very clear example is the work of Rapaport,[249] who shows that phenocopies (p. 79) may be induced by treatment with various chemical substances that are known to inhibit enzymes. The effects are produced by concentrations of these substances below, but not far below, the lethal. The substance appears to act in the same way as the mutations, which are regarded as modifying the enzyme-forming activities of the genes.*

There is no doubt at any rate that much genetic action is expressed in alteration of the rates of processes within the body.

* For fuller discussion of this whole subject with other examples, see [128] and [337].

The rate of almost any quantitative change in the body, from single chemical reactions to the complex growth of the body as a whole, may be under genetic control.

(b) *The time of action in the life-history*

It has been mentioned that Ford and Huxley in their work on the pigmentation of the eyes of *Gammarus* found that the melanin was laid down in the red-eyed mutation both more slowly than in the normal form and also later in the life-history. We have here an example of the type of action to be discussed in this section.

Another example of action of this type, and one that has been thoroughly investigated, is the action of the various allelomorphs of "vestigial" on the wing of *Drosophila*. The range of the adult phenotypes of these mutations has been shown in Fig. 27 (p. 66); they give a series in which the wing is more and more reduced in size until only a vestige remains. In the larval development of these wings (Goldschmidt [139]), the wing in the earliest stages is normal in all, but its further development is inhibited, at periods which differ for the various allelomorphs, by degeneration of the tissues at the edge of the wing (Fig. 31). The time of the onset of this degeneration is earlier the more abnormal the adult wing. The mutation thus seems primarily to cause some change responsible for the degeneration. The cause might be either lack of a substance necessary for normal development or presence of a poisonous substance not normally present. Which of these alternatives is correct was not determined, but Goldschmidt expressed the facts in the diagram of Fig. 32 on the assumption that a necessary substance is lacking.

The point of special interest to us here is that departure from the normal occurs earlier in the development of the more abnormal allelomorphs. The genes control not only the amount of the substance in the body but the time at which its concentration becomes abnormal.

Fig. 32 is remarkably similar to the figures in which Goldschmidt had earlier interpreted his results on intersexes in the gipsy-moth, *Lymantria dispar* (e.g. [133-4]). These will give us another example of genetic control of the period in development at which changes occur. He found evidence of a balance between two sex-determining substances, the one tending to cause dif-

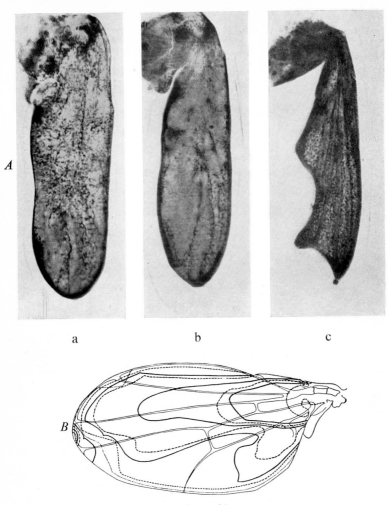

a   b   c

Figure 31

A. Three stages of the development of the wing of *Drosophila melanogaster* with the "scalloped" abnormality (vg/vg^{no}). a—Youngest; c—oldest.

B. Outlines of the wing with a number of allelomorphs of "vestigial", to demonstrate the path of the destructive process. (Both after Goldschmidt)

ferentiation in the male direction, the other in the female. All the animals, whatever their sex, contained both of these; the direction of sexual differentiation was determined, not by the presence of one or the other, but according as one or the other was in excess. He concluded that the male-determining substance was stronger in intersexual females (i.e. females with some male characters) than in normal females; and that in these intersexual forms a change occurred during development from excess of the female-determining substance (characteristic of

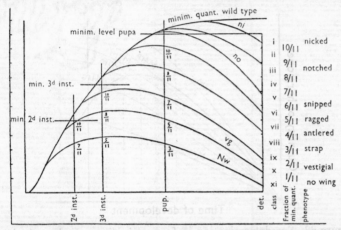

Figure 32. Action of the allelomorphs of "vestigial" on the wing of *Drosophila melanogaster*. Ordinates: amounts of some substance necessary for normal development. Each curve corresponds to one of the allelomorphs. Abnormalities begin at the stage of the life-history (plotted on the abscissa) where the curve leaves that for the wild type. (After Goldschmidt)

the earlier parts of the development) to excess of the male-determining substance (Fig. 33). As a result of this change, there was a reversal of the direction of sexual differentiation; organs which were formed early were of the female form, those formed later of the male form, so that the adult structure was intermediate between male and female. The grade of the intersex, i.e. the extent of its difference from the sex of the earlier part of the development, was determined by the time of the reversal. This was controlled by the strength of the male-determining substance and the rate of its increase, and these were ultimately controlled by the genetic constitution of the individual. Similar interpretations have been given of some types of intersexuality in vertebrates.[11, 52] Here again genes control the time at which developmental processes take place.

The pattern of colour on the surface of an animal's body does not seem at first sight to be in any sense a quantitative distribution, nor is it obviously linked with any restricted period of the development. One would not suppose that it is controlled in the manner we are considering. Yet in some instances, especially in the wings of moths, it has been shown that colour

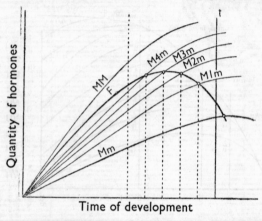

Figure 33. Sex-determination in *Lymantria dispar*. F: Female-determining substance. Mm, M1m–M4m: Male-determining substance as it occurs in females of various degrees of weakness. Mm is the normal female; M1m–M4m give intersexes. MM: Male-determining substance in the male. (After Goldschmidt)

pattern is the result of chemical processes in development and that variations in pattern may be due to changes in both the rate of these processes and the period in development at which they take place. In some instances both the rate and the period have been shown to be under genetic control. It is probable that much of the colour pattern of animals originates and is controlled in ways such as these.

The wing-pattern of the Lepidoptera is produced by distribution of differently coloured scales over the wing and is laid down in the pupal period when the scales are formed. The development of the pattern has been investigated [188] in the flour-moth, *Ephestia kühniella*, in which the most obvious feature of the pattern is a central band across the breadth of the wing bordered by lighter stripes (Fig. 34a). The wing-rudiment was variously damaged in the early pupal stage, and the resulting deformations of the central band in the adult wing were observed (Fig. 34b). It appeared that the deformations

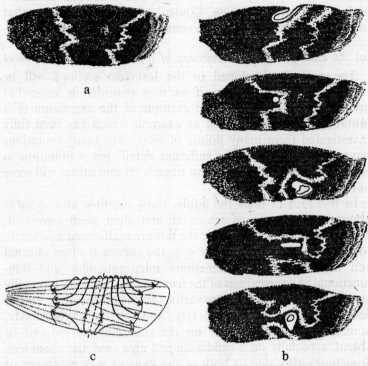

Figure 34. *Ephestia kühniella*, dark-coloured race. a—Normal wing; b—modifications of the pattern produced by damage of the wing rudiment in various ways; c—deduced course of the determination stream. (After Kühn and Henke)

were such as would result if the colour was due to a stream of some substance into the area of the band from the anterior and posterior margins of the rudiment (Fig. 34c), and that this stream was, in the damaged wing, deflected around the wounds that had been made. Pattern, then, in this instance, is due to a "determination stream", that is to say to the production of a substance in the developing body and its movements about the body. It has been shown that the genotype controls the production of this substance in *Ephestia*. A mutation is known which modifies the width of the central band in the undamaged wing; this can also be altered by heat treatment. The mutation was shown to act by altering both the amount of the determining substance and period of the life-history at which it is produced and spreads over the wing. Control of pattern similar to that in *Ephestia* has been found in some other Lepidoptera.

(c) *An example of the expression of a mutation in development*

The outlook developed in the last two sections will be brought into clearer focus if we now consider in somewhat greater detail a characteristic example of the expression of a mutation. For this we need an example which has been fully investigated from many points of view. Not many mutations have been investigated in sufficient detail, but a mutation in mice investigated by Little and Bagg [8, 195] and others will serve our purpose.*

In this race of mice the adults show multiple and variable abnormalities many of which at first sight seem unrelated. The eyes are often abnormal; the lids are malformed and small, so that they fail to cover the eye, the cornea is often affected and the whole eye is sometimes microphthalmic and nonfunctional. Abnormalities of the feet are very frequent, especially in the fore feet, and take the various forms of dorsal or ventral flexure, polydactyly, syndactyly and, rarely, hypodactyly. Sometimes patches of hair on the skin may be reduced or absent, especially on a saddle-shaped area over the shoulders. Sometimes also, one or both of the kidneys may be absent or abnormal. All these abnormalities occur irregularly, some individuals showing one and some another. They are commoner on the left side of the animal.

It was early shown that the condition was due to a single recessive gene in the homozygous state. It might seem at first sight that the various abnormalities were due to extensively pleiotropic effects of this gene (p. 68), though the irregularities of the expression among individuals of the same stock would be unusual. Further investigation has shown that this is not in general the true explanation.

* For a fuller summary of this work, see H. Grüneberg.[147]

In embryonic stages of the animals the abnormality appeared first in development of clear blebs or blisters below the ectoderm in the head region,[9, 23] when the embryo was about 7 mm. long. The blisters soon pass to a spectacle-like area above the eyes and to a saddle-shaped area over the back in the shoulder region. Bonnevie [23] believes that the fluid of the blisters is derived from that of the central canal of the nervous system which exudes, in both normal and mutant animals, through an opening, the foramen anterius, in the region of the myelencephalon; in the mutant an abnormally large amount of the fluid is exuded, and it is not, as it is in the normal embryo, resorbed, but remains to form the blisters. In opposition to this explanation it has been maintained (Plagens [239]) that the fluid is derived from the blood, being exuded from capillaries. The point is undecided. The movement of the blisters is probably mechanical, towards concavities of the surface over the head and in the shoulder region, and more frequently towards the left side because of the asymmetrical posture of the embryo. They may also be pushed along by greater tension in the regenerating tissues behind them as compared with that in the undamaged tissues before them.

While they are moving, the pressure in the blisters is small and they do little damage, but when they stop the pressure rises and the neighbouring tissues are damaged. In the head region this damage is chiefly to the eyes, most frequently to the ectoderm from which the cornea and lids are formed but sometimes to the eyeball. In the shoulder region it is chiefly the hair follicles in the ectoderm that suffer, but smaller blisters very often pass down the legs and cause the abnormalities of the feet. Other small blisters are found on the tibial border of the legs. Some of the smaller blisters may be resorbed during development and cause no abnormalities in the adult.

The action on the kidneys may be a true pleiotropic effect of the gene. It has not been fully investigated.

The action of the gene varies in different stocks, both in its immediate action of causing the blisters and in the adult abnormalities. The amount of the fluid in the blisters and the period of development at which they are formed both vary. Again, in some stocks almost every individual bearing the homozygous gene shows the abnormalities; the penetrance

4*

(p. 71) is nearly 100 per cent. But the penetrance can be altered by selection,[196] and a stock has been produced in which the mutation caused very few abnormalities. This variation can only be due to selection in the resistant stocks of modifying genes which reduce the expression of the mutation. Similar variation in the expression of the gene was obtained when a stock bearing many abnormalities was crossed with unrelated stocks not carrying the mutation.[23] Here the change in expression was clearly due to introduction of new modifying genes from the unrelated stocks. The specificity (p. 71) of the expression as well as the penetrance may vary; the relative frequency of the different types of abnormality varied between the original and the crossed stocks.

This example of the expression of a mutation in the developing animal shows us how complex the results of a relatively simple abnormality may be in later development and in the adult. Whichever explanation of the origin of the blisters we adopt, they are caused by effusion of liquid below the ectoderm. The immediate action of the mutation is an increase in the quantity of this fluid, presumably due to an acceleration of the process by which it is produced. The gene, then, is what we have called a "rate gene"; it exerts a quantitative control over the rate of this relatively simple process. It also controls the period in development at which the effusion of fluid occurs. All the various later abnormalities, except, perhaps, those of the kidneys, are secondary to these actions; they are the results of the abnormal conditions produced by the original changes in the highly complex organisation of the developing body.

The analysis also gives us a good example of modification of gene action by other genes. The expression may be altered in almost all its features—its penetrance, its specificity and the time of its occurrence in the development. Further, the modified expressions give a graded series from fully developed expression in the most sensitive stocks to hardly any expression at all in highly resistant stocks; the gene has not a simple all-or-none expression. This point is of great importance from the evolutionary point of view; we shall return to it later (p. 214).*

* For many other examples of developmental analysis of genetic change, the reader may be referred to the recent book by H. Grüneberg.[147]

(d) *Mutation and the origin of new structure*

In surveying the evolutionary changes displayed in palæontology, we found, besides allometric change in the relative sizes of parts correlated with change in body size, origination of new structural organisation, aristogenesis (p. 43). We took two examples of the latter. In one, the origin of hypsodontism in the horses, we found the new differentiation to consist in a change of the relative growth constants in the teeth. In the other, the increasingly complex teeth of the mastodonts, the aristogenesis consisted partly in reduplication of organs (the cusps and ridges of the teeth) already present in smaller numbers in the earlier teeth; partly in formation of new structures such as the cement. We have in these two last types of change a real and fundamental difference. Reduplication, like changes in allometry, is a modification of pattern already present in the body —in this case modification by increase in the number of the parts. It is not, as is the origin of cement in the elephant tooth, addition of *new* pattern of a kind not previously present in the body. There can be no doubt that both these types of aristogenesis, as well as changes in allometry, have played essential parts in evolution. Increasing complexity of the animal body is certainly present in evolution on any large scale and the formation of *new* pattern is clearly necessary for it. It is possible to deny this only if we accept the "pre-formation" theory of evolution in its entirety, the theory that the whole structure of later animals is inherent, but unexpressed, in all their ancestors. That theory is absurd: it is impossible to believe that an early metazoan, or even an early fish, had inherent within it all the organisation of a mammal. If the pre-formation theory is discarded, the only alternative is that *new* pattern has arisen in evolution.

We have now to ask whether there is evidence that mutation can give rise to all the types of change that occur in aristogenesis. Mutational control of allometry is undoubted (p. 80).

There can be no doubt that mutation can cause almost any modification of the pre-existing patterns of the body. We have discussed many examples of such action in the preceding sections, examples varying from changes in the relative sizes of organs to modifications of colour pattern, as in the wing of *Ephestia*. Many types of pattern besides those that we have considered may be genetically controlled. The distribution of chemical substances in the body is a true pattern, though not one of structure. Melanin, for instance, may be genetically controlled in distribution and amount, and its distribution may largely control the pigmentation of the organs in which it occurs. Dark (melanic) forms are varieties in which melanin is present in abnormal amount and its distribution more than normally extensive. Since melanin may not be evident in the normal form, it may seem at first sight that we have in the dark forms the production of a new substance, a new differentiation, but this is not so. Melanin is a widely distributed product of animal metabolism (cf. Onslow's work on rabbits, p. 81), and the gene should be regarded as increasing the amounts of this substance in the tissues and changing its distribution, not as causing the appearance of a new substance. The chemical patterns of the body have been altered by increase of the concentration of melanin; no *new* pattern has arisen.

Another type of change of pattern that may occur as a result of mutation is the loss of elements previously present. We have seen examples of this in the action of the mutations *v* and *cn* which prevent formation of the red pigment in the eye of *Drosophila* (p. 83). Another example is given by the allelomorphs of "scute" in *Drosophila*. These mutations alter the pattern of the bristles on the cuticle by loss of them. The numbers of bristles lost varies with the allelomorph. Other mutations may cause much larger deficiencies, e.g. "rump-less" in fowls, or microcephaly in vertebrates; the latter involves incomplete development of large parts of the head, and the former imperfect formation of the tail vertebræ. Probably most of these large structural effects are due to reductions of the growth rates, the reductions being so great that the organs appear non-existent in the adult.

Changes of pattern in which the number of similar parts in the body is altered can also be paralleled by the effects of mutation. Polydactyly is frequently under genetic control; it is often produced in man by a dominant mutation, and we have seen that it may occur in mice as the result of mutation (p. 88). The number of vertebræ in the different parts of the vertebral column of mammals (mice and rabbits) is genetically controlled, though the control is complex and has not been fully analysed

(147, pp. 191 ff.). There is no reason to doubt that variation in the number of similar parts in any region of the body may be controlled genetically.

Another type of change that is perhaps related to the last is that in which a pattern normal to one part of the body is transferred to another part. This is known as *homœosis*.* In *Drosophila* there may be formed in place of the antenna or

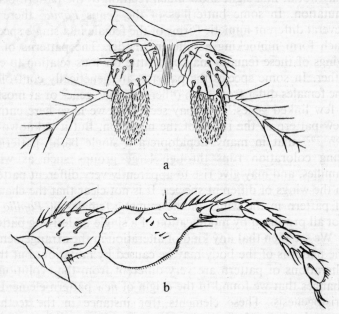

Figure 35. Aristopedia in *Drosophila melanogaster*. a—Normal antennæ; b—leg-like, aristopedic antenna. (After Balkaschina)

proboscis structures that resemble legs in general form (Fig. 35).14, 30 The conditions are known as "aristopedia" and "proboscipedia". That these abnormal organs are really legs is made more probable by the observation that some mutations that alter the structure of a normal leg have similar action on the leg-like antenna. "Four-jointed" reduces the number of joints of the tarsus in normal legs from five to four; it also shortens the "tarsus" of the antennal "legs".320 The antenna and proboscis are, morphologically, appendages of

* See 315 for review and discussion.

the segments on which they lie, as are the legs; and the most probable explanation of these extraordinary abnormalities is that we have here a modification of the pre-existing pattern, one in which a pattern normal to one part of the body has been transferred to an abnormal position. If so the novelty is again alteration of the pattern, not formation of a new pattern.

In some examples besides these, pattern modified by mutation may not at first sight show much relation to the pattern before mutation. In some butterflies of the genus *Papilio* there are several different mimetic forms of the female in a single species, each form mimicking a different model. The patterns of the wings of these females may bear little obvious relation to each other. In some species the patterns are genetically controlled; the females differ from each other by single genes or at most by a few linked genes.[118] It may seem that we have here entirely new pattern as the result of the mutation. But it is known [268, 269, 292,] that in many Lepidoptera a single basal pattern of wing coloration runs through large groups such as whole families, and may give rise to apparently very different patterns in the wings of different species. It is not clear that the changes of pattern in the wings of the mimetic females of *Papilio* are not all produced by modification of a single underlying pattern.

We see then that any kind of alteration in the arrangement of the patterns of the body may be caused by mutation, but these alterations of pattern are very different from the evolutionary changes that we found in the origin of *new* pattern elements in aristogenesis. These elements (for instance in the teeth of mastodonts, p. 42) first arise as very small new differentiations in a position where there was, so far as can be seen, no previous differentiation that could be modified into them. This is not an isolated example in evolution; many other organs can be shown to originate in this way, and indeed it seems to be a general mode of origin of new patterns. The horns of the titanotheres (p. 34) give us another example. They first appear as very slight thickenings on the upper surface of the skull.

We can say little of the causes of this mode of origin of new differentiation. We can only notice that we do not know of any examples in which such new differentiations have been produced by mutation. It may be suggested that mutational effects of this kind, if they occurred, would not be noted in our experimental animals; they would be too small. That may be so, but, at least, we have here a gap in our comparison between mutational and evolutionary change, and one which, at present, we cannot fill.

(e) The occurrence and frequency of mutation

Mutations being the material of most, if not all, of the changes of evolution, we clearly need to ask what is known of the circumstances of their occurrence and of their frequency, before we can discuss further how they lead to evolution.

In discussing the occurrence of mutation, distinction should be drawn between the large, easily recognisable mutations of genetic experiments (*macro-mutations*) and small mutations caused by modifying genes (p. 69), position effects (p. 72), etc. ("*micro-mutations*").[142] We will first consider the large mutations only.

The frequency of mutation may be measured as the proportion of genotypes that mutate in a unit of time. When comparison is made within a species, the proportion occurring per generation is an equally suitable measure, and is frequently used.

The frequency of macro-mutations varies with the external conditions. This is true whether we consider the frequency of mutation in a whole genotype or in a single gene. One of the most useful techniques of recent genetics has been treatment of organisms with doses of X-rays. It is found that this treatment greatly increases the mutation rate, and a large supply of mutations may be obtained by use of doses which are not large enough to kill the animal.[305] It appears that the rate is increased more or less generally in all the genes of the genotype. This is an example of the influence of external conditions on the mutation rate, but it is not one that need concern us further, for it will not occur in nature.*

Increase of mutation rate has also been observed as the result of treatment with ultra-violet light and with chemicals,

---

* The suggestion that spontaneous mutation might be caused by rays normally present in the atmosphere was made soon after the action of X-rays was discovered. It was soon shown that the radiation in the atmosphere was far too little in amount to be the true cause.[221] B. N. Rajewsky and N. W. Timoféeff-Ressovsky [248] have shown that isolation from cosmic rays has no effect on the mutation rate.

e.g. in mice by treatment with the carcinogenic sterol, methyl-cholanthrene.[286]

Temperature also influences the rate; the rate per unit of time increases as the temperature rises. In *Drosophila* the increase in mutation rate is greater than the increase of rate in the living process as a whole, so that more mutations occur in a generation at the higher temperatures. Muller [218] calculates for lethal mutations in the X-chromosome that one mutation occurs in 349 chromosome-months at an undetermined but cool room-temperature, and in 139 chromosome-months at 26·5 deg. C.

Further, there is evidence that the mutation rate may vary in a species from time to time without obvious correlation with external conditions. Spencer [279] kept a strain of *Drosophila* between March 1926 and April 1934, and counted the mutations that occurred in the strain. He found 25 mutations between the beginning of his observations and March 1928, none between that date and June 1931, and 29 between June 1931 and the end of his observations. Environmental conditions were kept as nearly constant as possible throughout the observations. Other cases of occasional outbursts of mutation are known.[141]

It is believed that there are certain mutations with the primary action of increasing the mutation rate. Their existence, if it is a fact, makes it possible that the rate may be altered by selection, and it has been suggested (but disputed [141]) that mutation in them may be the cause of the abnormal mutation rates, which have been observed. In any case, there is no doubt that differences in mutation rate per unit of time exist between animal species, and the differences may, perhaps, be caused by these genes. That such differences occur is shown by the fact that the proportion of mutant individuals in a population is approximately the same in *Drosophila* and man, although man's life-history is many times longer than that of *Drosophila*. The fly has presumably no more genes than man, and probably fewer; its mutation rate per unit of time must therefore be considerably higher than his.

It is clear that our knowledge of mutation rates in animals is very incomplete. We know nothing of the rates in any but a very few species, and even in these we are often unable to say what are the causes of the observed variations in the rate.

This is one of the largest gaps in our knowledge of the genetics of animals. For the understanding of evolution a wider knowledge of this subject would be very valuable.

So far we have considered the mutation rate in the genotype as a whole. When we examine the rates of mutation in individual genes (still confining our attention to the larger and more obvious mutations) we find these also variable. In *Drosophila* most genes mutate in not more, and often less, than 1 individual in 10^6, and very few in more than 1 in 10^5. These figures agree approximately with those for man; Haldane [156] finds that a new mutation to hæmophilia occurs in 1 in 10^5 individuals; Gunther and Penrose ([148], quoted by Haldane,[141] p. 146) that mutation to epiloia occurs in the same proportion of the population. These are examples of the most frequent mutations in man: many genes mutate less frequently.

A few genes are known to mutate at abnormally high rates in certain races of *Drosophila*. In these ("unstable") genes mutations may occur in as many as 1 per cent. of the cells bearing the genes. Since they occur in somatic cells, they may give rise to mosaic or variegated phenotypes.

Within an allelomorphic series the mutation rates are not the same for any two of the possible mutational changes. Even mutation and its reversal often have very different rates. The following table gives the number of mutations in allelomorphs

Mutations in allelomorphs of "White" in *Drosophila melanogaster*

	w	w^{bf}	w^e	w^a	w^b	w^x	W	No. of chromosomes tested
W (wild)	25	1	3	1	2	5	—	48,500
w^{co}	1	0	0	0	0	0	0	6,000
w^b	3	0	1	0	—	0	0	12,000
w^c	1	0	0	0	0	0	0	5,000
w^a	2	0	1	—	0	0	0	11,000
w^e	13	0	—	0	1	2	2	39,000
w^{bf}	1	—	0	0	0	0	0	5,500
w^t	1	0	0	0	0	0	0	7,000
w	—	1	1	0	1	1	1	54,000

(After Timoféeff-Ressovsky.)

of the "white" eye-colour gene ($W–w$) observed in a race of *Drosophila* by Timoféeff-Ressovsky.[304] These results were obtained in flies treated with X-rays, so that the mutation rates are far above the spontaneous rates (p. 95), but the rates probably illustrate the natural variability, for all the flies were given the same dose of X-rays. It will be seen that the frequencies of the various changes were very different; many of the possible changes did not occur in the numbers tested, whereas the wild form (W) mutated 37 times and to full white (w) 25 times. The reverse mutation from w to W occurred once.

In summary, we may say that the occurrence of these large and easily recognisable mutations is greatly variable in frequency though it is rare for any gene to mutate in nature in more than a very small proportion ($1/10^5$) of individuals. We have already seen that mutation is determined and not random in direction (p. 67); a gene can undergo at most a few different mutations, though some of these may take place in several steps (allelomorphs). In the whole genotype many different mutations can occur, but even so the changes will not be of every conceivable kind. Change of structure in a given direction will not occur unless the mutation appropriate to it is available. We therefore cannot assume that mutations of the required kinds will be available for any change of structure demanded by the adaptational needs of the animal. And, since mutation is normally a rare phenomenon, we cannot assume that all the mutations that are possible will be available in a population, except perhaps in very large populations.

These conclusions are strengthened by another consideration that we have not yet discussed. In this section we have considered only the occurrence of mutation; we have not considered how many of the mutations can be useful in evolution. The mutations we observe are recurrent, occurring again and again; they must have occurred many times in the history of the populations in which they occur. We have no accurate knowledge of the frequency of *new* mutations, but they certainly occur much less frequently. The recurrent mutations must have been tried out for selective value many times in the history of the population, and, since they are not now in the genotype, they must have been found of no positive value. We shall discuss later under what circumstances they may still play a part in building up evolutionary differences (p. 221). Except in so far as they can do so, the only macro-mutations that can be used in evolution are the much rarer new mutations.

Our discussion so far has given us the general picture of mutational change that we reach so long as we confine our discussion to macro-mutations. When we consider micro-mutations—mutations in modifying genes, position effects, and so on—the picture is different. We have little accurate knowledge of the frequency of these smaller changes, but at least we know that they are much more frequent than macro-mutations and indeed so frequent that in some species the genotype differs in these characters in every individual (cf. [197]). Extremely numerous mutations are needed for control of these individual differences.

4. DOMINANCE

We discussed the view of the early geneticists that dominance is due to the presence of a genetic factor and recessiveness to its absence (pp. 65–67). Incomplete dominance, the condition in which the phenotype of the heterozygote is intermediate between the phenotypes of the two homozygotes, is due, on this early view, to the weaker action of one, instead of two, genes in the zygotic genotype. We saw that this view soon met difficulties in the facts of reversed mutations and of multiple allelomorphs. Difficulties such as these suggested that mutation was a change in the potency of a gene, and a change that could take place in several steps, rather than an actual removal of the gene as the early theory postulated. Since that time much more knowledge on the nature of dominance has come to light.

We now know that*

1. The dominance of a gene may be altered by change in the environmental conditions, most easily by change of temperature.

2. A gene's dominance may be modified by changes in other genes in the genotype (*dominigenes*).

3. If a gene has pleiotropic action, the dominance may be different in the different parts of the body. A gene may be dominant in one organ and recessive in another.

4. Dominance may change during the life-history. A gene may be recessive in the young animal and dominant in the adult.

* Cf. R. Goldschmidt [140] for fuller discussion of the modern theory of dominance.

These facts are incompatible with the "presence-and-absence" theory in any form; a gene, for instance, cannot be absent in one organ and present in another, and the same mutation cannot be regarded as due to absence of a gene in the young and its presence in the adult. They are not incompatible with the view that mutation is a change in potency, for potency may vary in the different conditions of various tissues and of various times in the life-history. But they show clearly that, if it is such a change, the change can be modified by alterations of many kinds in the conditions within and outside the body.

In the light of our present knowledge of the manner in which genes act, it is not surprising that this should be so. We have seen reason to believe (p. 83) that genes act by controlling the efficiency of enzymes, and thus determining the rates of the chemical processes in the body that the enzymes control. It is to be expected that the reaction rates may be altered by change in the complex medium surrounding them, and that the action of the genes may vary with changes of the reaction rates due to these (and other) causes. Genes, in fact, are only part of the control of these rates: their action may be expected to vary with changes in other controlling conditions. We know also that the action of genes may be modified by change in other parts of the genotype (p. 69). We must now consider more closely how the phenomena of dominance and recessiveness are related to the control of enzymes by the genes.

Normally the rate of an enzymic reaction with a determined supply of the substrate, on which the enzyme acts, becomes asymptotic to a maximum rate as the efficiency of the enzyme increases, whether this increase is due to greater quantity of the enzyme or to some other change. A curve such as that of Fig. 36 is obtained. Where the curve is near the asymptote, variations in the efficiency of the enzyme will have very little effect on the rate of the reaction; where it is further from the asymptote, such variations will have larger effects.

If a mutation increases the activity of a gene, the gene will be least active in the unmutated homozygote, more active in the heterozygote, where one example of the mutation is present in the genotype, and still more active in the mutated homozygote where the genotype contains two examples of the mutation.

It is believed (e.g. Wright [334]) that a dominant mutation is one for which the efficiency of the enzyme is near the asymptote not only when the mutation is present as a homozygote but also when it is heterozygotic. The rate of the reaction, and therefore the phenotypic effect, will then be indistinguishable in both these conditions. But the unmutated homozygote being farther than the heterozygote from the mutated homozygote may give a different reaction rate and a different phenotypic effect. The supposed effects for a dominant mutation are

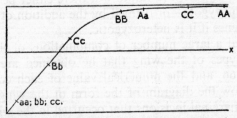

Figure 36. Diagram of the control of an enzymatic reaction by dominant (AA, Aa, aa), recessive (BB, Bb, bb) and incompletely dominant (CC, Cc, cc) genes. The ordinates give the efficiency of the enzyme, i.e. the reaction rate. This is supposed asymptotic to a maximum value. x—the supposed threshold value for change of the phenotypic effect from that of the recessives. The points marked give the efficiency with each combination of the genes.

illustrated by the points aa, Aa, AA, in Fig. 36. A recessive mutation is one in which the heterozygotic rate is far from the asymptote. If a threshold reaction rate (x) is necessary for the appearance of a phenotypic effect different from that of the recessive homozygote, the heterozygotic phenotype will be identical with that of the recessive if its reaction rate is below that minimum. This is complete recessiveness (bb, Bb, BB). If the heterozygotic rate is above the threshold but still far from the asymptote, we shall have incomplete dominance (cc, Cc, CC).

In series of multiple allelomorphs the dominance relations of the members to each other differ in different series. Sometimes, each allelomorph is dominant to all those with phenotypic effects further from the wild type than its own. Very often, the most dominant member, usually the wild type, is dominant to all the rest, and the others are incompletely dominant or recessive to each other. A series of this type, that of the "vestigial"

allelomorphs in *Drosophila*, has been investigated by Mohr ([213], cf. also [284]). He found that he was able to give numerical values to the activities of the allelomorphs, values representing the activities of the allelomorphs as shown on such a curve as that of Fig. 36. The values he gave to some allelomorphs were:

No-wing (vg^{Nw}), 6; vestigial (vg), 10; notched (vg^{no}), 15; nicked (vg^{ni}), 22; wild type ($+vg$), 30.

These values were for single genes. Since two genes are present in the diploid zygote, the values will there either be doubled— if it is a homozygote—or formed by the addition of the values of its two genes if it is heterozygotic.

He formed a large number of combinations of these genes. The phenotypes of the wing that he obtained are shown in Fig. 27, p. 66, and the numerical value of each combination is given below the diagram of the form of the wing. The percentage of marginal incisions that occurred in the wing in each combination is also given. The genes are pleiotropic and affect not only the form of the wing, but its posture—whether erect or not—the development of the haltères, the form of the scutellars, etc. His results are summarised in the following table.

Genotype	vg^{Nw}/vg^{Nw}	vg/vg^{Nw}	vg/vg	vg^{no}/vg^{Nw}	vg^{no}/vg	vg^{ni}/vg^{Nw}	vg^{no}/vg^{no}
Character of wing	absent	stumps	stumps	antler-like	ragged	scalloped	notches
Percentage of incisions	100	100	100	100	100	70·7	42·4
Numerical value	12	16	20	21	25	28	30
Divergent wings	++	++	++	+	+-	-	-
Erect scutellars	++	++	++	+	+-	-	-
Rudimentary haltères	+++	++	++	+	+-	-	-

Genotype	vg^{ni}/vg	vg/vg^{Nw}	vg^{ni}/vg^{no}	$+vg/vg$	vg^{ni}/vg^{ni}	$+vg/vg^{no}$	$+vg/vg^{ni}$	$+vg/+vg$
Character of wing	nicks	nicks	nicks	wild type				
Percentage of incisions	27·1	1·3	0·2	0	0	0	0	0
Numerical value	32	36	37	40	44	45	52	60
Divergent wings	-	-	-	-	-	-	-	-
Erect scutellars	-							
Rudimentary haltères	-							

It will be seen that the magnitude of these effects follows exactly the numerical value devised by Mohr. This is so for all the effects of this table, but in one other effect, a shortening of the second vein of the wing, this order was not followed in all cases—an example of the principle that dominance may vary in different pleiotropic effects. Mohr concluded that a reaction rate corresponding to numerical value 40 was necessary for the formation of a wild-type fly in all characters. When the numerical value was less than this, the fly was abnormal in one or more characters.

The regularity of these results strongly supports the theory upon which the interpretation was founded—the theory that dominance is determined by the rate of the reaction over which the gene exerts control. This theory is also in accord with our present knowledge of the manner in which genes act in the body. It seems very probable that the true explanation of dominance lies along the lines suggested by the theory.

It might be thought that, if the dominant gene is always the one giving the most active reaction rate, a dominant character should always be positive, one in which something is present in the body that is not present in the recessive. In fact, this is not always true (p. 67); for example, white coloration is sometimes dominant to the presence of pigment in the body. The explanation probably lies in the complexity of the conditions in the body. The production of a substance may be prevented not only by the absence of something necessary for the processes that cause its production, but also by anything that inhibits these processes, an anti-enzyme, for example. The dominant white gene, though it inhibits pigment formation, may still be in reality acting positively, producing a substance not present in the recessive. These dominant but apparently negative characters do not constitute a real difficulty for the theory.

5. PARTHENOGENESIS *

In asexual reproduction, in which the new body is formed from the somatic cells of the old body—bud-formation, fission, fragmentation, etc. (p. 49)—gametes play no part; and the only possibility of genetic change is by mutation in the somatic

* For fuller accounts, see [319], [323].

cells. This is rare in animals except in the few unstable genes that have abnormally high mutation rates (p. 97). It is not likely to have played any considerable part in evolution. We need not discuss reproduction of these kinds.

In the type of reproduction of interest to us here an unfertilised egg undergoes development of the same kind as that which follows fertilisation in sexual development. This is known in animals as *parthenogenesis*. It occurs also in plants, but in them other cells besides the egg-cell may sometimes function as gametes and develop—apogamy, apospory.

We have not space here to discuss the genetics of the various types of parthenogenesis in detail. We can only summarise the characters of these types of reproduction that seem likely to have had importance in the evolution of animals.

Parthenogenesis does not always play the same part in the life-history of animals. In some animals (some species of nematodes, ostracods and insects) males are either very rare or do not occur; parthenogenesis is the normal method of reproduction. In other animals (aphids, rotifers, some Branchiopoda such as *Daphnia* and *Artemia*) parthenogenesis occurs at certain periods of the life-history, the reproduction at other times being bisexual. In these forms the type of reproduction is often under the control of environmental conditions; parthenogenesis appears to be the reproductive process by which a population increases rapidly in favourable conditions. In many Hymenoptera (bees and wasps) the males develop parthenogenetically from unfertilised eggs, the females from fertilised eggs [108]; similar types of reproduction occur in some rotifers and gall-midges (Cecidomydæ, Diptera [325]). Occasional (facultative) parthenogenesis occurs in several other groups of animals.

In bisexual reproduction the essential processes, so far as genetics is concerned, are: (1) meiosis (with crossing-over and reduction of the chromosome number) and (2) fertilisation (with return to the double chromosome number). In parthenogenesis, meiosis, including both crossing-over and reduction as well as fertilisation, may be absent (ameiotic type); but crossing over is often present where there is no reduction. There is always crossing-over where there is reduction. If there is no reduction, the ripe egg is diploid, and the reproduction is known as *diploid* parthenogenesis; parthenogenetic development of an egg with the reduced number of chromosomes is known as *haploid* parthenogenesis. In diploid parthenogenesis, activation, the change in the egg that initiates development, may either be spontaneous, as, for instance, in those species in which males do not occur, or it may be caused by a spermatozoon, the nucleus of which degenerates without fusing with the egg nucleus (some nematodes). In most forms of haploid parthenogenesis activation is spontaneous, but in some (e.g. species of Rhabditis, Nematoda) activation is caused by a sperm that penetrates the egg and then degenerates. In all types of haploid parthenogenesis, doubling of the chromosome number usually occurs soon after the start of development.

The cytology of meiosis varies greatly in the different forms of parthenogenesis. In the meiotic form of diploid parthenogenesis, oogenesis may be more or less normal up to the end of the second meiotic division (so that the chromosome number is reduced), but this is followed by fusion of the egg nucleus with that of the second polar body. This occurs, for example, in some sawflies. It is in fact a condition of intracellular fertilisation, and has been called *pseudo-fertilisation*; the nucleus of the second polar body takes the place of the sperm nucleus in normal fertilisation. In such cases crossing-over occurs, and the egg after fusion with the polar-body nucleus has the unreduced number of chromosomes. At the other extreme we find completely ameiotic oogenesis, with entire absence of the reduction division and crossing-over. The egg nucleus when ripe is then in the same condition as the somatic cells of the parent. *Daphnia* has this type of parthenogenesis. Very many types of oogenesis intermediate between these extremes occur. In *Artemia*, for example, there is an ineffective reduction division, and the chromosome number of the ripe egg is diploid.

Haploid parthenogenesis is less variable in its details. It is also more widespread. In general oogenesis is normal. In the bees and wasps, for example, there is no difference during meiosis between the eggs that will produce the two sexes, and the egg develops parthenogenetically if it is not fertilised.

From this summary of the cytological facts we can deduce the genetic effects of parthenogenesis.

In all forms of parthenogenesis genetic differences between parent and offspring will be less than in bisexual reproduction, for there can be no interbreeding between different individuals and therefore no transference of genes. Except for mutation, genetic differences between parent and parthenogenetic offspring can only occur if crossing-over or reduction is retained, for it is only in these processes that differences can arise. If the parthenogenesis is diploid with crossing-over, and exchange of the genes between the chromosomes occurs at a crossing-over, differences will be present between the gametes in the genes they carry, but only in those genes that were heterozygotic in the parent (Fig. 37). In haploid parthenogenesis recombination is possible at crossing-over and reduction, but only in the first of a series of parthenogenetic reproductions, for in the offspring

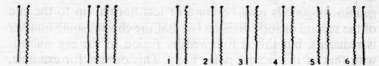

Figure 37. Meiosis in diploid parthenogenesis with crossing-over.
(After Waddington)

of such reproduction either the haploid number is retained throughout the life-history, when there will be no meiosis at later reproductions; or (as is more usual) the chromosome number is doubled during the life-history, when the genotype becomes entirely homozygotic.

It results from these characters of parthenogenesis that the course of evolutionary change to be expected in a parthenogenetic species differs in important respects from that to be expected in a species with bisexual reproduction. First, since interbreeding between individuals is absent, and recombination of genetic characters therefore greatly less, a parthenogenetic population should be much less variable than one with bisexual reproduction. Also, in all forms of parthenogenesis except diploid parthenogenesis without reduction and crossing-over, homozygous individuals are rapidly produced—in diploid parthenogenesis with reduction and crossing-over some of the gametes become homozygous even for characters that were heterozygous in the parent, as can be seen in Fig. 37; and in

haploid parthenogenesis the whole genotype becomes homozygous in the second generation. From this it results that a
recessive mutation becomes homozygous and is expressed in the
phenotype almost immediately after it occurs; it will not be
concealed for a long time by crossing with individuals that do
not possess it, as it will be in bisexual reproduction (p. 180).
Thus in parthenogenesis, all mutations, recessive as well as
dominant, will be at once exposed to the competition of
selection; the distinction in this respect between dominant and
recessive mutations that is present in bisexual reproduction
(and of great evolutionary significance, p. 217) is effectively
non-operative.

Again, we should expect animals reproducing parthenogenetically to separate more readily than those with bisexual
reproduction into stocks differing in genetic constitution. We
should expect this because recessive mutations are more rapidly
expressed in them and because, since they do not cross, the
stocks will remain distinct. Parthenogenetic populations will
develop as numerous distinct stocks (*clones*) between which
selection will occur; those with bisexual reproduction will form
large interbreeding populations.

It is also to be noted that most of the animals in which
polyploidy naturally occurs are parthenogenetic. This is true
of all those mentioned on p. 64—*Artemia, Trichonyscus* and
the curculionid beetles. The probable reason is that a polyploid
condition introduces difficulties in meiosis which do not occur
in parthenogenesis ([323], p. 181, [324]). It seems that parthenogenetic animals have here the possibility of a type of genetic
change not open to those that reproduce bisexually.

The effects of parthenogenetic reproduction in the male sex
only, such as occurs in the Hymenoptera, must be mentioned.
In these animals the male will carry only the genes of his
mother, and will pass on his genes in the next generation to the
female offspring but not to the males. In this respect the
inheritance is similar to that of recessive sex-linked characters
in bisexual reproduction.

Lastly, the effects of hermaphroditism may be compared with
those of parthenogenetic reproduction. In almost all hermaphrodite animals (Turbellaria, Oligochæta, Pulmonata, etc.) the
egg is not fertilised by the sperm of the same individual.

Conditions are then the same as in normal bisexual reproduction. Self-fertilisation may occur between the proglottides of some cestodes, if the proglottides are not regarded as asexually produced individuals, and it has been said to occur occasionally in some hermaphrodite molluscs. It may also occur in animals of other groups. Its genetic effects will be similar to those of pseudo-fertilisation (p. 105).

6. CONCLUSIONS: THE ORGANISATION OF THE INDIVIDUAL GENOTYPE

We have now to consider the general view of the organisation of the genotype to which we are led by the facts we have surveyed. In particular, we must ask how our present conceptions differ from those of the early geneticists.

1. Re-arrangement of the genes in the chromosome is frequent, and indeed a great deal of what has been thought to be gene mutation may in the future be found to be re-arrangement. Such changes are the cause of position effects, and also, in duplications and deletions, the cause of other changes in the phenotype.

2. It is clear that the mosaic conception of the action of the genes must be abandoned; the body is not a mosaic of parts each under the control of one or a few genes. The whole genotype is spread through the body, present in all its cells. Genes certainly have their most obvious (primary) effects on certain organs, but even in those organs their action is modified by many other genes and perhaps, though often to a small extent, by every other gene of the genotype. Genes do not act singly and independently. It is the genetic background constituted by the genotype as a whole that determines the nature of the expression of a gene, and modification due to other genes, position effects, and so on, may be great in extent. The real unit of genetic action is the genotype, not the gene. It follows from this that evolutionary change is best regarded as an evolution of the genotype, rather than of genes in isolation. This "polygenic" conception of genetic action does not imply that we necessarily accept Goldschmidt's view of the chromosome, which was mentioned on p. 73.

3. The old conception of genetic change as being always discontinuous, all-or-none, with large differences between the

normal and mutated conditions, cannot be upheld. Changes in modification and in position effects lead to small, gradual and quantitative changes in the expression of a gene. The same gradual, quantitative nature of genetic change is evident where a character is under the control of series of allelomorphs, though the steps in which the change occurs may then be larger. The reason that genetic change has this nature is not that mutation is itself a continuous change—it is not; each mutation is a sudden, "all-or-none", discontinuous change. But the mutational changes are numerous and each small, so that together they give in effect a continuous change. We must conclude that the fact that a change is gradual and continuous is no evidence against the belief that its control is genetic.

4. These various facts concerning interaction between genes lead us to a conception of conditions within the genotype, which has not so far been discussed. This is the conception of *harmonious co-ordination* between the numerous genes composing the genotype of an animal living in nature. If genes modify each other's action in these various ways, so that we are forced to regard the genotype rather than the gene as the unit of heredity, it follows that the parts of the genotype will, under natural selection, become so adapted to each other that the whole may give as efficient and viable an organism as possible. Position effects, modifying genes, etc., will all be selected to give this result. This harmonious co-ordination in natural genotypes will be preserved by extermination of any variations that are less harmonious. It must be preserved throughout the whole course of evolution.

5. We have today a great deal of knowledge, not available to the early geneticists, of the manner in which genes and their mutations bring about the alterations they cause in the phenotype. Much of this knowledge is recent, but the general picture of their mode of action is becoming concrete. Genetic action may be exerted at any stage of the life-history, but very many of the changes we see in the adult are caused by modification of developmental processes. Genes, very frequently at least, act upon metabolism by controlling the efficiency of the enzymes that are in control of the metabolic reactions. They probably do so by controlling the formation of the enzymes. Their control is quantitative, modifying both the activity of

the enzyme and the time in the life-history at which it is active. By these means they control the supply of much of the chemical material used in the organisation of the body, for this material is normally produced by the action of enzymes. Among other material, they control much that is used in the production of the body's patterns. They modify the elaboration of these patterns by altering the activities of the various processes that take part in their expression. Whether mutation can initiate new patterns, as distinct from alterations of the pattern already present, is more doubtful and cannot be said to be established. New pattern does, however, certainly arise in evolution.

It is on this background of the organisation of the individual genotype and of its action in the body, that we must base our discussion of the means by which animals have come to evolve.

CHAPTER III

THE SPECIES IN ZOOLOGY

THE present aim of zoological systematics is double: first, to catalogue animal forms, to give each a name and a description by which it may be recognised again; and, secondly, to make the catalogue of such a kind that it will express the evolutionary relationships of the animals.

Zoologists were attempting to build up a systematic classification long before they accepted the truth of evolution. Systematics, in fact, dates from Aristotle, many of whose primary divisions of the animal kingdom agree with those we accept today. In the eighteenth and early nineteenth centuries, before zoology became an evolutionary science, systematics was the most active branch of zoology, but the second of the two aims of systematics was simpler than today, no more than to express the structural similarities of animals, classifying together those that showed fundamentally similar structure. When the truth of evolution was accepted, similarity of structure came almost always to mean community of evolutionary descent, and the second aim of systematics came to be the expression of evolutionary relationships. That is the position today. We now call a classification that succeeds in this aim "natural".* It will in general agree with earlier systematics, for similar structure and closeness of evolutionary relatedness normally go together, but it will have to reject resemblances due to causes other than relatedness, those due to parallel evolution, convergence or chance.

The systematist uses for the classification of animals a hierarchy of categories of increasing extension and decreasing closeness of relatedness as one passes up the series. The better

* Some biologists, but probably few zoologists, do not accept this as the aim of a natural classification. Cf. J. S. L. Gilmour,[131] who would call a classification based only on structural similarity "natural".

111

known of these (phylum,* class, order, family, genus, species) are used in the classification of all groups of animals. The steps between them may be subdivided (subclass, superorder, etc.), and thereby the hierarchy may be made elaborate enough to express the most complex relationships. Below the species the systematist has a range of smaller (infraspecific) categories (subspecies, races, clines, varieties, etc.), but these are of different kinds rather than arranged as a hierarchy (ch. IV). If the classification is natural, each of the supraspecific categories should include a distinct part of the phylogenetic tree, and a part that becomes larger, and extends further back in evolution, the higher the category.†

The categories are not completely defined by this aim. Even if the aim is attained, the extension of each category would not be defined. We must therefore consider the extension of the categories somewhat further.

It is possible that the systematist is free to establish each category at the grade of extension that is most convenient to him—that he, and he only, is to say what grade of structural difference is appropriate to specific, generic or other distinction. If so, he is acting in exactly the same way as a librarian when he sets up categories among his books for convenience in cataloguing. The librarian divides his books into classes according to the subjects with which they deal, but the selection of the content of each class is his, and is determined only by his convenience. So, it may be suggested, the systematist is imposing on nature, for his convenience, categories of his devising. The categories are undoubtedly founded on the natural data of the relationships of the animals, just as the librarian's classes are founded on the subject material of his books, but the standard of relatedness that justifies inclusion in a species, genus or family will, on this interpretation, be a matter solely for the systematist; the extension of the categories will be his and his alone.

Another possibility is that some or all these categories are

* This is the zoological use of the term—a major division of the animal kingdom in which should be included animals with the same fundamental organisation. The term is used in a different sense by palæontologists—any group of animals, however small, that can be shown to be descended from a common ancestry.

† For palæontological cases in which such a classification breaks down, see F. A. Bather,[18] W. J. Arkell and J. A. Moy-Thomas.[6]

present as such in nature, that animals *naturally* classify them-selves into groups of various sizes which the systematist, perhaps unconsciously, describes as species, genera and families. Books so divide themselves by size into quarto, octavo, duodecimo categories, and the librarian would be behaving as we are now supposing the systematist to act if he used these categories for his classification. On this supposition, observation of nature should tell us whether a difference is generic or specific.

In the past the systematist has almost always assumed that his categories are not so given in nature, and therefore that he was free to delimit them in the way most convenient to him. A result of this has been that the use of the categories by differ-ent systematists has varied greatly. For instance, as time has gone on, there has been a tendency to reduce the size of most of the categories, to make superfamilies or orders of the larger families, and families of genera, so much so that in some groups, such as the birds, genera are today tending each to contain only one species. In addition to these changes with time, there has been much disagreement concerning the right extent of the categories among contemporary systematists. This has been especially true of the species; some have divided species on small structural characters so as to increase their number almost indefinitely; others have retained relatively few larger species and relegated the smaller differences to infraspecific categories. So long as the determination of the categories is regarded as a matter for the judgment of the systematist, such disagreement is inevitable.

Few zoologists believe that the categories above the species are given as such in nature. We are free to choose at what levels we set them up.* Some years ago most systematists said the same of the species. Thus, Haeckel wrote ([150,] vol. I, p. 34): "The general adoption of the theory of evolution has definitely closed the controversy as to the nature and definition of the species. The word has no *absolute* meaning whatever, but is only a group name or a category of classification with a purely relative value." In other words, the species is in exactly the same position as the supraspecific categories. Darwin held similar views. Of the effects that acceptance of his theory of evolution would have on systematics he wrote ([66,] p. 664): "Systematists

---

* But cf. for genera in plants, W. Wright Smith.[277]

. . . will not be incessantly haunted by the shadowy doubt whether this or that form be a true species. . . . Systematists will have only to decide (not that this will be easy) whether any form be sufficiently constant and distinct from other forms, to be capable of definition; and, if definable, whether the difference be sufficiently important to deserve a specific name. . . . In short, we shall have to treat species in the same manner as those naturalists treat genera, who admit that genera are merely artificial combinations made for convenience."

Today this is not the general opinion. Wider biological and ecological work in the last thirty years has led to its becoming recognised that animals are organised *in nature* into groups that correspond closely to those that have been called species, and it is now widely accepted that the species category should be used for these and not for larger or smaller groups. If this view is to be held, it is necessary for us to do our best to define the species group.

THE SPECIES PROBLEM

Darwin, holding the views we have just quoted, refused to attempt a definition of the species ([66], p. 51). Later, so long as zoologists agreed with him and Hæckel that the species was a category of the same nature as the higher systematic categories, an exact definition was not to be hoped for. Even if we accept the species as a natural group, definition is still difficult. There are many reasons for this.

First, the species groups into which animals are organised are not necessarily equivalent throughout the kingdom. Reproductive processes, behaviour and indeed the whole natural history vary greatly among animals of the different major groups, and it is to be expected that the species organisation will vary with them. It may not be identical in animals with sexual reproduction and in those that reproduce asexually; or in animals whose gametes are broadcast into the surrounding medium and in those in which male and female need to meet. Social behaviour largely influences the organisation, especially when it is highly developed as it is in many of the vertebrates and in the social insects. Many other characters of the natural history have each an influence on the organisation. The species organisation is most obviously different when we compare it in the Protista and the Metazoa; it may indeed be doubted whether the species of the Protista are sufficiently like those of the Metazoa to justify a common definition. But even among the Metazoa the organisation is not everywhere the same; we do not necessarily mean exactly the same thing when we speak of a cœlenterate, an insect and a vertebrate species. Since our definition must allow for these differences, it must to some extent lack precision. This does not mean that a definition is impossible. We may confine our definition to the species of bisexual metazoan animals, since these have been far the most important in evolution. For these it should be possible to frame a definition that will be almost, if not entirely, general.

Another cause of difficulty in framing a definition is that species are studied by zoologists from different points of view, and the term has not been used in the same sense by all who have used it. The systematist chiefly thinks of the species as a category in his classification; the biologist or naturalist thinks of it as a natural group of animals that he observes and studies in the field; and the palæontologist as a step of a certain size in the changes that occur in his evolutionary series. We may for the present leave aside the palæontologist's use of the term; we shall return to discuss it later (p. 138). But if we consider only the systematist's and the naturalist's uses, the difficulty remains. It is not to be expected that both will use the term in the same sense unless their work is closely correlated.

The systematist usually works in a museum on dead and preserved material. He has always tried to make his classification natural, but, until recently, he has not often appreciated any need to make his species agree with those of the naturalist. The species as a natural group has not been impressed on him, and he has often tended to use the term in the same way as he uses his other categories, exactly as the librarian uses the classes into which he divides his books. Many circumstances have led to this lack of correlation between the systematist and the naturalist, but perhaps more than any other circumstance the immense quantity of material that the systematist has always had before him, all requiring identification and description, but almost all without biological data. For it is always easier, and needs far less time, to collect animals for a museum than to study their natural history; collections of specimens rather than biological data have been the material sent to the museums. The systematist has generally not considered the natural history of animals because he has not had the data on which to do so.

The naturalist, on the other hand, is interested in fewer species and is able to study those in which he is interested in greater detail. The concept of the species as a natural group is forced upon him by his whole experience. He tries to define the category not so much on morphological characters, which the systematist must mainly use, as on its properties as a group in the natural life of the animals.

It is then at first sight surprising that, in the result, naturalists and systematists have largely agreed in what they call a species. Perhaps it is more true to say that naturalists have agreed with the majority opinion of the systematists, disagreeing chiefly with those who held extreme views of the appropriate size for the species in either direction. In many groups of animals there is no doubt about the definition of the species. In the mammals, for instance, there is disagreement only in a few of the sub-divisions of the class—among the smaller rodents, for example. The same is true of a great many others of the major groups of animals. In fact, the groups in which species are difficult to define are much fewer than those in which there is no difficulty. Also, it is not among the better known animals that difficulties arise. No one, naturalist or systematist, has any doubt that the lion and the tiger, the horse and the ass, are true species, and few wish to make species out of the races of these animals.

This very general agreement implies that both systematists and naturalists have, at the back of their minds, essentially the same idea of what a species should be. At the present time many systematists admit this. Many admit that the true species is that of the naturalist, and hold that it is their aim to recognise among their material the naturalist's biological species. They say that the criteria on which they define their (systematic) species are useful simply as indicators of the distinctions between the biological species. This indeed may be taken to be the out-look of the New Systematics,[177] which has in recent years been replacing the older conceptions of systematics. Nevertheless, the criteria on which systematist and biologist are accustomed to recognise species are very different. We must consider these criteria and try to understand why those of the systematist lead so often to determination of species equivalent to the naturalist's, and what are the characters of the species that both sets of criteria define. Our own interest is in the biological species, for it is these natural groups that are important as a stage in evolutionary differentiation. But it is important for us to know how they are related to the species of systematists, for it is by their systematic names that animals are defined.

THE SPECIES OF SYSTEMATICS

The ideal of the systematist is that his species should be "good", that is to say that they should be recognised and accepted by other systematists. Since his description is mainly morphological, this implies in the first place that the morphological difference between the species and those nearest to it should be distinct and large enough to be accepted as of specific rank. This is a criterion to which he attaches importance. It is vague, and indeed no more than an appeal to the experience of those who are accustomed to deal with species. But the morphological differences between species vary so much in the different groups of animals that it is probably impossible to make the criterion more exact.

A distinct morphological difference in typical examples of his species is not the only criterion that the systematist uses. A "good" species should be clearly distinguishable from related species *in all examples*. This implies, besides sufficient morphological distinction in typical examples of two species, that forms intermediate in structure do not occur, i.e. that the species do not intergrade. To apply this criterion the systematist needs an extensive range of specimens on which to define the species; single specimens may be taken as "types" representing the typical form of the species, but definition of a species on single specimens is dangerous. For variation is present in all species, and it is impossible to say that the species is distinct unless it can be said that the range of variation is not great enough to allow the species to intergrade with others.

We used a criterion similar to this in distinguishing a single population from several mixed populations in our discussion of evolving palæontological faunas (p. 26). There it was pointed out that a curve expressing the variability of some character in a population should be a simple curve with a single apex if the population is single, but a curve with more than one apex, if the population is mixed. So, here, if such curves are drawn for two species, they should be distinct if the species are "good" and do not intergrade. Preferably, the curves should not overlap, but if they do they should at least have two distinct apices.[274] Even from the curves for a single character it should be possible to say for all specimens, or at least for all but a few, that they belong to one species or the other. But species differ in many characters, and variation in these characters is very often independent. Decision to which species an animal belongs should always be easy on the aggregate of its characters; it may be intermediate in one character, it will not, if the species are good, be intermediate in all. For this reason the systematist will always include many characters in his definition.

Absence of intergrading is a second very important criterion to the systematist. He has still others. One is that the species should be stable. It will change in form with evolution, but evolutionary change is always slow and the systematist will not expect his species to alter appreciably in his own experience. If he collects it a second time after an interval of some years, the mean form should have changed little. This is not to say that every species will be identical in form wherever it is collected and under all conditions. Many species vary in the different parts of their geographical range, under different environmental conditions, at different times of the year, and so on. These variations should normally be less in extent than the specific difference, and the systematist will describe them in infraspecific categories. They will be discussed in ch. IV. Such forms frequently intergrade.

Finally, the systematist finds evidence for the specific difference from geographical distribution, which should be of such a kind that it is possible for him to believe that the whole group has had a common descent from a single ancestral group. A species must be a single group with a single origin.

In whole or in part, these criteria are contained in the definitions of the species given by the systematists when they are speaking only of the systematic definition. Thus Tate Regan [252] says: "a species is a community, or a number of related communities, whose distinctive morphological characters are, in the opinion of a competent systematist, sufficiently definite to entitle it or them to a specific name." Here it should be noted that the systematist must be competent, and that the morphological characters must be not only distinctive (i.e. with clear differences from the neighbouring species), but definite; they will not be definite if the species intergrades with other species or is unstable. Vavilov [314] has a similar definition of plant species. He says: "We are coming to the concept of the Linnean * species as a definite, discrete and dynamic system, differentiated into geographical and ecological types, and comprising sometimes an enormous number of varieties." Here again the emphasis is laid on the species being definite; we shall discuss below its dynamic character, i.e. its modifiability with time. It should be noted that it is not assumed in these definitions that the morphological species will be an identical category in all groups of organisms. The specific differentiation must be acceptable to a competent systematist; presumably he must be competent in the systematics of the group to which the species belongs.†

BIOLOGICAL SPECIES

In his observation of animal life in nature, the naturalist finds that animals are very generally organised, at least at some period of their life history, into populations that live and breed together. These communal populations vary much in size and organisation in the different species of animals. In size they vary from the few individuals of a family group of apes or a herd of deer to the vast numbers of a shoal of herring or an assemblage of a planktonic species living in a lake or the sea. In social animals the communal organisation is usually strict throughout the life of the animal. At the other extreme, in large assemblages such as that of a herring shoal, the organisation may show itself in little else than the behaviour that makes the fish swim and breed together. Often the organisation is not permanent. Non-social animals may live independent lives except at the times at which the individuals meet for reproduction;

---

* In distinction from other groups to which the name species has been given, such as the jordanon. With these we are not concerned.

† The use of serological tests to give an objective criterion of the relatedness of animals would seem of more value when categories above the species are compared.[24, 25, 127] For its use in the species of *Drosophila*, see R. W. Cumley.[60]

the organisation is then at a minimum, but it cannot be said to be entirely absent even when only two animals meet. Though the organisation is absent at other times, it may be elaborate at the breeding season. Many birds collect in large flocks to breed, and complex sexual behaviour may then be necessary for successful breeding [7, 174, 175]; after the breeding season the flocks often break up. Not only birds behave in this way. To take but one other example, frogs collect in spring from considerable areas to lay their eggs together in the same ditch, leading a social life for only a few days in the year. Another feature of the organisation is that the population is often organised on different levels of size at different times. Many birds breed as family groups, but congregate as the population of a district when they are choosing their mates [7]; many migratory birds breed as pairs but migrate in large flocks.

This communal organisation is necessary, in at least a simple form, at the breeding season if not at other times, for all bisexual animals in which contact between the sexes is required for reproduction. But not only these animals have it. When fertilisation is external, the gametes being shed into the external medium, we often find correlation between the sexes in the time at which the gametes are shed. This is so, for instance, in the sea-urchin, where the one sex is stimulated to shed its gametes by chemical stimulation produced by gametes of the other sex, if they are present in the surrounding water [115]; or by stimulation associated with the full moon.[116] Some organisation of the population is required for these results. It is only in those few animals in which the egg develops asexually (and this type of reproduction is continued indefinitely), and in the few self-fertilising hermaphrodites, that the organisation is unnecessary so far as reproduction is concerned.

This organisation has value in other features of the biology of animals besides their reproduction: it may even be important in the biology of completely non-sexual animals. Many animals get protection by living together in large numbers. Also, there may sometimes be advantage in the search for food, if it is to be found in large masses scattered at wide intervals; the foraging ants give an example of its use for this purpose. Again, the work of Allee [2, 3, 4] shows that many animals modify their environments when they live together in associations above a

minimum density, whatever may be the means by which they
so modify it. He has found that growth of the community is
optional only when the density is at this optimum; if the
density is less, the environment is less modified and so less
favourable to the life of the species, and if it is greater, growth
is inhibited by other factors such as lack of sufficient food. The
communal organisation is useful to animals in many ways, but
there can be no doubt that its reproductive advantages are the
most general and the most important.

Without doubt this organisation into communal populations
is a general and fundamental fact of natural history.[76] For these
populations the name *deme* has been proposed [132, 178] and is
convenient. We must next consider the relation of these demes
to the species.

Clearly the species is a much larger unit than the deme; it
consists of a large number of these populations, which may or
may not be differentiated as subspecies, races and so on. We
have therefore to ask what is the common character in a group
of demes that justifies their inclusion in a species.

The layman, when he speaks of a kind of animals, by which
he normally means a species, thinks of it as an aggregate of
individuals " of the same kind ". By this he means that, besides
being similar in form, they are capable of living the same kind
of life and of producing offspring that will be members of the
same aggregate. All dogs or cats, lions or tigers can so live
together, however differentiated they may be as varieties; all
the members of each species will also breed together unless
prevented by mechanical difficulties such as those due to the
differences in size between the races of some species (as in
some domestic races of the dog), and they will produce offspring
of the same species as the parents. Different species do not in
nature live together as single communities and interbreed. This
is true even though the species are closely related.

This last statement is not disproved by the fact that we find
in nature many examples of different species of animals, even
distantly related animals, living in association with each other.
Insects of various orders live in the nests of ants and other social
Hymenoptera; ants keep aphids as cows; rooks and jackdaws
form common feeding flocks; in tropical forests birds of many
species associate in flocks, probably for the protective advantage

5*

of association in large numbers. There are also all the facts of parasitism and commensalism. Association of two or more species is common in natural history, but these associations never extend to *complete* sharing *on an equal footing* of a single communal life. The association may be for only a single purpose such as protection or feeding, or the associates may be differentiated in their biological relations to each other, as in parasitism or in the use of aphids by ants. These associations differ most clearly from the communal population in that the species that form them do not normally breed together. In that respect, and in other ways also, communal life in such associations is not complete. No one, layman or naturalist, would wish to include the different kinds of animals that form one of these associations in a single species.

The naturalist's conception of a species is in close agreement with the layman's. It is the general view of naturalists that the character that justifies inclusion of a number of demes in a species is that any two of the demes should be capable of living together as a single, completely integrated population, and will do so whenever they get the opportunity by meeting.[76, 214] The demes will then usually * fuse into a single population if they belong to the same species; they will not do so if they are of different species. The nature of the characters that allow this living together in one case and prevent it in another differs from species to species. Very often they will be biological or psychological rather than morphological, differences of habit and behaviour rather than of structure. Food habits probably play a large part in them. When one population has developed the habit of feeding on some food which the other does not use, it is unlikely that they will be able to live together. But any marked difference of habit or behaviour may prevent their doing so.

The species is, then, to the naturalist, a group of animal populations capable of living a *complete* communal life together. Now, as two races evolve in isolation (as they must to diverge into new species, p. 142), they will develop simultaneously the differences of habit that make communal life between them difficult and those, genetic and other, that tend to prevent interbreeding. We should expect, then, that communal life and

* See pp. 242–4, for qualification of this statement.

normal, successful interbreeding will be associated; that inter-breeding will normally occur within the species, but that between two species it should not occur, or at least should be difficult. This we find, and it is so general a character of the species difference that it is very often given as its chief biological criterion. The view taken here is that the absence of normal and successful interbreeding should be regarded as a part of the lack of a complete communal life, which rests on the broader basis of the whole natural history of the animals. As a criterion, the absence of such interbreeding will in general be a sound guide to the recognition of biological species, and it may often be more easily recognised than other characters of the specific difference.

Whatever view we take of the absence of normal interbreeding as a criterion of the specific difference, it is important to realise the distinction between this criterion and that of sterility in interspecific crosses. The interbreeding criterion is not that the cross between the species, if it can be made to occur, is sterile, but that in their natural life the species do not *normally and successfully* interbreed, that the cross between them does not normally occur. The differences that tend to prevent interbreed-ing between animals are not solely, or even mainly, the genetic differences that are the cause of sterility in a cross. Two animals may refuse to interbreed for many reasons, morphological, physiological or psychological; indeed, differences of almost any kind in their natural history may have this result.

In nature adaptations to prevent interspecific breeding are of many kinds, and extremely wide-spread and frequent. These adaptations are of special interest to us at this point because their prevalence indicates the great biological importance of the prevention of interspecific breeding. There can be no doubt of the biological importance of maintaining the organisation into species (cf. p. 158), and the emphasis laid in nature on preventing interspecific breeding may be regarded as confirming our con-clusion that the absence of interbreeding between species is an important part of the specific organisation.

Morphological examples of these adaptations are, for instance, the fine and elaborate correlations in structure in many insects between the accessory sexual organs of the two sexes. These make copulation difficult between members of different species.

Many others of these adaptations are physiological. For instance, eggs are almost always more readily fertilised by sperm of the same species than by foreign sperm. The adaptations, already mentioned, by which eggs and sperm of a species are released at the same time also tend to prevent interbreeding. Often physiological and psychological adaptations are combined. In birds elaborate sexual behaviour is often necessary for ripening of the gonad of the female [168]; psychological stimulation is required before the cyclical changes of the animal's physiology can take place, and this stimulation will not be provided if attempts are made to breed across the species, for the behaviour is never the same in two different species. Highly developed sexual plumage may also be necessary for breeding, having a similar effect on the sexual cycle [174]; again, the stimulation will be ineffective if the mate is of another species. The fact that a colony above a minimum size is necessary for successful breeding in many socially-breeding birds [4] and mammals [63] probably has a similar basis. Here again the sexual cycle of the female is probably involved, stimulation being insufficient in a smaller colony. Other adaptations are of behaviour only, involving no obvious reactions in the animal's physiology. Organisation of many of the higher animals into family groups, herds and flocks will prevent interbreeding, since it will ensure that the main contact of the animal is with members of its own species. This may be one reason for the gregarious habit; there are undoubtedly others. Even if it has no influence on the ripening of the female, any elaborate sexual behaviour will prevent interbreeding, for it always differs from species to species ([209], p. 255), and, if the behaviour is necessary for breeding, its abnormality when two species cross will make interbreeding difficult. This indeed may be a main cause of the evolution of such behaviour.

In fact, the natural history of animals is everywhere organised to prevent interspecific crossing. These adaptations are the chief reason why crosses between species are rare in nature, even when they are possible. Many species that do not naturally cross are interfertile, and can be made to cross by man's interference—the mule, for instance, is not a natural animal. This is because man can deny to an animal the opportunity of breeding with its own species, and it may then breed outside the species if this is allowed. In nature hybrids will occur only in the rare circumstances in which an animal is for some reason unable to breed with its own species and yet has the opportunity of doing so with another species. Their occasional occurrence will not show that the two forms belong to the same species; the criterion of the specific difference is that the forms do not *normally* interbreed. In the normal circumstances of the life of the species, hybridisation will not take place: it will occur only in abnormal circumstances, and therefore rarely.

We may conclude that complete or almost complete absence of natural interbreeding between two demes that are in contact will be reliable evidence that they do not live communally together, and therefore that they are of different species.

Sterility in interspecific crosses is, as we have seen, a different phenomenon from the absence of normal interbreeding. Yet it has often been proposed as a criterion of the specific difference, and we must consider its value as such.

It is undoubtedly true that some degree of sterility is very general between animal populations that live independently and do not interbreed, that is to say between those that on our definition are species. This is to be expected, for any such populations living apart will in time differentiate in genotype as well as in biological characters; and genetic differences, when they become large enough, will probably cause sterility.* But sterility is not a universal character of crosses between groups that are recognised on other criteria as species. It is found that the grade of sterility between species is very variable. Occasionally, though not often, interspecific hybrids are completely fertile. Some species-hybrids in birds, e.g. in pheasants, are fertile. More often, provided the species are closely related, incompletely fertile hybrids are produced; their sterility may be of any grade from fertility only slightly less than that of the parents to complete sterility. The great majority of interspecific hybrids belong to this class. Often, again, especially if the species are less closely related, the hybrids are not viable, and the cross is sterile in the first generation; the mule belongs here.

---

* Cf. Stern.[286] See also pp. 235, 242 below, on relative sterility as a result of loss of harmonious correlation of the genotype when differentiated forms are crossed.

Complete sterility in a cross will imply that the animals are of different species, for they cannot then interbreed successfully and are unlikely to form a single communal population. But hybrid fertility, even if it is complete, is not proof that the animals are of the same species, and there is no close parallel between the grade of sterility in the cross and relatedness of the animal.[86] It is clear that sterility in a cross is a far less reliable criterion of the specific difference than absence of natural interbreeding.

We may sum up this discussion in the following biological definition of a species. "An animal species is a group of animals organised into communal populations or demes, which are often differentiated into groups within the species differing both morphologically and in habit, but which will all live together a complete communal life and will naturally breed together. They will not readily do so with animals outside the species group." * Such a definition will certainly not apply to many of the plant species recognised by botanists ([178,] p. 162)—we are concerned only with animal species. Even among animals the definition is not free from difficulty in exceptional cases, especially where the reproductive mechanism is unusual (mating types of Protista, self-fertilising hermaphrodites, animals with obligatory parthenogenesis) [209]; these cases are not of any great evolutionary importance. It also meets with difficulties where the range of the species is large and its populations considerably differentiated. We shall consider some of these last difficulties when we are discussing infraspecific categories (p. 155).

It will be noted that, besides being inapplicable to some classes of species, our definition is to some extent inexact. Animals of a species will not *readily* breed with other species, but we do not define the exact frequency of hybrids that will show that two forms belong to the same species. We shall discuss this point again (p. 230). Very few biological definitions can be made entirely exact.

Many geneticists and some systematists prefer a slightly different form of the definition of a biological species. They prefer to define it as a group of animals within which transference of genetic material from one individual to another is

* Modified from Mayr.[209] Cf. also [82], [208], [311].

possible in the natural life of the animal. This definition is in almost all circumstances equivalent to ours, for transference of genetic material can only take place by interbreeding. We shall later (p. 157) come upon some exceptional circumstances in which the two definitions are not equivalent, and we will discuss the matter there. Our definition seems preferable, since a communal life is a more general feature of the natural history of the animals than the genetic results of interbreeding. It therefore emphasises more clearly the unquestionable fact that the species is a phenomenon in the general natural history of animals. A genetic definition may delimit the species group with considerable accuracy, but it cannot describe the general characters of the group as it occurs in nature. A definition that does this must be based on the whole natural history.

BIOLOGICAL AND SYSTEMATIC SPECIES COMPARED

It will now be clear why the systematist's species so often agree with the naturalist's. The systematist's first criterion is, as we have seen, the necessity for a certain standard of morphological distinctness. Constant morphological difference between two populations in contact with each other implies that they do not interbreed, otherwise the difference would in general disappear by mixture in the hybrid population.* It is therefore in accord with the biological definition. But if the populations are not in contact, owing to geographical isolation or some other cause, morphological distinctness will not be proof that the populations would be unable to live and breed together if they were brought into contact, and therefore that they are different biological species. Yet the larger the morphological difference the less likely it is that they will do so; a large difference will generally imply greater likelihood of incompatibility between the genotypes, and this will reduce the chance of successful interbreeding. Nevertheless, morphological distinctness, even if large and definite, is not a sure criterion of specific difference in the biological sense.

Still less is absence of morphological distinctness proof that two forms belong to the same biological species. Here the practice of the systematist differs unmistakably from the conclusions of the naturalist. The systematist is loath to describe

* But cf. pp. 241–4.

forms as different species unless they have morphological differences of a standard that he thinks species should have; the naturalist knows of "species" that satisfy his definition but have little or no morphological distinction. There are, for instance, two races of *Drosophila* that are included in the systematic species *D. pseudo-obscura*, and are known as races *A* and *B*. These are partly sterile when crossed, and breed by preference within rather than across the race. Biologically they appear to be species, though not well-defined species. Their morphological differences are minute.[207] Again, *Gammarus zaddachi*, a brackish water species, has two forms with only slight morphological differentiation. These are adapted to different salinities, and where they meet do not intergrade and presumably do not interbreed.[272, 281, 282] They seem to be true biological species. Many other such "cryptic" or "physiological" species are known.[291, 302] They will not be recognised as species on any morphological criterion, and usually have not been called species by the systematist; to the naturalist they are species. Thus, biological species may include some forms that are not "good" systematic species.

The systematist's other criteria are even more closely in accord with the biological definition than the morphological criterion. Absence of intergrading means no more than absence of interbreeding. Systematist and naturalist are here using two aspects of the same phenomenon. Stability of a species will imply (1) that crossing with related forms does not occur, for no form that is frequently crossing with forms of different structure will remain stable,* and (2) that the morphological distinctions on which the species is founded are based on genetic differences and are not due to action of varying environmental conditions on the phenotype. As a criterion, stability will only exclude some forms that no naturalist would wish to call species. Lastly, a geographical area of distribution in agreement with descent from a common ancestral group is as necessary a character of the biological species as of the systematic.

There is therefore no real reason for surprise that the species of the systematist and the naturalist so often agree. The chief differences in the two uses of the term are in the extent of the

---

* Provided the hybrids are fertile, i.e. the interbreeding is ultimately successful, p. 243.

group to be called a species. In physiological species the biological use is the narrower; we shall see immediately that in some cases where systematic species hybridise in nature the biological use is wider. These differences are on the whole exceptional. Nevertheless, the biological definition cannot be used by the systematist, for he has not the knowledge to apply it to his preserved material. He is bound to continue to work on the basis of his own criteria, even though he may regard them only as indications of the biological specific differences.

We have reached a reasonably clear definition of the biological species. There are, however, many zoologists, both systematists and biologists, who would deny that species can be defined so distinctly. Reasons for this are numerous. There is, first, the desire that the definition should be applicable to every species both in animals and plants. There is no doubt that there are many plant species to which the definition will not apply, for plants differ from animals in their genetic mechanisms (e.g. in the prevalence of polyploidy), in the types of their communities, in the means by which fertilisation is brought about and in many other ways ([209], p. 273). Since there are these many biological differences between animals and plants, we cannot expect that the species differences that result from the biological characters should be similar. Even among animals the species organisation is, as we have seen, variable and our definition cannot be expected to apply to all its varieties. It will not apply to any animals to which the criteria of communal life and interbreeding are not applicable, e.g. to some hermaphrodite and self-fertilising animals (p. 107). The species organisation may be entirely different in these animals, and a definition that will apply to their species and also to those of bisexual animals may be unattainable. Animals of these types have, however, not played a large part in evolution, and for our purpose we need not discuss them further. It seems unnecessary to look for a definition that will be universally true of all animals and plants.

Another reason why biologists hesitate to define the species accurately is that they still wish to accept the species of the systematist, although many of these were established before the natural history and behaviour of the animals were known, with the result that the species as defined by the systematists often conflicts with the biological species as we have defined it. Thus, the fact that some animals of different systematic species or even genera have been found to hybridise normally in nature has been thought to discredit the absence of normal interbreeding as a criterion of the specific difference. Hubbs and Miller,[171], [173] for instance, have worked on minnows (Cyprinidæ) of the Mohave desert of western North America. Forms of these fish were differentiated in the Pluvial period, probably in habitats of different types. Their morphological distinctions have been thought by systematists sufficient to be reckoned of specific or even generic rank (*Gila orcuttii* and *Siphateles mohavensis*). With the desiccation of their habitats they were forced into cohabitation in the remaining waters, and they now hybridise readily, so that considerable proportions of hybrids are found in waters where both forms live. Biologically they do not behave as species * and, if our definition is accepted, they should not be called species in spite of the considerable morphological differences. In some other fish besides these Hubbs [172] has found hybrids between forms that have been placed in separate genera.

Another possible explanation of interbreeding in these structurally well-differentiated forms is possible. It may be that the barriers to interbreeding and communal life, evolved as the forms became distinct species, might break down in further evolution, so that the forms became again able to interbreed. It would not seem likely that this would often happen, but it might be the explanation of these exceptional cases.

It is clearly impossible to define a term accurately so long as it is used in more than one sense. If the species is to be defined, either the biological or the systematic sense must be accepted and allowed to control the use where the two senses conflict. For any discussion of evolution and especially of its theory, the biological sense is essential, for, as we shall see later (p. 158), it defines a very important stage of evolutionary divergence. For the purpose of this book we need at least to recognise biological species as of this importance, and for this we need a name for them. If it were shown that the biologist's and the systematist's species were fundamentally different, it would be necessary to give a different name to the biologist's

* But cf. p. 138

species,* for the systematist's use of the term is the older and has priority. It is possible that this might ultimately be the most reasonable procedure, but, so far as one can see at present, it does not seem to be necessary. Systematics is also an evolutionary study. The stage of differentiation that we have called a biological species, being of importance in evolution, must surely be so in systematics, and we have seen that at least the great majority of systematic species agree closely with biological species. It seems that we may conclude that systematists intend a stage of evolutionary divergence by what they call a species, and that this stage is the same as that of the biological species; that is to say that systematists and biologists mean the same thing when they speak of a species. We may perhaps leave the few cases in which they disagree to further investigation, and hope for future readjustment on one side or the other. At any rate in the remainder of this book, since we are concerned with evolutionary problems from a biological standpoint, we shall use the term in its biological sense. For us the species is a phenomenon in natural history.

THE GENETICS OF THE SPECIFIC DIFFERENCE

In ch. II we saw that a genotype may change either by rearrangement of the material of the chromosome—chromosome mutations and alterations of the chromosome number—or by changes in the genes themselves—gene mutations. Among the latter we distinguished the major mutations recognised and named by geneticists (macro-mutations) from mutations of smaller phenotypic effect due to changes in modifying genes and to position effects (micro-mutations). We have here to ask what part these various types of mutation play in the genetic differences that occur between species.

To answer this question we need to compare the structure of the genotype in related species. But its organisation is known in very few genera in sufficient detail to allow the comparison. The genotype has been accurately compared in several species of *Drosophila*. In another fly (*Sciara*, Mycetophilidæ, fungus gnats) some comparison has been made, and this is also true of some mammals, chiefly rodents, but of very few other animals.

---

* The term *commiscuum* has been suggested.[62]

Beyond this, all the evidence we have is indirect—from the results of crossing and other biological work.

The species of *Drosophila* show very clearly that every type of chromosome re-arrangement has occurred in their differentiation, but the amount of this type of change varies greatly between different pairs of species. We saw (Fig. 29, p. 74) that the arrangement of the whole chromosomes and their number vary in different species of the genus, and our dis-

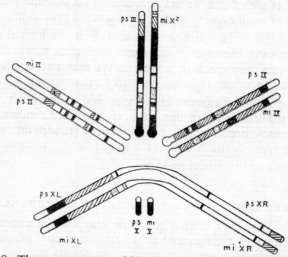

Figure 38. The arrangement within the chromosomes of *Drosophila pseudo-obscura* (ps) and *D. miranda* (mi) compared. Sections having the same gene arrangements, white; translocations, stippled; inverted sections, cross-hatched; sections of which the homologues are not detectable in the other species, black. (From Dobzhansky after Dobzhansky and Tan)

cussion on pp. 74–6 showed that these variations imply that chromosome mutations have taken place in the divergence of the species. This is confirmed when the finer structure of the chromosomes is compared, either by preparing linkage maps of the chromosomes in the different species or by observing their structure in the salivary glands. This has been done for a few pairs of species.

One of the most accurate comparisons of this kind that has been made is between *Drosophila pseudo-obscura* and *D. miranda*. The results are given in Fig. 38.[80, 88] It will be seen that the re-arrangements are numerous and complex. Large parts of the chromosomes show inversions, there are some translocations, and considerable parts are so altered that comparison of the structure was not possible. It was calculated that forty-nine re-arrangements are necessary to account for the changes in the parts that could be compared; the number would be considerably higher if account were taken of the other parts.

It is noticeable in Fig. 38 that the altered segments, especially those with inversions, tend to be more extensive and numerous in some chromosomes than in others. Reasons can be given for this.[290] An inversion will be heterozygotic at its first appearance in almost all the animals in which it occurs (p. 180), and in this condition it will reduce crossing-over and recombination, especially if it is not long enough to allow the formation of a loop at meiosis (p. 60). The reduction of recombination must be to some extent deleterious. This will not necessarily lead to the removal of the inversion by selection, for the deleterious effect will be in balance with any advantage that the inversion may bring; if the latter is greater, the inversion may become established. But it can be shown that succeeding inversions in the same chromosome will have less effect in reducing recombination than similar inversions in other chromosomes. So, it is to be expected that established inversions will tend to collect in single chromosomes.

Other pairs of species may show either more or less re-arrangement than these two. Between *Drosophila melanogaster* and *D. simulans* the only re-arrangements are a long inversion in the third chromosome and some alteration of structure at one end of the *X* chromosome.[288] On the other hand, in *D. melanogaster* and *D. pseudo-obscura* the structure is so different that it has been found impossible to compare it in the salivary glands,[88] though some comparison has been made by linkage maps. It is interesting to note that the races *A* and *B* of *D. pseudo-obscura*, which behave as biological species but have little morphological differentiation (p. 128), differ by five inversions in four chromosomes. Re-arrangement does not always mean any large morphological change in the phenotype.

Thus, large chromosome mutations have been numerous in the evolution of some at least of the species of *Drosophila*. It is not certain that they have been equally important in the evolution of other animals. They may not have been, for Rohm [257] found comparatively few of them when comparing chromosome structure in two species of *Sciara* (*S. ocellaris* and *S. reynoldsi*); smaller re-arrangements, especially small duplications and deficiencies, were numerous (as they also are in *Drosophila*). Outside *Drosophila* this is almost all the evidence of this kind that we have.

In *Drosophila* the chromosome re-arrangements that differentiate races are of the same kind as those between species, though smaller and less numerous. This is one example of the general truth that genetic differentiation is of the same kind at all stages of specific divergence. The only possible exception to this truth is that, as we shall see later (p. 136), one character of the differentiation, the development of hybrid sterility, may be independent of other characters and not necessarily continuous. But if this is true of the evolution of hybrid sterility, it is exceptional. In general, infraspecific genetic differences are less in extent than specific but not otherwise different.

There is no doubt that gene mutation plays at least as large a part as chromosome mutation in specific differentiation; indeed, it is probably of much greater importance.[220] For direct evidence of its occurrence we need to find genes that are homologous in two species and then to compare them as allelomorphs. In the species of *Drosophila* the homologies of many genes have been established, and they often occur as different allelomorphs in the various species. Here it is clear that gene differences are numerous between the species, but in the rest of the animal kingdom our knowledge is not so sound. Haldane [152] gives a table of the occurrence of numerous genes in several rodent species, and discusses their homologies, coming to the conclusion that there is good evidence for homology in many cases. The genotypes have been compared in few other animals with sufficient accuracy to allow the homologies of the genes to be determined.*

There is more evidence of gene differences between subspecies and races. Goldschmidt [136] found that numerous races of the gipsy moth (*Lymantria dispar*) differed in characters— strength of the male-determining factor, pigmentation of the

* For other examples, see E. Mayr, [209], pp. 73–74, 79.

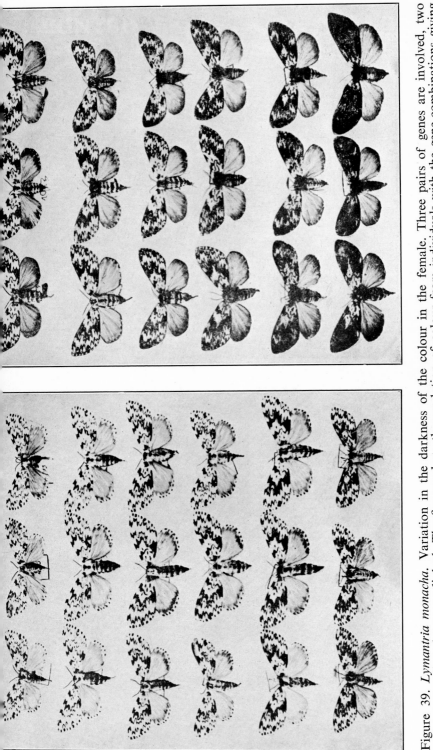

Figure 39. *Lymantria monacha*. Variation in the darkness of the colour in the female. Three pairs of genes are involved, two autosomal and one sex-linked. The figures show the gradation of colour from individuals with the gene-combinations giving the lightest colour to those giving the darkest. (After Goldschmidt)

larva, the latent period before hatching—controlled by series of allelomorphs, and the members of each allelomorphic series present in the genotype differed among the races. In *Lymantria monacha* he analysed [135] the factors producing melanism and found three dominant genes, two autosomal and one sex-linked. Fig. 39 shows the variation resulting from the possible combinations of these genes. The snail *Partula* is differentiated into a large number of forms in small isolated environments in the Society Islands.[47, 49, 50] They differ in many characters, some of which are inherited in a Mendelian manner and are therefore controlled by mutation. A lady-beetle, *Harmonia axyridis* (Coccinellidæ), differs in geographical races in Asia, which vary in colour pattern. These have been shown to segregate and to be controlled by three genes.[299] Other examples could be given.

These examples are not many, but this must not be taken to imply that gene differences between natural forms are rare. In fact, they are present in large numbers between every pair of natural forms, though many of them are of small phenotypic expression. Only a very few can be demonstrated by their behaviour in breeding. This is because natural forms differ in so many genes that it is hard to find differences between two forms that are controlled by one or a few genes. Almost always, the character is controlled by many genes, and it is then impossible to recognise the segregation of the separate genes in a cross; the hybrid is intermediate between the parents, its form being determined by all the genes in combination. The inheritance is, in fact, "blending", and gives the proportions found by Galton [120] in pre-Mendelian days for inheritance of characters in man. This is no evidence against the belief that the characters are inherited in the normal genetic manner; it merely implies that numerous genes are involved—in fact, that the genetic control is "polygenic" (p. 108). There is one piece of direct evidence that the inheritance is genetic. When natural forms are crossed, it is normally observed that the variation in the F_2 generation is greater than in the F_1. This is a necessary result of Mendelian segregation. It should always occur in a second generation formed by crosses within the first, heterozygotic, generation, if the heredity is genetic.

This polygenic control of characters is so frequent in crossing of natural forms—not only species but also subspecies and races —that it is recognised as a character that distinguishes naturally evolving forms from the occasional aberrations—mutants, etc. —that arise suddenly and spasmodically.[81] Very many examples of it could be given. Spencer finds control of this kind in many characters of crosses between *Drosophila virilis* and *D. americana*.[279] Hubbs [170] observed it in his naturally-occurring fish hybrids. It was evident in Sumner's crosses of deer-mice (*Peromyscus*).[293] It occurs also in many crosses of plants, for instance in crosses between species of cotton.[160, 161] It is, in fact, the usual experience in crosses between natural species and races.

For our discussion of evolution, it is these naturally divergent forms that are of interest to us, and it is for us an important conclusion that their genotypes differ in a large number of genes in addition to the differences in chromosomal arrangement that we have already discussed. It is also of importance to us that many of these differences are of small effect in the phenotype, and are presumably due to micro-mutations, in modifying genes, position effects, etc.—and, in fact, that the genetic control of differences between natural forms is very generally polygenic.

When considering the definition of the specific difference (p. 125), we noted that interspecific sterility often accompanies morphological differentiation, though its grade is variable and does not run closely parallel to the differentiation. We must consider what is known of the genetic basis of the sterility and of its development in diverging forms.

The assumption is often made that hybrid sterility is always a secondary result of the accumulation of genetic differences as the evolving forms diverge. It is undoubtedly true that such accumulating differences will tend to cause sterility in the hybrid. As they increase in number, chromosome mutations will interfere with meiosis and therefore lead to sterility; gene mutations will also do so when the cross is between forms differing in many genes, for the viability of a phenotype depends on the aggregate of its genes which must be so co-ordinated among themselves that together they will give a viable organism (p. 109). This co-ordination will almost certainly be reduced when two genotypes are mixed, as they are in a hybrid—the mixed genotype cannot be expected to have the co-ordination of the original genotypes, which will have been improved by selection during a long period of existence in nature. Indeed, genes which are harmless in their original genotypes may be harmful or even lethal when their action is altered by other modifying genes and position effects. Some grade of sterility is to be expected in the hybrid whenever the parents have considerable genetic differentiation of any kind, and the sterility will increase with the differentiation (cf. [285]).

This cannot be the whole cause of hybrid sterility for, if it were, there should be close correlation between the extent of genetic (and morphological) differentiation and the grade of sterility, and this correlation is always incomplete and sometimes absent (p. 125). There must, at least in part, be an independent evolution of hybrid sterility.

The most direct cause that could be suggested for this would be an accumulation of genes with the immediate action of causing the sterility—"sterility genes".[86] Such a course of evolution is probable, for Fisher ([104,] cf. [217]) has shown that any genes that increase hybrid sterility will accumulate in differentiating forms that are in contact and liable to inter-breed, if there is slight infertility between the forms before they interbreed. In these circumstances, genes tending to decrease hybridisation will have positive selective advantage, for such genes will decrease the number of the relatively infertile hybrids. Sterility genes will have this advantage, and will therefore be selected and become established in the genotype.[289]

This independent evolution of hybrid sterility will only occur if the two forms have already developed slight mutual sterility in the course of genetic differentiation before they interbreed, and only if they are in contact and therefore able to interbreed. It will develop in the parts of the habitats where both forms occur, but it may later spread through the whole of the populations of the forms. Forms that are not in contact should not have any tendency to evolve hybrid sterility, except as the direct result of genetic differentiation. Perhaps this is the reason why sterility between species is so variable [86]; species that give completely fertile hybrids may not have been in contact during their differentiation. After they have become species and ceased to interbreed, they might come into contact without any evolution of sterility taking place.

There is evidence that in some cases hybrid sterility may arise before the animals cease to be able to interbreed. Distinction between the forms may then be maintained though they are in contact and interbreed freely. An example of this has been described by Hovanitz.[169] Two races of a butterfly (*Colias chrysotheme*) were found to give numerous intermediates in regions where they met. These intermediates could only have been produced by interbreeding, so that the races were not biological species. The races remained distinct in spite of the interbreeding. The explanation seemed to be that the intermediates were sufficiently sterile to be unable to give rise to a permanent hybrid population which could maintain itself and interbreed with the parent forms. If this were so, there could be no fusion of the two races even though the intermediates were viable. Hubbs' hybrid fish populations (p. 130) seem to be another example of the same phenomenon. Here again the parent forms remained distinct in spite of interbreeding. Such cases are probably common. As we shall see later (p. 235), it is to be expected that some grade of intersterility will normally develop as soon as differentiation between parts of a species becomes marked. Well-differentiated subspecies will often be not fully fertile with each other, though they should interbreed since they belong to the same species. If sterility between two such forms increases, it may well result in a situation such as Hovanitz found in *Colias*.

PALÆONTOLOGICAL SPECIES

The palæontologist's outlook differs most clearly from that of the zoologist in that he is presented with a succession of forms in time, whereas the zoologist's material is almost entirely contemporaneous. It results that the palæontologist is able to study the course of evolutionary divergence much more directly than the zoologist can; we have already summarised his conclusions (ch. II). But, the palæontologist cannot, as the zoologist can, learn much of the natural history and behaviour of his forms. In this respect he is very much in the position of the systematists of the last century, and his use of the species category is similar to theirs. The basis of the biological conception of a species being outside his data, his definition is necessarily morphological, and he uses the category in exactly the same way as he uses the higher systematic categories. To him the species difference is that grade of morphological change in an evolving series that has come to be accepted as specific by the majority opinion of palæontologists. This being so, it is not surprising that the palæontologists' estimates of the correct size of the specific difference have varied as much as the systematists'. In fact, they have, perhaps, varied even more.

Such is the position when the palæontologist is able to work out clear lines of evolutionary descent. But he cannot always do so, chiefly because he often finds it impossible to distinguish resemblances due to common evolutionary descent from those due to parallel evolution. One reason for this is that in almost all his series the environment changes with time, and many of the changes in the fauna may be adaptive to these changes in environmental conditions. If so, they may have arisen independently in several animals by parallel evolution. An example of this, in *Gryphœa* (p. 27), has been mentioned. In these circumstances some palæontologists are inclined to remove all phylogenetic meaning from the species, and to give the same specific name to all related forms that sufficiently resemble each other, whether the resemblances are due to parallel evolution or evolutionary relatedness.[6, 19] When this is done, the species group becomes solely an expression of morphological resemblance; it ceases to have any significance as an evolutionary category. Since we are concerned only with the relation of the species to evolution, we need not discuss this use of the term further.

CHAPTER IV

INFRASPECIFIC CATEGORIES

IN this chapter we have to consider how the communal inter-breeding populations, the demes, which we have seen (p. 121) to be the basic units of animal populations, are organised within the species. For our purposes we shall find two categories above the deme, the subspecies and the cline, to be sufficient to describe the infraspecific organisation.

We are not here concerned with the manner in which differences between demes arise in nature; this will be the subject of a later chapter (ch. VI). Our present aim is only to describe and classify the differences. Also, we are not concerned with differences within the deme. Of these there are many types, and it will be as well to mention them immediately, so that we may exclude them from further discussion.

First, there is the fluctuating variation that is present in all natural populations. This is non-genetic and for this reason cannot be of interest to us, since it cannot form the basis of permanent evolutionary change.

Secondly, there are abnormalities that occur in no more than a few individuals of a population. Some of these will be genetic —mutants of various kinds; others non-genetic—abnormal structural or physiological characters due to such causes as individual aberrations of development—monsters such as Siamese twins, animals with more or less than the usual number of limbs, and many less extreme abnormalities. These are clearly not differences between populations as wholes.

Thirdly, there are phenotypic variations due to action of environmental conditions on smaller populations within the deme. One part of a deme may be exposed to a higher temperature or a drier climate than another, and this part may differ from the rest in structure or physiology. Such geographical forms * are often known as *ecotypes*. They are more noticeable in plants, but may occur in animals. They will be most common and evident where the range of the deme is large. Variation of this type is non-genetic, and is therefore not of interest to us, but in some circumstances we shall find it difficult to distinguish —except by experiment—variation of this kind from genetic variation (p. 209).

Not all phenotypic varieties have geographical distribution distinct from the rest of the population. Differences in seasonal form, in so far as they are controlled by environmental conditions and are not genetic, belong here. They occur in insects— seasonal forms of butterflies; mammals—colour pattern in arctic animals; and in other groups. Here too should be included some differences that are produced during development by conditions external to the animal, if they are between subsidiary groups within the deme. Well-known examples are the differences between workers and females in wasps and bees, and those between the various worker castes in ants and termites.[22, 226] These are phenotypic, being controlled by the standard of nutrition given to the larva during development.

Lastly, there are genetic differences between classes of individuals within a population. Of these the example that first comes to mind is the difference between male and female, where that is genetic, but some other differences should be included in this category. There are, for example, the frequent cases of polymorphism, in which individuals, often of the same sex, occur in different forms in the same population. Some at least of these have a genetic basis, e.g. the differences between the mimetic females of certain species of the swallow-tail butterfly *Papilio*.[118] The subject of polymorphism is wide,[109, 111] and includes phenomena of more than one kind. We shall refer to it again (p. 259).

All these types of variation are outside our present subject, since, even when they are genetic, they are variations within demes and not between them. Some of them are of interest from the point of view of the origin and development of differentiation—mutant forms may spread through a population and lead to a change in the characters of the whole; polymorphic forms

---

* The term "form", though it is sometimes used as a systematic category, is here used as a neutral term for any differentiated group or individual.

may become separated from the rest of the species and then evolve in isolation to give rise to new species. We shall discuss these again when we consider the evolution of differentiation (ch. VI).

THE NATURE OF THE DEME

Before we go further, something more must be said of the nature of demes and of their distribution in natural habitats.

If our definition of the deme is accepted—a communal interbreeding population within a species—it is essential to distinction of the deme from others of the same species that it should be in some way isolated. Interbreeding will normally occur throughout the species if there is opportunity for it, and unless the deme is isolated, there will be interbreeding between it and the other demes with which it is in contact, and they will all fuse to form a single population.* This isolation is almost always geographical. The demes live in places where the conditions are appropriate to their life, and these habitats are separated by regions of unsuitable conditions. Thus, the organisation of the species into demes depends first on the fact that animals are not capable of living effectively in every type of habitat within the broad range of their species. Almost every species is adapted to a narrow range of conditions, and areas with these conditions are normally separated by wider areas of different conditions. The species can live only in the restricted areas. Even so, the distribution would be discontinuous, but in nature it is normally still more so. A species will live most successfully where the conditions are not merely possible for its life but optimal, and it will be forced to find and live in these optimal conditions by pressure of the struggle for existence; it will generally be unable to maintain itself in less favourable conditions. The optimal conditions will be distributed at still wider intervals than those in which the species might be capable of living if not subjected to pressure.

That the normal distribution of a species in nature is in fact discontinuous cannot be questioned; this is a commonplace

* When demes are so greatly differentiated as to be incompletely interfertile, fusion may not take place—cf. the races of *Colias chrysotheme* (p. 138). We shall discuss this again (p. 243). Occasionally a form may arise within a population that is sterile with the rest of the population, and it may perhaps in exceptional circumstances perpetuate itself (p. 219).

of natural history. It is true even of the commonest species. The hare and the rabbit occur throughout England, but they are not found in every locality; they select areas suitable for them and these are separated by regions in which they are not found. The distribution of rarer species is still more clearly discontinuous. In general they are rare because the optimal conditions for their life occur only in widely scattered and infrequent localities. A rare species is not often one that is distributed over the country as a continuous population at a low concentration; it is much more often one found in only a few localities.

There must be isolation between a deme and its neighbours sufficient to allow them to live independently and to prevent their fusion, but this does not mean that the isolation need be complete. The grade of isolation between two demes will be measured by the frequency with which individuals succeed in crossing from the habitat of one deme to those of others, and *vice versa*. It will vary from almost complete mixing to complete absence of interbreeding, but there will be some degree of isolation wherever two demes are separated by a barrier of unsuitable conditions, however narrow this may be. We shall find later (p. 230) that occasional interbreeding with a stray member of another deme will not necessarily break down the independence of the deme, but for the present we must leave discussion of the necessary grade of isolation. Here we need only note that the isolation must be sufficient but need not be complete.

The size of the isolated habitats of the demes is extremely variable among the species of animals; they may be very large or very small. As examples of habitats at the upper limit of size we have the large areas of sea in which shoals of many fish swim, or the still wider ranges of schools of porpoises or whales. Within these ranges there may be no geographical isolation, and the population of the whole range can then be divided into demes only on biological grounds such as lack of interbreeding between distinct shoals, if there is more than one in the habitat. On land one factor that largely determines the size of the habitat of the deme is the extent of the locomotory powers of the species. Far-travelling birds and mammals may range over wide spaces, and it is possible that some such species (but not all, as we shall see immediately) form only single demes in these wide areas.

At the other extreme, the habitat of the deme may be very small, especially among the smaller invertebrates. Cladocera, copepods and rotifers living in a pond, or even in a small pool of water in a gutter or the axil of a leaf, will be almost completely isolated from the rest of their species. Spontaneous locomotion is often ineffective in conveying such animals to new habitats; occasional chance transport by wind or other animals seems often to be their only means of getting from one habitat to another. Parasites in a single host body are equally isolated. Many parasites have biological adaptations that ensure their transference to new hosts, but these do not often ensure mixture with the rest of the species. In all these cases the deme is composed of the inhabitants of one micro-habitat. Between the extremes of large and small habitats there is every gradation, both in the size of the habitat and in the number of the individuals of the included deme.

Whether the population in one of the habitats of a species is a distinct deme must depend on the grade of its isolation from other populations of the species, and this will largely be determined by the geographical features of the habitat and its surroundings. Often the isolation is certain. Island populations, even birds except species accustomed to long flights, are almost completely isolated if the island is separated from other land by any but a very narrow strait. In continental areas a barrier of forest or desert may isolate many species even though it is narrow. But isolation need not be due solely to geographical features; the habits of an animal often ensure isolation where with other habits mixing would certainly occur. The Amazon has been found to be an effective barrier to many species of birds which have certainly sufficient powers of flight to cross it; they are competent to cross, but in fact never do so because it is not their habit to fly over a wide stretch of water.

It is probable that there are some species in which no population is isolated sufficiently to be regarded as a separate deme. Some species of such animals as whales and far-flying birds are in this condition. So also may be many small animals (protistans, tardigrades, rotifers, etc.) which have almost cosmopolitan distributions and show very little differentiation throughout their ranges ([209], p. 212). The cause of their wide distribution is undoubtedly that they are carried, usually in inactive states, on wind currents, so that there are no effective barriers to the extension of their range. It is possible that the organisation into demes does not apply to these small animals, but this is by no means certain. Most of them form populations in separate micro-habitats, and it is hard to believe that these are not effectively isolated. If these populations are demes, the lack of differentiation in the wide ranges of the species must be due to other causes, probably genetic. We have not the knowledge needed to discuss the question.

Among the larger animals, there are many species of which we cannot say with certainty that the populations should be regarded as isolated demes. Are we to say that the rabbits of a warren or the rats of a farm distant from other buildings form separate demes? Whether they do or do not will depend on the grade of their isolation, but we have little concrete knowledge to guide us here. However, such as it is, the evidence suggests that isolation is greater in natural populations than it would at first sight appear to be, and that this is true even of species with great powers of locomotion. It may appear to superficial observation that there is nothing to prevent the spread of such an animal as a bird throughout its range, and that therefore the whole population of the species must be regarded as a single deme. In fact, this is far from being the case. The narrow range of the optimal conditions is as true for these species as for others, and results in their distribution being discontinuous though the species may spread over a wide range. They live where they find these conditions, not elsewhere; and it appears that often migration from one habitat to another is much rarer than would seem at first sight likely. A. H. Miller [211] discusses the distribution of mammals and birds in California and finds everywhere small interbreeding populations, such as a flock of birds at a nesting site or a colony of a small mammal in a wood; he concludes that there is little crossing between the populations. Lack [189] for birds in England, and Dice [73] for deer-mice (*Peromyscus*) in America, give accounts that are in general similar. Sanderson [266] points out that even in the tropical forest, where the conditions appear peculiarly invariable, many species are closely adapted to small habitats and are only to be found there.

A.E.—6

These habitats are often astonishingly restricted. A special type of tree, a patch of ground where the soil is more than usually wet or dry, a fallen log at a special period of its decay, will each have its peculiar fauna. These restricted habitats only occur at widely scattered intervals in the forest, and exchange between them must be infrequent, though the fact that they become colonised by the species peculiar to them shows that it does occur. In the higher animals division of a species into numerous small demes may be carried further by features of their biology. The habit of forming flocks and herds, and the very general preference for breeding within the flock rather than outside it, are important in this respect.

We may conclude that very many species are organised into relatively small demes. But, as we have already noted (p. 143), the deme is not always small. Demes, not only of many species of fish and of planktonic invertebrates in lakes and the sea but also of many other marine species with external fertilisation and of many common species of terrestrial invertebrates, are very large. The numbers of individuals in the population of wire-worms in an acre of agricultural land may be as high as 1,000,000, and the total population of arthropods as high as 1,000 millions,[265] including 664 million mites and 245 million Collembola. There cannot be effective isolation between parts of this population (except by distance, p. 185). Some other insect populations, e.g. those of the house-fly in summer, may be very large. So may some populations of birds and other strongly locomotory vertebrates, especially those that breed in large flocks.

In many species we have not at present the knowledge to determine the size of the deme accurately. Better knowledge of this subject is perhaps our greatest need towards an understanding of the natural history of animals and towards a solution of the many problems of evolutionary theory that would be enlightened by it. We shall discuss later (p. 253) the effects of cyclical rhythms in the size of the deme.

DIFFERENTIATION IN THE DEME

Wherever demes are effectually isolated, they will differentiate genetically (p. 179). The differentiation will be partly by mutation and partly by recombination, re-arrangement among the individuals of the population of the genes that were previously present in the genotypes (cf. p. 208). We shall discuss the relative importance of mutation and recombination later (p. 249).

The extent of differentiation within the deme will vary with many conditions, such as the period of isolation and the genetic variability of the species, as well as with the grade of isolation. Chance will play an important part in the differentiation. Mutations are rare (p. 97), and the differentiation of a deme will depend to a considerable extent on what mutations happen to arise within it. These chance factors will be of more importance when the deme is small. Much of the differentiation will be adaptive to the conditions of the habitat; that some may be non-adaptive will be made clear when we come to discuss differentiation in more detail (p. 212). This non-adaptive differentiation is also likely to be greater when the population of the deme is small. Thus, the differentiation of demes depends on many conditions, so many that it will always be difficult to predict what the course of differentiation in a deme will be.

However this may be, it is clear that the demes of a species as we find them in nature should be differentiated from each other, if their isolation is effectual. But, since chance plays a considerable part in their differentiation, we must not expect any great regularity in the distribution of differences between the demes across the range of the species; it is rather to be expected that the differences will be distributed more or less indiscriminately. Observation shows that this is so in nature. Mayr [208] gives the data of Fig. 40 for variation in the wing-length in a species of cockatoo (*Cacatua galerita triton*) in New Guinea. Here there is some tendency for similar forms to occur close to each other—perhaps the result of incomplete isolation—but the regularity is far from complete. The genetic basis of this character is unknown, but it is almost certainly controlled by a large number of genes and therefore capable of graded variation (p. 135). The same type of distribution is found when variation based on known changes in the genotype is observed. In Fig. 41 the occurrence of different types of arrangement in the third chromosome among populations of *Drosophila* *pseudo-obscura* and *D. miranda* is plotted.* There is here the same largely indiscriminate distribution.

Not many other species have been studied with sufficient accuracy to give parallels to these results. Welch [322] gives a similar account of variation in a snail (*Achatinella mustelina*); Diver [75] has comparable results on the snails *Cepæa* (=*Helix*) *nemoralis* and *hortensis*; and Dice [72] found the same type of variation in the deer-mice (*Peromyscus*).

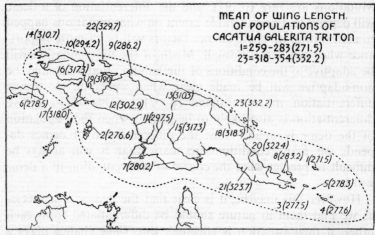

Figure 40. Variation in a cockatoo (*Cacatua galerita triton*) in New Guinea. The numbers give, first, the order of the populations in wing-length from the smallest (1) to the largest (23), and, secondly, in brackets, the mean of the wing-length for each population. (After Mayr)

Crampton [47] found similar differentiation among local populations in his studies of snails of the genus *Partula* in the Society Islands. The islands are divided into numerous wooded valleys separated by high ridges. In these valleys many partially isolated populations of the snails, differing in many characters, were found. Specific, subspecific and smaller differences were all present between the populations. The differentiations of the populations were in some cases found to have altered when they were examined again after fourteen years (1909–23).

* From H. J. Muller,[209] after T. Dobzhansky, A. H. Sturtevant and P. C. Koller.

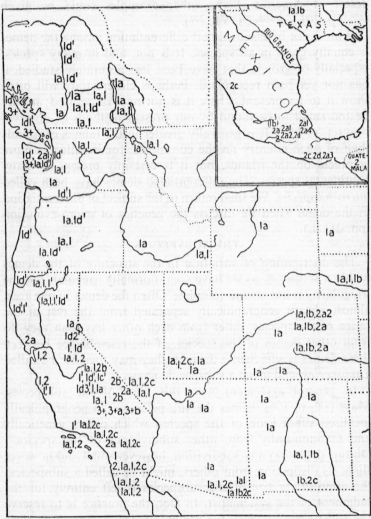

Figure 41. Distribution of races of *Drosophila pseudo-obscura* and
D. miranda as determined by the characters of the third chromo-
some. *D. pseudo-obscura*, race *A*—1a–c, 2, 2a–d; race *B*—1c, d;
D. miranda, 3+, 3+a, b. (From Muller after Sturtevant and
Dobzhansky)

Hubbs ([172], cf. p. 130) found similar differences between populations of fishes isolated in small bodies of water in the Mohave desert of America. Some other examples could be given ([178], pp. 201 ff.; [209], ch. VI; [303]).

It must not be assumed that differentiation among the demes is equally great in all species. It is not, and in many species, especially of groups that have been less accurately studied, it has not yet been recognised. Perhaps closer study will often show it to be present where it is not now recognised; it may be too small to be found by our present methods of observation (cf. p. 151). It is generally greater in the faunas of islands than of open country on the continents, for isolation is more complete on the islands, but it is certainly present in many continental species. The differentiated demes have been called *micro-subspecies*. We shall return to the subject of differentiation in the deme when we discuss the genetics of micro-evolution (pp. 211 ff.).

THE SUBSPECIES

The distribution of variation in the structure of the demes within a species is, as we have seen, normally irregular, but the irregularity is not always complete. Often the demes in one area, almost always geographically separated from the rest of the range of the species, differ from each other less than they do from other demes of the species. If the resemblance between these demes is sufficiently distinct, they may together be called a *subspecies*, and given a subspecific name.

In general agreement with this view of the subspecies, Mayr ([209], p. 106) defines the subspecies as "a geographically localised subdivision of the species, which differs genetically and taxonomically from other subdivisions of the species". On this definition any subdivision, however small and however slight its distinction from others, might be called a subspecies; the appropriate size of the subspecies is left entirely for the judgment of the systematist. In fact, the practice is to reserve the subspecific category for groups of demes that show clear and distinct demarcation from the rest of the species (cf. Lack [192]). The systematist treats the subspecies as a major subdivision of the species which will normally contain many demes. Logically, the subspecies is in the same position as the supraspecific categories (p. 113). It is founded on the natural differences between animal forms, but its correct extension is not defined in nature. Only the species and the deme are so defined.

Not all species can be divided into subspecies; those that contain more than one subspecies are called *polytypic*, others *monotypic*. Many of the monotypic species, if they vary in form at all to present observation, vary irregularly throughout their range, and in many others local differentiations, though they occur, are not distinct enough for definition of subspecies. But as systematics progresses it is found that more and more species can be divided, especially those of wide range; and it is noticeable that the proportion of polytypic species is much higher in the better-known groups. Many forms that were previously described as species are now treated as subspecies of larger species.

The organisation of subspecies within a species, like that of the demes, varies with the natural history of the species and especially with its power of locomotion. Species that are unable to travel far are more likely to be polytypic than those with greater locomotory powers. This is to be expected. Rensch [253] gives the following data for palæarctic birds:

Type of bird	Percentage of total number of species monotypic	Number of subspecies per polytypic species
Large . . .	54·5	1·6
Small, migratory .	39·9	3·2
,, non-migratory .	29·6	7·2

Many other features of the natural history of the organisms influence the occurrence of subspecies within a species.

The differentiation of an isolated subspecies is a stage in the inevitable, continuous differentiation that, as we shall see (p. 179), always develops between isolated populations. In course of time subspecific differences will be evolved from the original identity of the forms, and with further evolution these differences will become specific. The evolution is continuous, and the subspecific stage is not distinguished by natural criteria from other stages of infraspecific differentiation.

A good example of independent evolution in closely related groups living in isolated habitats is given by the finches of the Galapagos Islands observed by Darwin and more recently

studied by Lack [192] (Fig. 42a). These birds were apparently
evolved from one stock brought into the islands by a single
invasion (Fig. 42b). In the numerous islands of the archipelago
they have differentiated into 14 species, which Lack divides
into 4 genera.

The species are recognised as such by Lack on the extent of
their morphological differences and because in many cases two
or more of them live in contact on the same island without
interbreeding. These species must have differentiated in isolation to the stage at which interbreeding ceases, and have come
into contact only after that stage had been reached. The differentiation has therefore in some instances gone far beyond
the subspecific stage, but it is variable in extent—varying, as it
appears, not only with the period of isolation on the different
islands but also with other conditions of the natural history
and with the inherent characters of the species. On neighbouring
islands some of the species occur as forms which, from their
slight morphological differences, are not regarded as separate
species. Lack calls these subspecies if he is able to say for at
least 75 per cent. of the individuals that they clearly belong to
the one form and no other. The single species of *Certhidea*
(*C. olivacea*) is thus differentiated into eight subspecies. Many
less distinct forms occur; these are not described as subspecies.
We see here very clearly the distribution of differentiation that
results from continuous evolution among isolated but closely
related groups. The differentiation is variable in extent, as it is
bound to be in an aggregate of groups evolving at different
rates—differences may be subspecific, specific, or even generic in
size, and many are less than subspecific. The whole forms a
differentiated aggregate (or *plexus*) of evolving forms.

Many other examples of this type of distribution could be
given. Mayr ([209] ch. VI) has described many among the birds
of New Guinea and the Pacific Islands.

Correlation has sometimes been observed between the extent
of the differentiation and the conditions of the habitat. Thus,
Kramer and Mertens,[187] who studied races of the lizard *Lacerta
sicula* on islands of the Dalmatian coast of the Adriatic, found
that the differences between the races increased in size with the
depth of the water in the straits separating the island from
neighbouring land and with its breadth, and decreased with

Figure 42a. Forms of the body in the male and female of various species of finches (Geospizinæ) from the Galapagos Islands. (After Lack)

1. *Geospiza magnirostris.*
2. *G. fortis.*
3. *G. fuliginosa.*
4. *G. difficilis.*
5. *G. scandens.*
6. *G. conirostris.*
7. *Camarhynchus crassirostris.*
8. *Camarhynchus psittacula.*
9. *C. pauper.*
10. *C. parvulus.*
11. *C. pallidus.*
12. *C. heliobates.*
13. *Certhidea olivacea.*
14. *Pinarioloxias inornata.*

6*

increasing size of the island. They took the breadth and depth of the strait to give a rough estimate of the period of isolation, and we shall find (p. 183) that non-adaptive differentiation (as was much of the differentiation in these lizards) will proceed more rapidly in a small population, as that on a small island is likely to be. The results are therefore in accordance with theory. Examples of correlation such as these are not un-common. To take one example from this country, the St. Kilda wren is well known as a distinct derivative of the widespread British species, and has differentiated on a small island. Lack found subspecies of *Certhidea* on the smaller islands, whereas

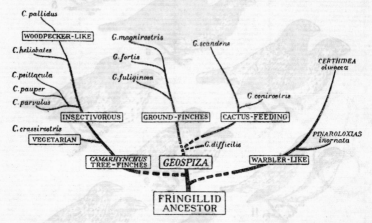

Figure 42b. Suggested course of evolution by which the species of Figure 42a might have been evolved. (After Lack)

there was no subspecific differentiation on many of the larger islands.

In continental areas isolation of parts of a species may be less easy than on islands, but even continental species are often polytypic. Our discussion of the conditions under which demes are isolated (pp. 142ff.) makes it easy to understand that larger groups may often evolve independently even on the continents. Sometimes indeed the isolation of continental species may be as complete as that of island forms; species living on the higher parts of mountains or in the oases of a desert may be able to cross the surrounding land no more easily than the sea around an island can be crossed. Distance, also, between the habitats of a species, if it is large enough, will make the isolation complete except for the most actively locomotory species. It must also be remembered that isolation may be caused by the habits of the species where with different habits the barriers could be easily crossed. The example of the Amazon serving as a complete barrier to certain species of birds has been previously mentioned (p. 144). Many smaller barriers may be effective for similar reasons. Small areas of desert, marsh, forest or, indeed, country of any type may be complete barriers to species that do not live in them.

It is therefore not surprising that we find many continental species to be polytypic. It might be expected that subspecies would be commoner among the smaller animals, and especially among the less strongly locomotory animals. In the present position of systematics this is not evident, probably because the systematics of these groups are less well-known. We have already noted that there is correlation between subspecific differentiation and locomotory powers in such a group as the birds (p. 151). The general position is that polytypic species are much more frequent in continental faunas than we might at first sight expect, and that the number of described subspecies is continually increasing with the progress of knowledge in systematics.

Often, owing to the habits of the animals and the lie of the land, the habitats of a species are not scattered indiscriminately over a continental area, but follow natural features—the course of a river, a chain of mountains, or the sea-coast. A good example of this type of distribution is that of the "species" *Larus argentatus*, the herring-gull. These gulls occur as many subspecies around the shores of the Arctic Ocean (Fig. 43).[208] The probable course of their evolution from a central form, *L. a. vegæ*, in north-east Siberia has been worked out by Mayr, and is shown in the figure. The subspecies have been evolved along two lines of descent passing east and west from the central form. Another distribution in linear chains of sub-species has been described by Ticehurst [303] in the warblers of the species *Phylloscopus trochiloides*, an Asiatic species of the genus to which our willow- and wood-warblers belong (Fig. 44). Here the chains follow the high ground of mountain ranges.

In both these examples the subspecies are arranged in chains

and the terminal members of the chains come into contact,
L. a. argentatus and *omissus* (the British and Scandinavian
herring-gulls) with *fuscus* and *grællsii* (the British and Scandinavian lesser black-backed gulls); and *P. t. plumbeitarsus* with

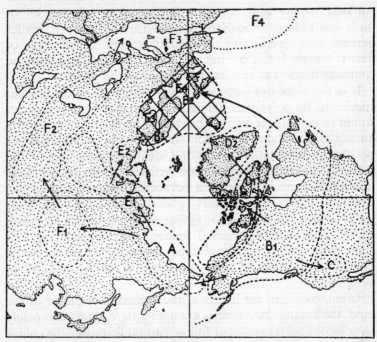

Figure 43. Distribution of forms of *Larus argentatus* around the
North Pole. A, B1, B2, etc., various races. The arrows give the
probable directions of migration. In the cross-hatched area
L. a. argentatus (B2), which has reached the area by migration
through America, meets the race *grællsii* (E4), which has
migrated through Asia. Also the race *omissus* (B3) meets the
race *fuscus* (E3). (After Mayr)

viridanus. Where this happens it is found, in these instances
and some others, that the terminal forms do not interbreed.*
They thus behave as biological species. Here our definition of
the biological species appears to break down, for these forms
are connected by unbroken chains of forms and each member

---

* Chains of subspecies which may include forms that will not interbreed have
been called *Rassenkreise*.[254]

of the chain is not more than subspecifically distinct from its neighbours. On this ground it would be natural to call all the members of the chains subspecies of a single species. Nevertheless, *L. a. fuscus* and *grællsii* are regarded by some systematists

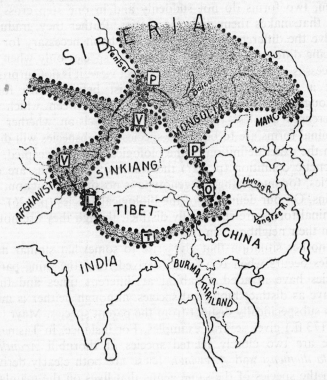

Figure 44. Geographical distribution of subspecies of *Phylloscopus trochiloides*. V, *P. t. viridanus*; L, *ludlowi*; T, *trochiloides*; O, *obscuratus*; P, *plumbeitarsus*. The arrows give the course of migration. Cross-hatched area, the region in which *viridanus* and *plumbeitarsus* meet. (From Mayr after Ticehurst)

as varieties of a second species *L. fuscus*, the lesser black-backed gull, distinct from *L. argentatus*, the herring-gull. Certainly, if the intervening forms were not there, the terminal forms would, since they do not interbreed, appear to be species and would undoubtedly be called species.

This is a difficulty of nomenclature rather than of interpretation. The same difficulty would arise if we possessed all the stages by which *any* two species arose from a common ancestral species. It implies that a specific difference can arise by summation of steps no one of which is large enough to constitute the specific difference by itself. In these cases, and perhaps very often, two forms do not suddenly and in one step cross the line that makes them different species. Rather they gradually evolve the differences of structure and habit necessary for the specific difference, and they are distinct species only when the process is complete. If this is the correct view, it is not surprising that a specific difference should exist between two forms although they are connected by others between which the differences are less than specific. The decision whether the terminal forms are to be called species or subspecies will differ with the exact definition of the biological species accepted. On a genetic definition (p. 127) the whole of the chains are one species, for interchange of genotype is possible throughout the chains. On our definition of the biological species (p. 126), the terminal forms are specifically distinct, though they are not so from their neighbours in the chains.

Another situation that gives rise to somewhat similar difficulties occurs when two forms derived from the same parent species have invaded a habitat at different times and there behave as distinct biological species, although neither is more than subspecifically distinct from the parent species. Mayr (209, pp. 173 ff.) gives several examples. For instance, in Tasmania there are two closely related species of thornbill *Acanthiza fusilla diemensi* and *A. ewingi*. These are both clearly derived from the species of the same genus that lives on the mainland of Australia, *A. fusilla*, but they do not intergrade, behaving as good species. Clearly one must have been differentiated to the specific stage before the other came into contact with it. But if they had not met they would have been regarded as subspecies of the continental species—*A. ewingi* would not have been given a specific name. The two invading forms are biological species on our definition. The difficulty is again one of nomenclature, not of interpretation.

It is only when differentiation has reached the specific stage that it is permanently added to the capital of evolution. After that stage interbreeding with related forms no longer occurs, and the characters of the new species can be lost only by its extinction; before this stage there is always a chance that the differentiation will be submerged in the general characters of the species by interbreeding. The differentiation then ceases to be characteristic of any form that could give rise to another species, though it may be retained in part in the characters of the original species (p. 246. Because a new form reaches permanence with the specific stage of differentiation, this stage is of primary importance in the analysis of the process of evolution.

CLINES

Species are not always organised into clearly distinct groups of demes to which subspecific names can be given. We have already noted that many species show no organisation into infraspecific categories above the deme; these species are monotypic. There is another type of distribution of variation within a species that has not yet been mentioned. The characters of the demes may vary gradually and continuously as one passes from one deme to another across the specific range, so that there is no break of larger size than that which occurs between neighbouring demes, in either the geographical distribution or the characters of the species. Such a distribution has been called by Huxley ([178,] p. 206) a *cline*. At the two ends of a cline the characters of the populations may be largely different, but the differences are reached by a continuous gradient in each character from deme to deme along the cline. There are nowhere isolated subspecies.

Many of the changes that occur along the course of a cline will be adaptive to changing environmental conditions in the different parts of the range. Clines are therefore more clearly defined if the species have large ranges in which there is space for considerable variation in environmental conditions. Of this adaptive element in the characters of a cline part will be non-genetic, consisting of phenotypic reactions to the different environmental conditions. This type of variation is relatively unimportant in the higher animals in which isolation from the environment is better developed than in lower animals. It is not of direct interest to us, since it is non-genetic and cannot serve as a basis for evolutionary change. But its existence must be noted, for it is often difficult to distinguish it from genetic variation except by experiment (p. 163). It is with the genetic variation in a cline that we are primarily concerned. This may be either adaptive or non-adaptive. The non-adaptive element cannot be disregarded and we shall later (p. 212) discuss how large it is likely to be in this and other types of subspecific differentiation. Adaptive variation will also be present.

Graduated variation correlated with varying environmental conditions has been well known for many years to students of the geographical distribution of animals. As the environment changes in some way across the range of an animal—from warmer to colder, or from drier to wetter—it is found that changes in the characters of many species run parallel to the environmental changes. These observations have been summarised in certain rules which are generally known by the names of those who have proposed them. The evidence on which these rules are founded is chiefly derived from the terrestrial vertebrates, for which the rules have been found to be generally true. Most of the rules are also true of some insects, but on our present knowledge they cannot be said to be certainly true of all animals. The best-established rules are [209]:

1. Bergmann's rule—related animal forms are smaller in the warmer regions, larger in the colder. This is true of altitudinal changes of temperature as well as of those due to latitude. It is in general well established, but exceptions occur where some other environmental condition interferes, e.g. a short growing season in a cold environment may prevent the animal attaining large size. The rule appears to be adaptive, since loss of heat from a larger body will be relatively less, and this will be of value in a cold climate.

2. Allen's rule—tails, ears, beaks and other projecting parts of the body tend to be shorter in a cool environment. Its results will be adaptive, since reduction of surface area will reduce heat loss.

3. Gloger's rule—dark colour due to melanin pigmentation is more strongly developed in warm and humid environments.

4. In addition Mayr ([209], pp. 89 ff.) gives some rules that apply only to birds. The number of eggs in a clutch is larger, the digestive and absorptive parts of the alimentary canal are larger, wings are longer, and migratory habits are better developed in birds of colder climates.

These rules are founded in the main on comparison between different species or subspecies, and not on the changes within clines. Nevertheless, they illustrate the type of correlation that may be expected between the characters of animals and the conditions in which they are living. They are therefore worth our notice here. The changes of characters on which the rules are founded are in general genetic and not phenotypic. Most of them are probably adaptive, though their value as adaptations is not always clear—Gloger's rule, for example.

Of clines there are two kinds. In the one the rate of change in the characters along the cline is not constant. There are areas in which there is very little change and these are separated by narrower zones in which the change is rapid. This has been called by Huxley ([178], pp. 206 ff.) an *intergroup* or *stepped* cline. In the other kind, the *internal* cline, there are no such variations in the rate of change, the gradient being more or less constant throughout.

As we find it in nature, the intergroup cline is hardly distinguishable from a linear series of differentiated forms—subspecies, if the differentiation is sufficient—in contact at zones of hybridisation (p. 241); in these zones the changes in the characters will be rapid, in the rest of the range of each form it will be slow or absent. It must not be assumed, however, that the differentiated forms of a cline have evolved in isolation and later come into contact (see immediately below).

Intergroup clines are frequently found. Mayr [208] gives more than one example. One is that of the birds of paradise of the species *Paradisæa apoda* in New Guinea (Fig. 45). Only the coastal lands are habitable to these birds. They occur as several forms that replace each other round the island and have been called subspecies. At least some of these hybridise with neighbouring forms in zones of intergrading. The changes in two characters are shown in the figure, and both characters show a gradient round the coast, though their variations are independent. This example will illustrate the organisation of an intergroup cline. It is probable that, as distribution within species becomes better known, clines of this type will be recognised in increasing numbers.

The internal cline is much rarer. In it no distinct differentiated groups that might be called either subspecies or smaller groups can be recognised, and the whole series of forms can only be treated as a single aggregate of demes.

That these clines should be rarer than the intergroup clines is not surprising; it is indeed more surprising that they should occur. An internal cline can only develop when the range is of considerable size, for unless its parts were at some distance

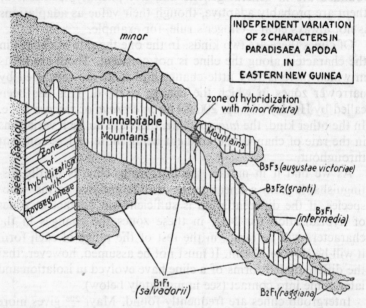

Figure 45. Linear distribution of races in the Bird of Paradise, *Paradisœa apoda*. The races replace each other round the coast of New Guinea, and some hybridise with neighbouring races. Two characters (B, F) are irregularly distributed. B, colour of back: B1, entirely black; B2, upper back yellow, lower back brown; B3, entirely yellow. F, colour of the flank feathers: F1, red; F2, orange-red; F3, orange. (After Mayr)

from each other gene flow between them (due to interbreeding) should prevent differentiation (p. 241). But when the parts of the cline are thus isolated by distance it is to be expected that the aggregate of demes in the cline will break up into smaller aggregates, which would differentiate in adaptation to the varying environmental conditions in the cline, and form sub-species or smaller groups. Even non-adaptive variation might be expected to arrange itself in such groups of demes owing to the action of distance isolation (p. 185) in the cline. Thus, one would expect the internal cline to become an intergroup cline. It is not easy to see how a regular gradient could be maintained, so long as the variation was genetic. Phenotypic variation might readily be graded with the environmental conditions.

Nevertheless, internal clines do occur, and in some there is no doubt that much of the variation is genetic. A clear example is that investigated by Alpatov [5] in the honey-bee in Russia. There is here a north to south cline with regular gradients, expressed in many characters. The length of the tongue and of the legs increases from north to south (Allen's rule), the body size diminishes (Bergmann's rule), and there are parallel gradients in colour, the form of the wings and behaviour. To the south of the main cline, the gradients extend into the Caucasus. Here they are continued in a north to south direction in some characters but reversed in others, presumably in correlation with decreasing temperature at the greater altitudes. Other examples of internal clines are given by Robson and Richards. [256]

In some of these clines, for instance in the Russian bees (so far as many of the characters are concerned), the variations are genetically controlled. But when one of these clines runs parallel with a gradient in environmental conditions it is usually only possible to decide that the control is genetic by experiments designed for the purpose, and this evidence is often not available. In its absence the possibility that the variation in the cline is phenotypic cannot be disregarded.

Natural organisation of populations within the species can, so far as we know at present, be described by use of the three categories of the deme, the subspecies and the cline. Many other terms have been used for groups of individuals within the species. Some are of value in systematics ([339], pp. 107–110), but it seems unnecessary for our purpose to define them. Others, such as those mentioned at the beginning of this chapter, describe modifications of individuals within the deme. Others again, for example, "race", "variety", and "form" are used so loosely and in so many senses that it is advisable to avoid using them as infraspecific categories.

CHAPTER V

COMPETITION, ISOLATION, NATURAL SELECTION

Up to this point we have tacitly assumed that natural selection is an effective agent in evolution. We have not discussed the basis for believing it to be effective. This will be the general subject of the present chapter.

Darwin's argument for his theory of evolution (pp. 3–4) is open to dispute at only one point. There can be no doubt that the reproductive powers of animals are much greater than are needed for maintenance of their numbers, and therefore that, in the animal world in general, many of the offspring die before they are able to reproduce. Even species that reproduce relatively slowly may increase rapidly when conditions allow. The fulmar petrel lays only one egg a year but its numbers have increased by 300 per cent. in the last sixty years.[100] The human population of India increased by 70 per cent. in the sixty years between 1872 and 1931, and that of Java almost trebled between 1850 and 1900.[33] There is also no doubt that animals vary, and that some part of the variation, that part that has a genetic basis, is inherited. It is irrelevant to the argument that another part, phenotypic variation, is not inherited; this must simply be set aside and disregarded in any discussion of Darwin's theory. When this has been done, there is undoubtedly sufficient material in genetic variation for natural selection to act upon. But to accept these facts and propositions does not make it necessary to agree without further argument to the conclusion that natural selection is effective in controlling evolutionary change. It is that point in Darwin's argument that is still open to discussion. His conclusion has been disputed by some zoologists at all times since the theory was proposed, e.g. recently by Robson and Richards.[256] It has always been accepted by most and is so accepted today, but, clearly, a reasoned belief in its truth demands more discussion than we have so far given it. Before we can accept it unreservedly, there are many questions that need answer, and to some of them an answer cannot yet be fully given. When animals are killed as the result of excessive numbers of a species, is it really, in all or a significant proportion of cases, the best adapted that survive? Natural competition is not always, or even usually, between the members of a single species living in isolation from other species; more often the competition is between numerous species in the same environment. How does this affect the conclusion? Will the species live together giving a mixed population in which they all survive, or will some drive out the others completely? How perfect must the isolation between two closely related forms be to allow them to evolve independently? How great a selective advantage is needed to allow a variation to be perpetuated in a species, and how rapidly will it then spread through the species? These are some of the questions that we must discuss before we can give an answer to the final questions whether and how far natural selection is effective in nature.

It is here that mathematical analysis of populations, based on the accepted genetic theory of heredity, has been of most value in the study of evolution. In discussing these subjects we shall often be unable to follow the analysis, for it is intricate and requires more difficult mathematics than it is possible to introduce into a book of this type. Nor do we need to follow it. Without doing so we can consider the conclusions to which it has led.

COMPETITION

Competition occurs between animals living together in the same environment. We may distinguish the following types:

1. There is first competition between members of the same population for the satisfaction of their needs. Such competition will occur when the numbers are more than the environment can support. We may call this internal competition, since it is within the population.

2. Members of two different populations may compete for the resources of an environment in which they both live. The two populations are not then *directly* competing with

each other; there need be no *direct* interference between them. We may call the competition indirect and external.

3. Lastly, two populations may compete directly. One interferes in some way with the life of the other—by using it as food, by preventing it from finding sufficient living space, from reproducing, or in some other way. This we may call direct external competition.

Both the direct and indirect types of external competition are very general between forms living in the same environment, but they are not necessarily present between all the animals that live together. The resources of an environment may be enough to provide sufficient food for all the members of a population living in it. Two populations may not make the same demands on the environments for food or for any other of their needs, and they may not interfere directly with each other by attack or otherwise. *Paramecium* is not obviously in competition with plants living in the same environment; the plants may indeed improve the chances of survival for the *Paramecium* by increasing the aeration of the water. Two species are not in competition unless their biological requirements overlap in at least one feature; either they must make the same demand on some constituent of the environment, or one of the species must make some demand on the other. The *biological* niches occupied by the species must overlap as well as the geographical.

The severity of competition between two species will vary with the densities of their populations in the environment. If the individuals of both species are scarce, there may be enough room, food materials and other resources for them all to live in the environment without interference; and, if their multiplication is inhibited by some cause unrelated to interaction between them, competition may be absent for an indefinite time. Multiplication of ciliates in a culture may be so greatly inhibited by some unfavourable physical condition such as an unsuitable pH, that their numbers cannot increase. There may then be sufficient food for all the organisms present, and no competition. But these conditions are unusual; more often two species in the same environment are both able to multiply, and if they interact in any way competition between them must then arise sooner or later. The competition will become more severe as the populations increase in number.

It will be clear that competition between animals in an environment varies with all the conditions of the environment, both biological and physical. Change in any condition may affect two competing forms unequally and therefore alter their relative efficiencies in the competition. An animal's competitive efficiency with another animal can be defined only in relation to a defined environment. It will be different in other environments.

With these preliminary remarks we may consider the results obtained by investigation of competition between animals. The subject, like many others in ecology, is at present difficult to study in the field owing to the great complexity of natural environments. Up to the present time, more valuable results have come from experiments carried out in the laboratory, where the conditions can be simplified. Conclusions to which these experiments lead can then be compared with observations made in the field.

Competition between the members of a single population will be considered in the next section. For the present we will discuss competition between the members of two distinct populations in the same environment, i.e. external competition, and, first, indirect external competition in which the animals do not directly interfere with each other.

A simple form of competition is that in which two forms compete for the same food but not in any other way. Gause [122] studied an example of this type of competition, that between *Paramecium aurelia* and *P. caudatum* for bacterial food. The protistans were grown in test-tubes in a known volume of a culture medium containing the bacterium, *Bacillus pyocyaneus*. The environment was made as simple as might be. It was homogeneous and contained no other organisms beyond *Paramecium* and the bacteria. The culture medium was renewed daily so as to avoid, or at least reduce, the effects of any changes due to excretion of substances by the organisms. By this means, also, the density of the bacterial population was kept as nearly as possible constant throughout the experiment.

Each species cultured separately under these conditions increased in number and "volume" (i.e. the estimated volume of the protoplasm in their bodies) along an S-shaped curve to a maximum at which the population remained constant (Fig. 46). At this time the available supply of food was being completely used in maintaining the population, and the

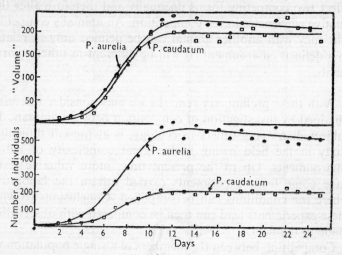

Figure 46. Increase of numbers of the individuals and of "volume" in separate cultures of *Paramecium aurelia* and *P. caudatum*. (After Gause)

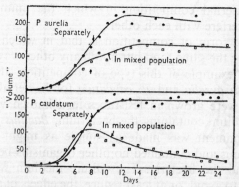

Figure 47. Competition between *Paramecium aurelia* and *P. caudatum* for bacterial food. (After Gause)

multiplication of the organisms was matched by their deaths.

When the two species of *Paramecium* were grown in the same culture (Fig. 47), both populations at first increased in number and volume almost as quickly as they did in the separate cultures; competition between them at that stage was slight—there was sufficient food for the increase of both. But as the numbers increased competition soon took effect and the rate of multiplication fell off. The effects of the competition on the two species were very different. *P. aurelia* continued to multiply until the volume of the population reached a maximum which was clearly less than that reached when the species was cultured alone. After this the volume remained constant at this value. *P. caudatum* also multiplied until its volume reached a maximum, which was also below the value it attained in isolation, but the volume did not remain constant at this maximum; it immediately began to decrease until the species entirely disappeared from the culture. After this *P. aurelia* behaved as in single culture. Thus, *P. aurelia* had the advantage in the competition, and the final result was that it alone survived. The competitive advantage is probably due to *P. aurelia* being more efficient in the capture and use of the food and perhaps also in other ways.

Results similar to these are almost always obtained when two species are allowed to compete for food in a homogeneous environment. Gause ([123,] p. 112) also studied competition between *Paramecium* (*aurelia* or *caudatum*) and *Stylonychia pustulatum* for bacterial food. In these experiments he found that the *Stylonychia* disappeared from the environment. Crombie [53-55] studied competition between certain beetles living in and feeding on flour. All the species compete for the food, but there is also direct competition between many of them; some species attack the eggs, larvæ and pupæ of other species. In numerous combinations of two species he found that one always has the advantage in the competition, and the other is in the end completely eradicated. In reviewing the subject,[56] he quotes many other examples in which experiments have given similar results. We must conclude that mixed populations of animals that occupy the same niche and compete for food or other resources of the environment, cannot be permanent in a homogeneous environment unless the species are exactly balanced in selective advantage. In nature such a balance will hardly ever be effective, for to be so it must be very exact, and small changes of the conditions, from which natural environments are never free, will be enough to upset the balance. It seems certain that in natural homogeneous environments one species will always sooner or later drive out the other.* Volterra and Lotka ([316]—cf. [44]—[199], [186]) have analysed the competition mathematically and have shown that these results are to be expected.

Direct competition usually leads to similar results. Gause and Witt [126] studied competition between *Paramecium caudatum* and *Didinium nasutum* in a medium containing bacterial food. The *Paramecium* feed on the bacteria, and the *Didinium* on the *Paramecium*, which are eradicated. After this, the *Didinium* die out for lack of food. Gause and Witt found that the two protistan species could not live permanently together unless he renewed the *Paramecium* at intervals from outside the culture. Crombie's results with insects, quoted above, are also relevant at this point, for in his experiments there was direct as well as indirect competition. Mathematical analysis shows that these results are to be expected as much as those of indirect competition.

In any natural environment, the species that compete, both directly and indirectly, are not two but many. But there is no reason to think that conditions will be widely different when the species that compete are more than two. Another difference between conditions in the experiments and nature is that it is rare in nature for two species to be adapted to exactly the same niche; almost always habits differ sufficiently to make the competition no more than partial.[124, 191] We may at least conclude that if in nature any two or more species compete for exactly the same niche in a natural environment the competition will normally lead to dominance of one species over the others. If the species do not compete, there is clearly no reason why they should not live together as a mixed population.

There is one way in which we can make the experiments approach natural conditions somewhat more closely. The environments we have considered have been homogeneous, and homogeneous environments are rare in nature. Natural environments always differ in their parts, and species are never adapted

---

* Where one species is present in more than one form, and the forms have different selective values, a balance may be set up. An example of this is the balance that occurs when a heterozygote is favoured by selection and the homozygote unfavourable (pp. 199, 260).

to exactly the same range of conditions. There are very often parts of the environment to which the weaker of two species may retire and in which it may live in isolation from the stronger species. It is secure from interference in that part of the environment.

If in the experiments the weaker species can escape from the stronger in a part of the environment, the results of competition may be very different from those in a homogeneous environment. Gause [123] found that he could provide a refuge for *Paramecium*, living in mixed culture with *Didinium*, by allowing sediment to collect at the bottom of the culture tube. This produced variable results. In some cultures the *Paramecium* was eradicated after a time, the refuge being inadequate; in others the *Didinium* died out, the available *Paramecium*—outside the sediment— being insufficient for their food, and this was followed by increase of the *Paramecium* as in the cultures in which they were grown alone; in still other cultures a mixed population of *Didinium* and *Paramecium* continued for some time. Clearly there must be an accurate balance between the advantage provided by the refuge and the destructive powers of the predator if the mixed culture is to persist.

Crombie [55] gives another example of the importance of a refuge in modifying the results of competition. He found that mixed cultures of insects would sometimes persist when they were cultured on whole wheat, though they did not persist in flour. The difference was due to the weaker species being able to find protection and isolation within the grains of the wheat. He was also able to produce a permanent mixed culture of *Tribolium confusum* and *Oryzæphilus surinamensis* by providing glass tubes into which the larvæ of *Oryzæphilus* could retire. There they were safe from destruction by the *Tribolium* larvæ. Without this protection they were killed and the species disappeared from the culture.

Thus, to survive in direct competition, the weaker species must be able to find protection from the stronger in a part of the environment outside the range of the stronger species.* Competition will then drive the weaker species to this region, and in most cases it is only there that it will survive. It seems,

---

* It may be sufficient that the stronger species should be the weaker in the refuge. There seems to be no experimental evidence on this point.

then, that we have here a principle that will lead to the isolation of two similar species whose ranges overlap. And, since both the isolated species are likely to adapt further to the conditions of the regions in which they are isolated, the principle will also result in exaggeration as well as perpetuation of differences between them—evolutionary differentiation between them should be more rapid and easier than it would otherwise be. We shall find this of importance when we discuss speciation (ch. VI). The principle should apply at all levels of differentiation, below as well as above the specific level. For a similar principle in a very different context the name *schismogenesis* has been proposed ([17,] cf. [56, 206]).

We must consider one other result that has been demonstrated by experimental study of competition. Mathematical analysis indicates that under certain conditions two forms living in the same homogeneous environment and competing directly may be expected to live together for an indefinite time undergoing rhythmic changes in population density. Each species should increase and decrease in numbers rhythmically, and the two should do so alternately, the one being numerous when the other is scarce. As has been said, this does not usually happen in experimental cultures. Usually the stronger species eradicates the weaker—in Gause's cultures of *Paramecium* and *Didinium* the *Paramecium* were first killed out and the *Didinium* then died of starvation; there was no rhythmic increase and decrease of either species, and no permanent mixed culture. Gause [123] was able to observe the rhythm under certain circumstances. He found that if he repeatedly added new *Paramecium* to the mixed culture at intervals after those originally present had been killed but before the *Didinium* had died out, the *Didinium* increased for a time after each addition of *Paramecium*, but soon again decreased. This is clearly what we should expect. But he also found that rhythmic changes in numbers occurred without interference from outside, if he used an example of competition in which the predator has a less deadly action on the prey than *Didinium* has on *Paramecium*. The example he chose (see also [227]) was competition between *Paramecium* and a yeast. The yeast will grow in the culture and serves as food for the *Paramecium*, which prey on it. In these cultures, both the

Paramecium and the yeast increased and decreased in numbers rhythmically. In one culture he observed three of these cycles in the *Paramecium* and two in the yeast (Fig. 48). The biological explanation is easy. The predator first increases as it feeds on the prey, but later the supply of the prey falls off and the numbers of the predator decrease. This decrease in the predator gives opportunity for renewed increase of the prey, and this is followed by another increase of the predator. So the cycle may continue indefinitely. The rhythm did not occur in the

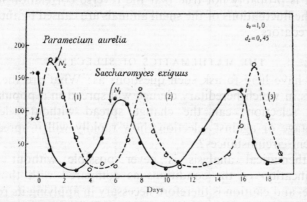

Figure 48. Rhythmical changes in population density in a culture of *Paramecium aurelia* and *Saccaromyces exiguus* living in competition. (After Gause)

cultures of *Paramecium* and *Didinium* because all the *Paramecium* were killed before reduction in the *Didinium* population gave an opportunity for them to increase again. Occurrence of the rhythm will depend on the relative efficiency of the predation and on the growth-rates of the two species.

Rhythmic changes in population numbers are very frequent in animal ecology and are important in the study of evolution. It may be that rhythms due to the inherent conditions of the competition, such as those we have been discussing, occur in nature. They may be frequent and of ecological importance, but it is not easy to observe them. It is usually difficult to be sure that an observed rhythm is not the result of cyclical changes in non-biological factors external to the competition. We shall discuss the subject again (p. 253). Sometimes, however, natural rhythms extend through several members of a food-chain and the fluctuations in the numbers of the later members of the chain can then be shown to be caused by those in the numbers of the earlier members. Thus in Canada,[92, 93] the lemmings (*Lemmus richardsoni* and *trimucronatus*) fluctuate in a rhythm of about 10 years (cf. p. 247) and their fluctuations and those of the varying hare (*Lepus americanus*) and other small mammals are followed by fluctuations in the numbers of predators such as the lynx (*Lynx canadensis*) and the snowy owl (*Nyctia scandiaca*). But it is probably not true that the reverse correlation holds, that the fluctuations of the small animals are caused by those of the predators.

THE MATHEMATICS OF SELECTION

We have here to ask such questions as: What are the conditions in which hereditary change will spread in a population under selection; can the change spread without selective advantage or against selection; how rapidly will it spread in different circumstances?

Mathematical analysis is never possible without great simplification of the conditions as compared with those in nature, and caution is therefore necessary in applying its results to the problems of natural evolution. This must be kept in mind in all the discussions of this section. One simplification that is often made in mathematical analysis of selection is that of random breeding, so long as the population is continuous and not too large (p. 186); it is assumed that an animal has an equal chance of breeding with all the other members of the population to which it belongs. We have little evidence of the extent to which natural mating in continuous populations is truly random, but the assumption of randomness is undoubtedly to some degree unnatural; animals, for instance, have greater chance of breeding with their immediate neighbours, such as the members of their family (p. 185). Any selective element in mating in such populations may in certain circumstances modify our conclusions. Another frequent assumption is to assume that the environment is constant, neglecting the changes that occur from time to time in all natural environments. Here again the assumption is clearly unnatural. The need for caution in these and other respects will appear in the course of our discussion.

Nevertheless, mathematical analysis can tell us much of the action of selection in nature.

The conditions that control the spread of genetic change in a population are always complex, even when simplified for mathematical analysis. Numerous factors take part in the control. It is advisable that we should first define the more important of these factors, and the terms we shall use for them.

We shall find that the *size* of a population largely modifies the rate and nature of the changes that occur in it. Definition of what we mean by size in this context is necessary. For the purpose of studying evolutionary change, the size of a population may best be defined as the "effective" number of breeding animals. This is known as the "effective breeding population". It is not intended to be a direct measure of the size of the population but an estimate of the size-characters of the population as they will affect the course of evolution. We shall use for it the symbol N. It is never equal to the total of the individuals in the population, for that will include non-breeding young and old as well as breeding adults. It is not even the number of sexually mature adults; it may be considerably less. Wright has discussed how the effective breeding population may be estimated. Of it he says ([336], pp. 170–1, cf. [335]): "The effective size of the population may be much less than the apparent size for many reasons. It refers, of course, only to the sexually mature individuals. If mature individuals of one sex are much less than those of the other, the effective size is determined largely by the former. It cannot be as much as four times as great. If there are wide variations in the number of offspring reaching maturity, left by different parents, the effective number may be reduced. If the species goes through a more or less regular cycle of numbers, the effective size is determined largely by the phase of small numbers. The situation then is approximately as if the population was characterised by the minimum number, but with the interval between generations as long as the length of the cycle." This definition applies only to a single population completely isolated from other populations. We shall discuss later (p. 185) the conditions when isolation is not complete, and migration occurs between the population and others with which it can interbreed.

Secondly, we need a definition in accurate terms of selective advantage. We may define this as the proportional excess of individuals bearing the mutation favoured by selection that survive to the next generation. If 1000 of the favoured individuals survive for 999 of the others, the selective advantage is 0·001. It may have any value from 0 to infinity. For it we shall use the symbol s.

The spread of a mutation is influenced not only by its selective advantage but also by the mutation rates both towards the mutation and in the reverse direction, to the normal form. We shall use the symbol u for the mutation rate towards the mutation, and v for the reversed mutation rate: u and v are defined as the proportions of individuals in the population in which the mutations occur. For the resultant mutation rate we will use the symbol V.

Change in the populations will be controlled by other factors besides these. The others can be defined when we need to refer to them.

The complexity of natural conditions is so great that it will be well for us to start by considering the action of only some of the active factors, and thus further simplifying the problems. For the moment we will consider only the actions of selection and of the mutation rate, and only the distribution of a single gene. This last simplification is undoubtedly unrealistic, for we have seen (pp. 68ff, 108) that genes interact in very many ways, so that the genotype behaves in heredity rather as a whole than as an aggregate of independent genes. Any change in one gene will alter the selective advantages of other genes, and its own advantage will be altered by changes in many of the other genes. But the assumption of independence will give us an approach to the problems.

If a mutant is favoured by selection, and the mutation rate towards it (u) is greater than that in the reversed direction (v), selection and the resultant mutation rate will act in the same direction and the mutation will spread until it becomes universal —or "fixed"—in the population. We will discuss the conditions of its spread later (p. 182). For the moment we will consider the case of an unfavourable mutant—with u still greater than v— so that the resultant mutation rate and selection are opposed. A balance will then be set up between them.[336] This is illustrated in Fig. 49, which shows the nature of the balance when the mutation is unfavourable and recessive, and the selective advantage 25 times the resultant mutation rate. The abscissa gives a scale of the proportions (q) of individuals in the populations carrying the mutation; the ordinate gives the rate of change in q (symbol Δq) that will occur in a population having any given proportion of mutated individuals. There is a balanced position ($\hat{q}$) at which the rate of change is zero. Populations on either side of this proportion will move towards it and will not then leave it. It is in fact a position of stable equilibrium. It is therefore clear that in circumstances such as these, so long as the conditions remain unaltered, the mutation, though unfavourable, will never disappear from the population; there will

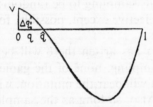

Figure 49. Tendency for change in the proportion of individuals bearing a deleterious recessive mutation under the opposed pressures of the resultant mutation rate (V), and of selection ($=25V$). Abscissa, proportion of individuals bearing the mutation (q); ordinate, rate of change in this proportion (Δq). (After Sewell Wright)

always be a proportion of the individuals bearing it. The proportion of mutated individuals will be smaller the more active is the selection against the mutation, and larger the greater the resultant mutation rate in favour of it. With a normal mutation rate—$1/10^5$ or $1/10^6$ (p. 97)—the selection must be weak if the mutation is to be present in more than a very small proportion of the population. Still it will always occur in spite of the fact that selection is against it. On the other hand, an unfavourable mutation will not spread to the majority of the population unless the pressure of selection is less than that of mutation. For this to be so in nature, the selection pressure must be very small.

For this result repeated mutation, i.e. a definite mutation

A.E.—7

rate in the population, is necessary, but we have seen (p. 98) that mutations normally occur repeatedly. Indeed, it is true that a single mutation is unlikely to persist even if it is favourable. This results from the action of a factor in the life of the population that we have not so far considered. All animals produce many more gametes than survive in the individuals of the next generation. Even those that succeed as far as fertilisation do not all reproduce. The individuals of each generation are therefore a sample, and usually a small sample, of those that might have been produced by the gametes of the last generation had all survived. There is thus in the production of each generation a sampling by which the successful gametes are chosen from the total number of gametes available. For our present purposes we may consider this sampling to be random; there is no reason to expect it to be selective except, possibly, for characters of the gametes themselves.

After a mutation has arisen there will be a chance that, as the result of the sampling, none of the gametes that survive to the next generation will bear the mutation, which would then be irretrievably lost. Also, so long as the sampling is random, the chance of a mutation's surviving will be the same whether it is favourable, neutral or unfavourable; the chance will be unaffected by the mutation's selective advantage. The sampling occurs at each generation, and its effects through a series of generations are cumulative. If a mutation occurred only once, it would be sure to be lost in time, for it has been shown [104] that for a neutral gene the chance of survival to n generations of a single mutation is $2/n$. Only if a mutation occurs many times has it a large chance of survival. A mutation with a 0·01 selective advantage (p. 176) has a 1:1 chance of survival if it has occurred 50 times, and a 100:1 chance after 250 occurrences. With normal mutation rates of $1/10^5$ or less survival is much more certain and rapid in a large population than in a small one, for a mutation will occur much more often in a large population. Abundant animals can take much more certain advantage of favourable mutation. But for any animal a mutation must occur repeatedly if it is to have a significant chance of spreading.

This random sampling of the gametes will modify the change that arises in a population as the result of mutation; some genes will be retained and others lost, and those to be retained or lost will be chosen by chance. It will therefore give rise to differences between populations, originally identical, that are living and evolving in isolation, and the differences will bear no relation to the selective advantages or disadvantages of the genes—they will be non-adaptive. The probable size of this effect at each generation is measured by the standard deviation of the sample of gametes that produces the new generation. This for a single gene occurring in a proportion q of the population is given ([336], p. 167) by the expression $\left(\dfrac{q(1-q)}{2N}\right)^{\frac{1}{2}}$. Since the size of the effect in a determined number of generations is inversely proportional to $N^{\frac{1}{2}}$, it is therefore much larger in small populations (p. 183). When N is large, it is very small, but, the variation being cumulative from one generation to another, it may in many generations become large even in large populations. The probability is that $1/2N$ of the genes that vary in the population will be lost or fixed in each generation.

Thus, isolated populations will differ in more and more non-adaptive characters as their isolated life continues. To random differentiation from this cause must be added that due to occurrence of different mutations in the separate populations. This differentiation will also bear no relation to the selective advantages of the mutations. The populations will also differentiate adaptively if the environmental conditions in their habitats differ. Together, these effects give a basis for the statement previously made (p. 146) that isolated populations may be expected always to differentiate. Some part of the differentiation will be adaptive, another part non-adaptive.

The rate at which genes which have arisen as rare mutations will spread through a population varies with many features of the population and of the genes. We shall later consider the population in relation to the spread of genes through it (p. 182); here we will consider the gene.

Various characteristics of the gene influence its spread— whether it is recessive or dominant; advantageous, neutral or disadvantageous; carried in the sex chromosomes or autosomes; and so on. Haldane ([151], p. 184) gives the following data for the spread of a dominant gene with a selective advantage of 0·001. This may be taken as a normal, but not large, advantage. By ordinary selection is meant that between the members of the population as a whole. Familiar selection is that between members of a family, as occurs, for instance, between the embryos in the uterus of a mammalian parent, or between the nestlings in a nest. Gametic selection is that between gametes, as between spermatozoa for speed of locomotion. The numbers in the last four columns give the generations required for each change in the distribution. The spread of a recessive gene with the same selective advantage is given by reading the table from the right and reversing the percentages at the top.

| Gene favoured | Type of selection | Sex favoured | Change in distribution; generations required | | | |
			0·001–1 per cent.	1–50 per cent.	50–99 per cent.	99–99·999 per cent.
Autosomal .	Ordinary	Both	6920	4819	11624	309780
,, .	Familiar	,,	13841	9638	23328	619560
,, .	Gametic	,,	13831	8819	6157	7112
Sex-linked .	Ordinary	Homo-gametic	6916	4668	5593	10106
,, .	,,	Hetero-gametic	6928	5164	11070	20693

In computing this table no account was taken of the action of random sampling or of repeated mutation. The figures cannot therefore be taken to give an accurate picture of the spread of a gene under natural conditions.* They do, however, show very clearly how the effectiveness of selection considered alone varies with the characters of the gene and the nature of the selection. In ordinary and familiar selection a recessive autosomal gene will take more than 40 times as long as a dominant gene with the same selective advantage to reach a distribution of 1 per cent., and nearly 13 times as long to reach 99 per cent. This result is not surprising, for the recessive gene will be expressed in the phenotype only when it occurs as a homozygote, and selection will act only then. Homozygotes of a gene that is still rare will be very few, since they will be formed only

* Repeated mutation will greatly increase the rate of spread of a gene so long as it is rare—when its frequency is of the same order as the resultant mutation rate. It will have much less effect when the gene is common.

when two heterozygotes meet. Selection will therefore have very slight effects during the early stages of the spread of a recessive gene, and its spread will be slow. A dominant gene is expressed in the phenotype of the heterozygote, and selection will be much more effective while it is rare. Its spread will be much more rapid.

It is also noteworthy that this difference in the rates of spread of dominant and recessive genes does not apply to gametic selection, nor, in anything like the same degree, to sex-linked genes in ordinary selection.

So far we have considered only selection between mutated and non-mutated forms. We have not considered the results of incomplete dominance where the heterozygotic phenotype differs from the phenotypes of both homozygotes, and will therefore have a different selective value from both. These cases are of considerable importance in evolution. An extreme example is that of a gene that is lethal as a homozygote but advantageous as a heterozygote. Such lethals are common in *Drosophila* and may have been important in evolution. In less extreme forms the same phenomenon occurs wherever the heterozygote has an advantage that differs from those of the two homozygotes.

With random mating two allelomorphs, Rr, will occur in the population as homo- and heterozygotes in the proportions $p^2RR:2pqRr:q^2rr$, where p is the frequency of the allelomorph R, q that of r, so that $p+q=1$. If the selective advantages of these types are as $a:b:c$, it has been shown ([104], p. 100) that the position is in equilibrium if $\dfrac{p}{q}=\dfrac{b-c}{b-a}$ and that the equilibrium is stable if b is greater than both a and c, i.e. if the heterozygote is the most favoured in selection. The population will move to this equilibrium and remain there so long as the conditions are unaltered. Such a gene will be preserved in the population even though the homozygotic mutation is lethal (and a is 0) (cf. p. 71). Its distribution will be

$$(b-c)^2RR:2(b-c)(b-a)Rr:(b-a)^2rr.$$

If b is less than both a and c, i.e. if the heterozygote is the most unfavourable, there will still be an equilibrium, but it will be unstable. The distribution will move away from the equilibrium. This condition is not frequent in nature.

On the basis of these results we can understand the presence in natural genotypes of genes that are lethal as homozygotes, provided that the heterozygote is advantageous. We shall consider this subject again when we discuss polymorphism (p. 260).

Up to this point we have discussed only single pairs of allelomorphs assumed to be acting in isolation. But we found earlier (pp. 68 ff.) that genes interact in very many ways and that characters of the phenotype are often controlled by many genes. Changes in these (metrical) characters have been of the greatest significance in evolution. What can be said of the action of selection upon them?

In these characters—the height of man is a typical example—the numerical value of the character is generally distributed among the individuals of a population in a curve of error about the mean. The population is maintained with the mean at its optimum so long as the conditions of selection remain constant.

If conditions change and the population is acted on by selection towards a new optimum of one of its metrical characters, the value of the character in the population will move rapidly to the new optimum ([104], p. 104), genes tending to alter the character in this direction being favoured. But Fisher has shown ([104], p. 111) that the change in the distribution of the genes does not necessarily cease immediately the new optimum has been reached. Selection will cease at the optimum, but some of the genes that were favoured during the movement may still increase in frequency after the selection has ceased. The change in the structure of the phenotype may overshoot the optimum. It is not possible to explain here the analytic basis of this surprising result. We shall return to it when we discuss orthogenesis (p. 291).

The minimum selective advantage that will be effective in causing the spread or eradication of a gene varies inversely with the size of the effective breeding population, N. Fisher ([104], p. 94) shows that in a constant environment the selective advantage must be at least as small as $1/N$ if the gene is to be effectively neutral. For large populations—10^6 or 10^7 individuals—this advantage is extremely small. Even for considerably smaller populations—10^4 or 10^5 individuals—it is smaller than we can hope to demonstrate experimentally. Indeed, Fisher concludes that in such populations it is impossible for any gene to be permanently neutral, for the environmental conditions are certain to alter from time to time, and the selective advantage of a gene will alter with them. The changes in selective advantage with time will be greater than is needed to make an originally neutral gene advantageous or disadvantageous; even if a gene were neutral it could not remain so for long. It should, however, be remarked that Fisher's original determination of the minimum effective selective advantage $(1/N)$ was reached on the assumption of an unchanging environment. He does not discuss whether this minimum will also hold in an environment in which the changes of advantage with time are much larger than the minimum effective advantage he finds for a constant environment.

When the population is small, the conditions of selection are very different. Wright [333] has given a detailed investigation of them.

Wright concludes that selection will be totally ineffective if the selective advantage (and resultant mutation rate) is less than $1/4N$. This, a somewhat smaller figure than Fisher's, gives an extreme lower limit for effectiveness. Where N is less than 1000, this implies that selective advantages of appreciable size may be ineffective. We shall discuss later (p. 212) the question whether these conditions are important in evolution in nature. Where they obtain, chance will play a much larger part in the control of gene distribution than in larger populations, and adaptive value a smaller part; genes may become fixed in the population or eliminated *by chance*, with no relation to their selective advantages. Non-adaptive differentiation should be considerable or even prevalent. This is Wright's theory of *drift*, indeterminate change of structure in small populations. If accepted, it gives a theoretical basis to account for the large amount of apparently non-adaptive differentiation that is found in animals (p. 47).*

Wright's conclusions are based on the facts of random

* Wright's theory has been disputed by Fisher.[106]

sampling among the gametes that we have already discussed (p. 178). We have seen that the effects of these phenomena should be most evident when the populations are small. The conclusions are illustrated by Wright in Fig. 50, which shows the variation in the distribution of a deleterious gene in the

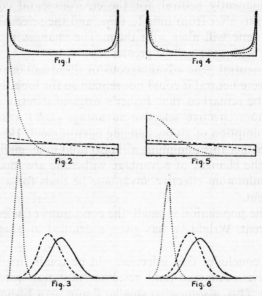

Figure 50. Forms taken by the variation of the distribution of a gene frequency in groups of populations of different sizes. Ordinates: proportion of the group of population with frequencies given by the abscissa. Absence of gene on the left of the abscissa, fixation on the right. 1–3, a deleterious gene in complete absence of dominance; 4–6, a completely recessive, deleterious gene. 1, 4, $N=1/40V$; 2, 5, $N=10/40V$; 3, 6, $N=100/40V$. In all figures the solid line represents the least selection $(s=-V/10)$; the broken line selection 10 times as severe; the dotted line 100 times as severe. (After Sewell Wright)

complete absence of dominance (Figs. 1–3), and of a deleterious recessive gene (Figs. 4–6), to be expected in groups of populations of different sizes. In the lowest diagrams of the figure, N is relatively large ($100/40V$, where V is the mutation rate) and selection is effective. Even with the weakest selection (solid line), the populations are normally distributed around the most frequent distribution, and with stronger selection they are crowded round this distribution more closely. Selection is here effective. With the smaller populations of the middle diagrams ($N=10/40V$), concentration of the distributions around the most frequent value is lost. Selection is no longer effective. In the smallest populations of the top diagrams ($N=1/40V$) the gene is either fixed or absent in almost all the populations, and this is so whatever the strength of the selection within the range considered. These diagrams demonstrate how strikingly the effects of selection change with changes in the size of the populations.

Wright [333] has also discussed the rate at which evolutionary change is likely to proceed in populations of different sizes. He finds that change is likely to be slow in small populations, where N is less than $1/V$ and $1/s$. This is largely because there will be few mutations in the small populations to give the basis for change. He also believes that change will be slow in large populations, because random sampling of the gametes will be almost ineffective in them. Haldane [154] is not in full agreement here. In medium-sized populations, where N is of the same order as $1/V$ and $1/s$, mutations will be sufficiently numerous and random sampling will also play its part. In these populations change will be most rapid. To this Haldane agrees.

ISOLATION

Groups of animals within a species are isolated when they are unable to breed freely with each other. In most types of isolation interbreeding is prevented by some form of barrier, but this need not be a physical barrier; differences in the biology or behaviour of the animals may prevent their interbreeding and so act as barriers. We shall discuss the relative importance of these types of isolation in the next chapter. We need not distinguish them here.

There is, however, one type of isolation that we need to distinguish. Isolation is possible without any barrier, physical or biological. In a continuous widespread population, an individual will not breed as often with those that are distant from it as with its nearer neighbours. It will be isolated from many of the individuals of the population by the distances between them and it. Animals may be isolated by distance alone.

We will first consider this isolation by distance, and for the

7*

moment assume that there are no differences of selective advantage throughout the range of the whole species. Around any individual there will be a group within which we may assume that there is complete interbreeding; as we pass away from this group the chance of interbreeding will gradually decrease. We may give the symbol N' to the effective breeding population (p. 175) of the group of complete interbreeding. Wright [338] finds that in such circumstances the conditions are equivalent to complete interbreeding throughout the whole species (panmixia), if N' is of the order of 1000 or larger. There is then no distance isolation. With N' between 1000 and 100, local differentiation will occur, but it will be fluctuating. There will not be fixation of different allelomorphs in the local populations unless N' for them is measured in 10's rather than 100's. Here we must remember that N' will differ from the total number of individuals in the group of complete interbreeding much as N differs from the total numbers of a population (p. 175). The group may in many circumstances contain considerably more individuals than the number given by N'.

Where there are differences of selective advantage within the range of a species, the effects of selection will vary with the size of N' according to the same principles as hold for differentiation in whole populations (p. 182 f.). The smaller N' is the less effective will the selection be, and the larger the part played in the differentiation by non-adaptive change. It must, however, be remembered that a change, although spread by drift and not by selection, may chance to improve the genotype and in fact be adaptive. Such a character may spread through the species beyond its original local population, and so give rise to evolutionary change in the species as a whole. There is therefore a chance that a mutation may cause improvement of the species even though its selective advantage is not large enough to be effective in its local population.

We may now pass to the effects of isolation due to barriers of some type between the populations. In a local population separated from other similar populations by barriers we may again call the effective breeding population N'. We may define the grade of isolation by the proportion (m) by which the effective breeding population is replaced in each generation by immigration across the barriers from neighbouring populations; m will bear approximately the same relation to the total number of immigrants that N and N' bear to the total number of individuals in the populations (p. 175).

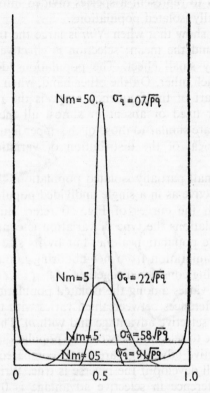

Figure 51. Distribution of frequencies of a gene in groups of partially isolated local populations of various sizes. Frequency in the species as a whole assumed to be 50 per cent. σq, standard deviation of the curve; q, frequency of gene; p, that of its allelomorph. (After Sewell Wright)

In a partially isolated local population conditions vary with the relative sizes of N' and m, and with the presence or absence of selection. Fig. 51 (from Wright) gives some calculated results for the variation to be expected in the distribution of a gene in assemblages of populations of different sizes. Each curve relates to a single assemblage throughout which $N'm$ has the same value. In the assemblages chosen the values of $N'm$ vary between 0·05 and 50. The mean frequency of the gene in the whole of each assemblage is assumed to be 50 per cent. There is assumed to be no differential selection. Each assemblage may be taken to represent a species divided into a number of smaller partially isolated populations.

The curves show that when $N'm$ is large the frequencies are crowded around the mean; selection is effective in them and drift has only small effect. The populations do not greatly differ from each other. On the other hand, when $N'm$ is small, the middle part of the frequency range is the rarest and the gene is either fixed or absent in almost all the populations. These results are similar to those of the upper figures of Fig. 50. They are typical of the distribution of variation controlled by drift.

Thus, in small partially isolated populations the same principles are effective as in a single undivided population, such as that to which the curves of Fig. 50 refer. But in partially isolated populations the type of variation is controlled not by the size of the population alone, but by its size and the proportion of immigration from neighbouring populations, these conditions being considered together.

If selection varies among the isolated populations, its power of causing differences between them varies with the size of the differences in selective advantage and with m. There will be no differences due to selection between the populations if the differences in selective advantage are small compared with m, but differences will develop if the reverse is true. Wright finds that when the difference in selective advantage is 0·001, a small value but one probably common in nature, local populations must be isolated so that not more than 0·1 per cent. of their effective breeding populations is replaced in each generation if they are to become adaptively differentiated. It is probable that greater differences in selective advantage occur, and, where they do, the proportion of immigration may be greater.

In obtaining these results it was assumed that the range of the species extends more or less regularly in all directions. But the distribution of animals is not always of this kind, and one other type of continuous distribution deserves mention.

This is the type in which the range extends along one or more lines, rather than in all directions. Many species are distributed along the lines of the seashore, of rivers, or of mountain ranges. Their distribution is linear rather than areal (cf. Figs. 43, 44, pp. 156–7).

When the distribution is of the linear type, the opportunities for local differentiation are much greater than when the distribution is areal. In Fig. 52 [335] the standard deviations between

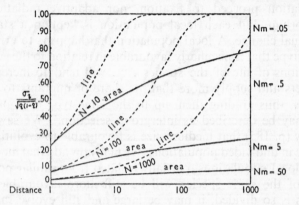

Figure 52. Standard deviations of mean gene frequencies in partially isolated local populations of different sizes and at different distances apart. Full lines: areal distributions of the populations; dotted lines: linear distributions. (After Sewell Wright)

partially isolated, local populations in linear and areal ranges are compared. The standard deviation gives a measure of the extent of differentiation that will occur among the populations, and the curves of Fig. 52 show its increase with the distance of the populations from each other. It will be seen that in all cases the standard deviation—and therefore differentiation among the populations—increases with distance much more rapidly when the range is linear than when it is areal.

Wright [336] concludes from his analyses that partial isolation of local populations is likely to lead to rapid evolutionary change. The reasons for this are (1) that immigration from neighbouring populations will bring in mutations not previously present in the population, and these will be tried out in recombination with the genotype of the population, and (2) that in small populations, as the local populations will often be, drift will be effective. The most important controlling conditions are the size of the local population, the proportion of immigration, and the sizes of the differences in selective advantage between the populations. Where both $4N'm$ and $4N's$—s being the difference in selective advantage between the populations—are in the neighbourhood of 1, the conditions will be the most favourable for rapid change. Then, "neither does random differentiation proceed to fixation, nor adaptive radiation to equilibrium, but each local population is kept in a state of continual change. A local population that happens to arrive at a genotype that is peculiarly favourable in relation to the general conditions of life of the species . . . will tend to increase in numbers and supply more than its share of migrants to other regions, thus grading them up to the same type by a process that may be described as intergroup selection." We saw previously (p. 185) that medium size is favourable to evolutionary change in undivided populations. We may now add that medium-sized, local populations, partially isolated from similar populations of the same species, will be still more favourable. If a species is so divided, it may be large and still evolve rapidly. We shall find this a very important conclusion, for many species are organised into demes, and demes are local, partially isolated, populations of the kind that we have been discussing.

THE EFFICIENCY OF NATURAL SELECTION IN NATURE

It is often assumed that direct proof of the effectiveness of natural selection in nature is unnecessary; the indirect evidence is thought to be sufficient to prove that it must be effective. This indirect evidence is of many kinds and certainly cogent. It is clearly true that many of the conditions that are required for selection to be effective in determining the characters of animals are present in animal populations. We know that animals vary and that part at least of their variation is inherited, and we know from mathematical analysis that small selective advantages will be sufficient as a basis for selection, so long as the populations are above a minimum size. Also, the broad facts of animal biology provide many powerful arguments for the effectiveness of natural selection, some of them developed by Darwin himself. Of these arguments perhaps the strongest is that from the existence of adaptation in animals. Let us first shortly examine that argument.

Adaptation consists in correlation of the structure and habits of animals with the needs of their lives. That this correlation exists is a biological fact that no biologist will deny. Every animal is adapted to the conditions of its life and could not live successfully if it were not so. This will be admitted, though some biologists may think the adaptation less general and exact than others believe it to be [256]; they think that many of the more elaborate examples of adaptation are imaginary rather than real.

For our purpose we need especially to note that many adaptations, the reality of which few find it possible to doubt, are most surprisingly detailed. No one who has seen the astonishingly *detailed* cryptic resemblances of many animals to objects in their surroundings, or the equally detailed resemblances of animals to other animals in mimicry, can seriously doubt their reality. It is impossible to doubt that the well-known likenesses between the closed wings of the butterfly *Kallima* and a dead leaf, and between a geometrid caterpillar and a twig, have some other explanation than coincidence. It is the detail and complexity of these resemblances, extending as they do to both structure and habit, that make them so convincing. It is difficult even for those who discredit many examples of adaptation to question the reality of these. When we remember that these are only the more extreme examples of adaptation, that adaptation is present in all animals and extends to all parts of the body, its reality becomes undeniable.

Either animal adaptation has been evolved in direct relation to the uses to which the structures are now put, or the structures arose in some way unrelated to their present use and have later been put to uses for which they are suitable, presumably by the animals choosing a habit of life in which they could be used. It is certainly true that choice of habitat and habit play a large part in animal life (p. 227); animals do select and live in habitats suitable for them. But this cannot account for all the facts of adaptation. It especially fails to account for the extreme detail of much of adaptation. A chance resemblance between the underside of a butterfly's wings and a dead leaf may have been the starting-point for the evolution of resemblance between them, and may have given rise to the habit of behaving in a manner which made the resemblance valuable in the animal's life. The structural *details* of the resemblance as we now observe it can only have been evolved in relation to the use to which it is now put; it must have been gradually perfected in adaptation to its present use. Chance may have originated the adaptation; to suggest that it has been responsible for the whole of its present detail is to ask too much of our credence.

If these adaptations have been evolved, at least in part, by some process that has resulted in their becoming increasingly efficient in their present uses, we need to find some means by which this could have been brought about. Only two naturalistic theories capable of explaining this process have been suggested. One, that of Lamarck, would undoubtedly produce the required result in many cases of adaptation (though it is hard to see how the similarities of protective resemblance could have arisen by Lamarckian evolution, and this is true of some other types of adaptation); but we found reason (p. 3) to disregard the Lamarckian theory on the grounds that we cannot find any generally accepted evidence in its favour, and that it is not possible to bring it into agreement with our knowledge of heredity.

The second theory is that of natural selection, which requires that selection should be effective in natural environments. This is the only theory at present in the field that may possibly account for the whole range of adaptation, and this by itself may be taken to give presumptive evidence in its favour. Also, the facts of adaptation are by no means the only indirect evidence for this theory. Our whole knowledge of the natural history of animals is, if not in favour of it, at least consistent with its truth. We have not space here to discuss this statement, nor is it necessary for us to do so. If direct evidence for the theory can be brought forward, the strength of the indirect evidence loses its importance. Biologists have been predisposed in favour of the theory of natural selection by the indirect evidence, but, if our theory of evolution is to be more than hypothesis, we need to show that selection is in fact effective in natural populations, that the more favourable varieties *are* preserved and the less favourable removed. Can we show that this is so?

It should first be pointed out that for proof that natural selection is effective it is not necessary to show that the *whole* death-rate in natural populations is selective. It is certain that very often it is not. Of the millions of eggs laid by a cod each year, the vast majority die for reasons unrelated to their selective advantages: the deaths of most are determined by chance. So also in all animals the sampling of the gametes by which only a few succeed in each generation is determined by chance. All we need to show is that a significant part of the death-rate is selective; it will often be enough even though the selective fraction is small. If at some time during its development a young cod that possesses a character of selective advantage is more likely to survive, there will be effective selection; the favourable variety will be more likely to be represented in the population of the next generation. And the selection will be measured by the excess proportion that survives *at the stage of the life-history at which the advantage occurs*. In the cod there will still be effective selection if there is significant advantage from some character in the relatively small population of young fish, although the death-rate of the much more numerous eggs may be wholly non-selective.

We must also note that it is the probability of survival that we are discussing. Often the selective process may fail and an advantageous form be killed, but it will be enough for our purpose if we can show that this is *less likely* to happen to an individual that possesses advantageous characters. It is no good argument against the effectiveness of selection that animals often die for reasons in which chance is the determining factor, and that favourable varieties do not always survive.

Evidence for the effectiveness of selection in nature is of several different kinds, but at present it is by no means as complete as we might wish. We will now summarise this evidence, such as it is.

We must first consider some further indirect evidence. This indicates the probability that selection is effective in natural populations, but does not prove it. Here we have first the fact that differences in genetic characters occur between natural populations. This is not direct evidence that selection is effective in the populations. Differentiation may, as we have seen (p. 183), be non-adaptive in nature. But it is not probable that all the differentiation in natural populations is non-adaptive. If any part of it is adaptive, it is clear that we find in natural populations the results that we should expect from selection if it were effective in the populations.

Differentiation of local populations has been found in every species that has been accurately examined. This subject has already been considered (pp. 147 ff.) and we need not repeat the discussion here. The opinions of Dobzhansky [85] from the extensive work that has been carried out on local populations of *Drosophila* may, however, be mentioned as confirming the conclusions of our previous discussion. Summarising the conditions found in a wide range of wild local races of this genus, Dobzhansky says: "Aside from 'macro-geographic' variability"—i.e. variation between the larger subdivisions of a species—"there exist also differences, usually of a quantitative nature, between populations inhabiting neighbouring or even contiguous localities. Moreover, the genetic composition of a population does not remain constant from year to year. . . . A species of *Drosophila* does not represent a single, panmictic population, but rather a mass of local colonies that are able to pursue within limits different evolutionary courses. The fate of a colony is, of course, controlled by natural selection, yet selection is not the sole determiner of the population dynamics. As predicted on theoretical grounds by Wright"—(p. 183)— "shifts in the genetic composition of a population may be due to the limitation of its genetically effective size." We must put aside, for the present, Dobzhansky's assumption that selection is effective, for that is the question we are discussing. We shall discuss later the evolutionary results of the organisation within the species that he describes (p. 245). All we need here is the undoubted fact that local populations are differentiated in a manner that selection might produce, if it is active. That not all the differences between the populations are due to selection is irrelevant at the present point.

Next we have the evidence that man is undoubtedly able to modify the structure of his domestic animals by selection. This evidence also is indirect. It does no more than make it probable that if selection is present in natural populations it will be effective there also. This evidence is weak in another way.

Much, though not all, of the differentiation between domestic races of animals is due to rearrangement of the genotypes of the species by recombination, and not to new mutation. In so far as the variation is of this type, caution must be used in applying it to the spread of new mutation in evolution, though there is no reason to think that this difference in the nature of the variation will significantly alter the effects of selection. Much of the variation between local races of natural species is probably due to recombination (p. 208).

We come now to direct evidence of active selection in natural populations. Here we have first the evidence given by the spread of new forms in nature. Many cases are known in which a new form, first observed as a rare variant at some point within the range of the species, has spread until it is now found over a large part of the range, and may sometimes have almost entirely replaced the original form in at least a part of the range. Probably the best known and most thoroughly investigated example of this is the spread during the last century of melanic varieties of several species of Lepidoptera, in Britain and other parts of Europe. Their spread is definitely associated with industrialisation of the country over which they have spread. All the species that show the phenomenon are cryptic, and it is easy to suggest that the darker colour of the melanic varieties is of selective advantage on the darker background of an industrialised countryside. But it seems that this is not the whole explanation. Ford [110] has shown that the melanic variety of one species (*Boarmia repandata*) is a genetic dominant and has higher viability than the original form. He believes that there is always, i.e. both before and during the spread, a balance set up between the advantage in viability and the disadvantage of the colour in concealment. In non-industrialised country, before the spread, the melanic form was the less cryptic and the selective balance was against it in spite of its higher viability; it remained a rare variant. But after industrialisation its disadvantage in concealment was reduced and the balance was reversed in its favour, so that it spread under selection. Probably the same theory will account for all or most of the cases of spread of melanic forms in industrial areas. If the theory is accepted, we have direct evidence of effective selection in nature.

Another example of spread of a new form is that of a black variant of the hamster (*Cricetus cricetus*, Rodentia) in Central Russia ([303], p. 99). This was first observed in 1771–2 in a small area in the part of its range where it is still commonest (Fig. 53). Between that time and today, it has increased so as to replace almost the whole population in this area. It has also spread

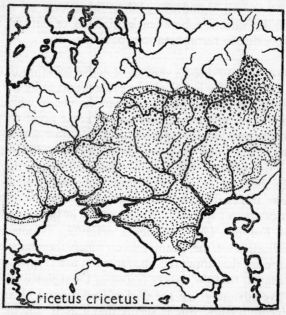

Cricetus cricetus L.

Figure 53. Distribution of a melanic mutation in the hamster (*Cricetus cricetus*). Small dots, distribution of the species; large dots, present distribution of the variety. The origin of the variety was at the point of greatest concentration of the large dots. (After Timoféeff-Ressovsky)

westwards more than 1000 miles, being now found on the Dnieper. In this and other cases there may have been repeated mutation, but there can be little doubt that the black form has a selective advantage (though we do not know what is the nature of the advantage), and that it has spread as the result of this advantage.

An example which shows selection in action, though the selective agent is not natural, is that of the spread of cyanide-resistant strains of red scale (*Aonidiella aurantia*, Hemiptera) and other pests in the citrus plantations of California.[247] After fumigation with cyanide had been used for some years to kill the pests, it was found that the treatment was less effective than it had previously been. The efficiency became less and less until the minimum effective dose was sometimes harmful to the trees. Also, the area in which the treatment was ineffective increased rapidly from year to year, though it was not the same for all pests. It was shown that these results were due to spread of resistant varieties of the pests. That of red scale was shown to be a genetic variation. In this example there is no doubt that selection, though artificial, was responsible for the spread of the resistant varieties.

The most direct approach to the problem of proving the effectiveness of selection is the experimental. Experiments can be planned to show that characters that appear to us to be adaptive, and therefore presumably to have selective value, are in fact favoured by selection. Experiments of this type have been carried out frequently, but the data that are given in accounts of these experiments are often incomplete. Although the conclusions are almost always in favour of selection, they cannot be said to be fully substantiated ([256], pp. 197 ff.). In particular, the results of selection are not often shown to be statistically significant. We will therefore not review this work here. But such criticism is not true of at least one recent example of work of this kind, that of Popham [241-4] on the feeding of a fish, the rudd, on a hemipteran *Arctocorisa* (=*Corixa*) *distincta*. This aquatic bug is able to adjust its colour during its larval life to that of the substratum of the water in which it is living, but does not do so as an adult; it then retains the colour it had as a larva. Popham took adults of various colours and exposed them to the attacks of the rudd on different backgrounds. He found that bugs that matched the tone of the background were eaten less readily and quickly than those that did not. If none accurately matched the background, those nearer to it in tone were protected, provided the difference in tone between them and the background was less than a certain maximum. The fish seemed able to distinguish all the insects when the difference in tone was greater than this.

Some of Popham's results are given in the following table.

By "tone" is meant the general darkness of the pigmentation; it was estimated by comparing the animals and the backgrounds with standard grey colours from Ostwald's colour chart. In these standards the proportion of black in each grey is known. In the table the tones are expressed in a series with equal standard tone-differences from 1 (lightest) to 7. These differences were also derived from the standards of the colour chart, and are separated by equal differences in sensation. The numbers in brackets after the figures of the table give the number of standard tone-differences between the fish and the background.

	Colour of insect					
Colour of background	7	6	5	7	6	5
	Percentages of insects taken by fish					
	Using 100 insects			Using 150 insects		
1	33 (6)	34 (5)	33 (4)	32·6 (6)	33·3 (5)	34 (4)
2	36 (5)	38 (4)	26 (3)	36 (5)	36 (4)	28 (3)
3	41 (4)	32 (3)	27 (2)	40·6 (4)	32 (3)	27·3 (2)
4	53 (3)	36 (2)	11 (1)	—	—	—

It is clear from the table that where some of the insects were close to the background in colour (bottom two lines) these had a definite selective advantage. But this was not so when the differences between the insects and the background were greater. The results were statistically significant.*

Another type of experiment consists in releasing animals bearing some mutation, believed to be advantageous or disadvantageous, and observing their fate after release. Many experiments of this type have been carried out on *Drosophila* under laboratory conditions, and from these experiments the "viability" of many mutations has been determined. All such experiments show that selection is effective in laboratory cultures, but they do not demonstrate its effectiveness in natural populations. Experiments in the field are much less numerous. An example is given by some work of Gordon,[143] who used the

* Frost and Macan (*J. anim. Ecol.* 17. 174, 1948) criticise these results as evidence of selection *in nature* on the ground that Corixids are not a large part of the food of the fish.

"ebony" mutant of *Drosophila melanogaster*. Ebony is out-wardly recessive—the heterozygotic phenotype is indistinguish-able from the wild form. In the laboratory the mutant persists in a mixed culture with the wild type, forming a balanced population with 20 per cent. of the homozygotic mutants ([194], cf. p. 170, note). This is probably because the heterozygote, though outwardly like the wild form, has a higher viability, and the homozygote a lower. In the mixed culture the advan-tage of the heterozygote is balanced against the disadvantage of the homozygote.

Gordon released near Totnes in Devonshire a population of *D. melanogaster* containing 50 per cent. of ebony mutants, i.e. the population was $\frac{1}{4}EE:\frac{1}{2}Ee:\frac{1}{4}ee$. The species is not present before the release; there was no danger of contamination of the population by native flies. He trapped flies at different places near the point of release and at intervals up to 128 days after release. No homozygotic mutants were caught more than 75 days after the release, though the wild form was still being taken at the end of the experiment. The results were those to be expected if there was complete selection against the homo-zygote, i.e. if none of this form lived long enough to reproduce. This is good evidence of the occurrence of selection in the conditions of the experiment, which were close to those of nature in all respects except that the habitat was not native to the fly. Incidentally, the results show very clearly how different the conditions of selection may be in a natural environment and in the cultures of the laboratory. In the laboratory, as has been mentioned, the ebony homozygote and the wild type can live together.

In all this evidence large differences between the competing forms, often caused by macro-mutations ([303], pp. 77–84) and usually giving rise to large selective differences, have been used. Not all the evidence of this kind has been given. As a whole, the evidence leaves little doubt that selection is effective for these differences. But we shall find reason to believe that these are not the differences on which the greater part of evolutionary change is based (p. 212). From the evolutionary point of view the more important differences are the small changes that result from micro-mutations. We have no experimental proof that these small changes are spread in nature by selection, and we can hardly expect this evidence, for demonstration of it in experiments would be very difficult. Nevertheless, we know that local natural populations differ by these small, often quantitative, differences (p. 194); and the mathematical analysis shows that the small selective differences to which they give rise should be effective, at least in populations above a minimum size (p. 183). Even in small populations some of the change should be adaptive. There is not the least evidence that these small and gradual changes are unsuitable as the basis for selection. We may say that all the evidence at present available is in favour rather than against the view that they as well as the larger evolutionary changes will be spread by selection.

Thus, the proposition that natural selection is effective in nature, even when the differences on which it acts are small and quantitative, may be looked upon as a very sound working hypothesis, so long as we add the reservation that it will be less effective in small populations than in large. In the future it may be shown definitely that small and gradual changes, as well as larger changes, come under the control of selection. Even today the probability that they are under its control is great enough to throw the burden of proof on those who deny it.

To conclude that selection is a reality in nature does not imply that this is the only way in which animals interact. It is certainly not. Without competition natural selection cannot be effective, but by no means all the interactions of animals are competitive. In many environments the fauna does not fill the environment at all times ([94,] and p. 272); when it does not, there may be no effective competition, either intra- or interspecific. More than this, active co-operation, the antithesis of competition, is a real fact of animal natural history; the chance of successful life may be actually improved for an animal by the presence of other animals in the environment. Within the species, animals associate in family groups, herds and flocks, and social species live in communities. There can be no doubt that these associations are valuable. Allee (cf. [4,] for references) has shown that some species live better with other members of the same species than alone, so long as the crowding is not too great. *Paramecium* cultured at unfavourable temperatures lives longer at an optimum concentration than at lower concentrations; flatworms (*Procerodes*) withstand unfavourable osmotic pressure for longer; echinoderm eggs develop better. Goldfish (*Cyprinus carassius*) grow better in water that has been contaminated by other fish of the same species. In nature advantage is often gained from symbiosis, from the living together of several species in feeding flocks, and from many other types of association.

We have already seen that natural selection may be an effective agent in evolution though only part of the death-rate is selective. Similarly, the reality of co-operation between animals does not prove that selection is ineffective. Indeed, it may be said that its existence supports belief in the effectiveness of selection. The effects of co-operation, either within a species or between species, are of value in any competition of the co-operating animals with species outside the co-operation. They tend to help the animal in its competition with other members of the fauna, and, in part, co-operation may have been evolved for this purpose. Where there is co-operation, it is likely that there is also competition; and, where there is competition, the facts we have considered in this chapter indicate that selection is effective. Co-operation is itself indirect evidence in favour of the effectiveness of selection.

PART II

The Theory of Evolution

Chapter VI

MICRO-EVOLUTION
pp. 205–263

Chapter VII

MACRO- AND MEGA-EVOLUTION: INTRODUCTION
pp. 264–8

Chapter VIII

PRE-ADAPTATION
pp. 269–290

203

204

MICRO-EVOLUTION

SO FAR our subject has been the background of biological knowledge on which a theory of evolution must be based if it is to be acceptable today. We have not considered the form the theory must take. We can now proceed to do this. In the present chapter we shall discuss micro-evolution, the early stages of the evolutionary process in which differentiation begins and is built up to the specific stage of divergence. The larger evolutionary changes of macro- and mega-evolution will be discussed in the following chapters.

It has been noted many times in the earlier chapters that evolution is not an identical process in all animals. The evolution of a species varies not only with the biological characters of the animal, but also with the nature of its environment. In many of its features the process of evolution must differ from animal to animal. We cannot here discuss all the forms of the evolutionary process; the most we can do is to interpret its general features. In one way in particular the discussion will be restricted. More than any other feature of its biology, an animal's reproductive mechanism determines the type of its evolution. We shall discuss micro-evolution almost solely in multicellular animals with bisexual reproduction. These, after all, are the majority of the animal kingdom. If we can understand micro-evolution in them, we shall have interpreted the form of the evolutionary process that has been responsible for the greater part of animal evolution.

Before we go further, it will be worth while to summarise the more important of the conclusions that have emerged in the discussions of the previous chapters.

The first point to be emphasised follows directly from the fact that the progress of evolution in an animal may be modified by changes of any kind in its biology or ecology. Evolution is a phenomenon in natural history; we must discuss it in relation to the whole life of the animal. And, since evolution goes on while the life of the animal is continuing, the animal throughout its evolution must be able to live in competition with other members of the fauna of its environment. It must always be viable and efficient. By modification of its organisation the animal becomes adapted to the conditions of the environment, but adaptation to special features of the environment is not the whole of evolutionary change. At least in the more successful groups of animals, there is throughout evolution a continuous improvement of the organisation of the animal's body whereby it becomes a more efficient living mechanism, more independent of changes external to it and with wider control over the environment. Evolution of this kind may also be regarded as in a broad sense adaptive. It is general adaptation to the art of living (pp. 19–20).

Evolution is then very largely the result of interaction between the animal and its environment. But not all evolution is adaptive in any sense. We have seen (p. 183) that, at least in small interbreeding populations, some part of evolutionary change may be wholly non-adaptive, caused by the chance spread of mutation. Whether any part of evolution is due to other kinds of non-adaptive change, in particular whether any part is the result of inherent directive tendencies in the animal itself—whether there is any orthogenesis—is a question that we shall discuss in a later chapter (ch. IX).

Success in evolution, first, enables the animal to compete successfully with other members of the fauna of its environment, and, secondly, to invade new environments and so occupy a larger place in the world of animals. But the rates at which animals succeed in evolution, and indeed the speeds of all kinds of evolutionary change, are greatly variable. Some groups are highly successful and evolve rapidly, others evolve slowly, and some, perhaps, hardly at all (ch. XI).

In micro-evolution we may distinguish two types of evolutionary change. There is first evolution within a single population of animals, such as we see in the successive strata of palæontological series (pp. 22 ff.). Its occurrence is probably almost general in animal populations. In unstable environments it results in altered adaptation to the conditions of the environment as these change, and in stable environments it leads to continually closer adaptation to the conditions. Secondly, there is the type of evolution in which an originally single population divides into two or more parts which then evolve independently. We may call these two types *successional* and *divergent* evolution. The distinction between them is by no means absolute, for successional evolution occurs in diverging populations as much as in any others.

When the reproduction is bisexual, it is the whole interbreeding population that evolves, not any smaller unit (p. 30). The mean characters of the population alter gradually. This is in agreement with the findings of the palæontologists, and is a necessary result of the reproductive mechanism of bisexual heredity (p. 142). It follows from this that some form of isolation is required if two populations which can interbreed with each other are to evolve independently, though the isolation need not be complete (pp. 186 ff.).

The biological species may be defined as the aggregate of animals that are capable of living a complete communal life together, and of normal interbreeding. But, in nature, the interbreeding population, i.e. the population within which interbreeding occurs in the natural life of the animals, is, as the result of the distribution of the animals in their environment, not in most cases the whole population of the species. It is usually much smaller, the species being organised into a large number of partially isolated populations, which we have called demes (p. 121). How far the evolution of the demes is independent varies with the amount of migration between them, i.e. with the grade of their isolation, but we know that in some species at least small local populations are capable of independent differentiation (p. 147). The demes are often organised into larger units within the species. These are (1) subspecies, groups of similar demes, differing in definite characters from the rest of the species and occupying distinct geographical areas within the specific range; and (2) clines, in which the characters vary continuously along gradients from one point in the cline to another. Not all species are organised into subspecies or clines; in many species there are no larger units than the demes recognisable within the species.

Owing to the great powers of multiplication that animals

possess, competition, both between the individuals of an inter-breeding population and between different populations, is present in almost all natural environments (p. 200). Natural selection resulting from this competition may be assumed to be effective and to play a large part in all evolution, but it must not be forgotten that non-adaptive evolutionary change due to drift (pp. 183, 194) also occurs. The smaller the inter-breeding population the larger the non-adaptive element in its evolution. In large populations non-adaptive change may be insignificant.

THE GENETICS OF MICRO-EVOLUTION

There are two ways in which the genotypes of animals may change during their evolution. One is by mutation, whereby new characters not previously present in the genotype are intro-duced; and the other by recombination, re-arrangement among the individuals of a population of the genes already present in the genotypes. Recombination is always possible in natural populations, for there is always variation in genetic characters among the individuals, and interbreeding will give rise to differ-ent combinations of the genes. The resultant genotypes will then be subject to selection, and the whole population will change by spread of new combinations of genes. Recombina-tion may often produce large changes in the phenotype. In domestic animals, such as the dog, it is probable that much of the differentiation between the various forms is due rather to recombination than to mutation. It is probable, also, that recombination plays a considerable part in the changes of micro-evolution in nature, though we know that many mutational differences are present between natural races (pp. 134–6).

However much of micro-evolutionary change is due to recombination, there is no doubt that evolution is impossible without mutation, for it is only by mutation that novelty can be introduced into the genotype, and evolution is impossible without new organisation (p. 91). As a basis for progress in evolution recombination has no real value, for it is nothing but re-arrangement of what is already present.

Before we go on to discuss the nature of the genetic changes of micro-evolution, we may ask whether it is true that *all* micro-evolution must have a genetic basis of one kind or another. Can any of it take place without genetic change caused either by recombination or mutation? It cannot be doubted that by far the greater part of micro-evolutionary change is based on alteration of the genotype. This is true not only of changes in structure but of changes of every kind in the physiology, behaviour and habits of the animal. But is all of it so based?

Certainly, changes that have no genetic basis do occur in differentiating animals. There are, first, phenotypic changes, modifications of the animals' structure and biology in direct response to the environmental conditions. In plants, the common differences between ecotypes are of this nature; in animals, almost every species is found to show phenotypic modification associated with change in the environmental conditions. An example has been recently investigated by Fox.[117] Species of the cladoceran *Daphnia* contain hæmoglobin in their blood in varying concentrations, and the concentrations differ among the individuals of a species as well as between species. The concentration is higher in animals living in ponds than in those in lakes, and it was shown that these variations were caused by differences in the conditions of the habitats. Pond water often has a lower oxygen content than the water of lakes, and a low oxygen content in the water was found to cause a high hæmoglobin content of the blood. It was also shown that some other (unidentified) substance in the pond water, perhaps an organic product of decay, has the same effect. When animals are transferred from one type of water to another, the hæmoglobin content changes in a few days to that appropriate to the new water. The variation is therefore phenotypic. The example is interesting as showing how difficult it may be to say without experiment whether a difference is genetic or phenotypic. This could not be determined in *Daphnia* before the experiments had been carried out. The difficulty is frequent.

Phenotypic variations are not inherited, and are therefore not themselves of evolutionary value, but they may prepare the way for genetic differentiation. An animal that finds itself in conditions in which its previous adaptations are not appropriate will first—and quickly—adapt by phenotypic modification, in so far as this is possible, and later the characters so acquired may be given a genetic basis by recombination or

A.E.—8

mutation, when these occur. By allowing the animal to live in conditions different from those to which it has previously become adapted, modification of the phenotype may give the opportunity for genetic adaptation to the new conditions (cf. [125], for a recent discussion).

The changes of feeding habit by which many animals have recently become pests give good examples of the value of phenotypic modification in the initiation of divergence. We shall later refer (p. 271) to the capsid bug (*Plesiocoris rugicollis*), which has recently become a pest on apple-trees, having previously fed on willows. The races of this bug on the willow and the apple are now genetically distinct; the change in feeding habit has been followed by genetic adaptation to the new conditions. But at the time of the change, so far as we have any reason to believe, there were no genetic changes; the whole change was one of habit and, accompanying this, of the ecology of the species. These phenotypic modifications paved the way for the later genetic changes. This is a clear example of the value of non-genetic change in enabling genetic differentiation to occur. Many other examples, not all from the biology of pests, could be given.

There is also the possibility that tradition may play some part in micro-evolution. In birds differences in the song are often found between local populations ([209], p. 256). The broad capacity for song is inherited genetically in birds, and in some birds the details of the song are also under genetic control ([178], pp. 305–6). But the details are not so inherited in all species; often they are learnt after birth from the parents. It may well be doubted whether the differences of song pattern which are often observed between local populations have a genetic basis; it seems more probable that they are, at least in some cases, learnt, and handed on traditionally from one generation to the next. If so, they give us another example of non-genetic differentiation. Similarly, Cushing [61] finds local non-genetic mating preferences in birds. All these differences will tend to maintain isolation in the populations between which they occur. They will therefore make genetic differentiation of the populations more likely.

In these examples traditional characters may set up and maintain isolation, and so prepare the way for differentiation.

But it is possible that tradition has a more direct part to play in evolution. Traditional characters may be handed on from one generation to another; in this they resemble characters genetically controlled. They are open to change when the conditions of the animal's life alter, and it may seem unlikely that they are by any means as permanent as genetic characters. They can form a part of the changes of evolution only if they are permanent on the evolutionary time-scale. Certainly, most traditional characters are not permanent in this sense and it may be doubted whether any are, though Hingston [166] has brought forward evidence that some—appreciation of various types of recognition marks—may be permanent in the higher animals. If they were, tradition would be a real, non-genetic, element in evolution and we should be unable to say that all evolution requires genetic change. We cannot do more than keep the possibility of traditional evolution in mind, but it is not possible at present to deny that there may be a small non-genetic element in evolution.

We have seen (p. 179) that differentiation will always occur between populations that are sufficiently isolated. We will next consider in more detail the course of the genetic differentiation that will occur in an isolated population.

As soon as a population is isolated and conditions in its habitat change, recombination will commence. It will be the earliest type of genetic change in differentiation, for it may start in the next generation after isolation is set up. It will accompany phenotypic modification.

Of the types of mutation one, chromosomal re-arrangement, is (pp. 133–4) less generally distributed in micro-evolution than the others; chromosome mutations have been found to be numerous between some pairs of species, much less so between others. Gene mutations of all kinds are always numerous between differentiated forms, micro-mutations so numerous that it is often difficult to find characters controlled by single or even by a few mutations (p. 135)—polygenic control (p. 108) is characteristic of natural races. This is of great importance to us in our attempts to interpret micro-evolution. It means that there is no difficulty in understanding that change may occur in any direction demanded by adaptational needs. If as the basis of change we had only the relatively few macro-mutations, determined in direction and of only a few kinds in each gene (p. 67), we should find it hard to understand how changes in all the required directions come about. But micro-mutations are extremely numerous in all natural populations (p. 136) and it is reasonable to suppose that a supply of this type of mutation will be available whatever the required direction of change, though the supply may not be large enough for change at any speed. Further, Fisher ([104], p. 39) has shown by mathematical analysis that small mutations are more likely to be favourable than large. This makes it still more clear that micro-mutations are the most suitable basis for evolutionary change.

It is then clear that micro-mutations, together with recombination, are responsible for the greater part of micro-evolution. This is the view that is generally held today (cf. [80], ch. III). It is in agreement with observation. The infraspecific differences we find in nature are very largely quantitative, differences either in the proportion of individuals in a population bearing a character, or in the size and other quantitative (metrical) features of the characters. Variation in the distribution of characters in a population is the type of difference that is most characteristically the result of recombination; metrical change is characteristic of micro-mutation. For modification caused by micro-mutation alters the action of genes quantitatively, strengthening or weakening them, altering the point in the life-history at which they become effective, and so on (p. 69). By such action all sorts of quantitative change in the body may be brought about, but not, generally, change of other kinds.

The fact that micro-evolution is more largely based on micro- than on macro-mutation has an important bearing, not so far discussed, on the nature of the evolutionary changes. If evolution is based on micro-mutation, it would seem that non-adaptive change, that is to say the spread during evolution of genetic change that has no selective advantage, may be more easy to understand.

Ford (e.g. [111], cf. [107]) has maintained that no genetic change in evolution can be wholly non-adaptive. There is no doubt that many of the small phenotypic characters that distinguish species and subspecies have themselves no significant value in the lives of the animals that carry them. This at least is the conclusion of almost all those who have dealt with the smaller systematic differences in animals (p. 47), and Ford does not deny it. But he points out that very many genes are pleiotropic. He believes that the characters that have no selective value are linked to others, less evident, controlled by the same genes, and that it is these other characters that have positive selective value. He also points to Fisher's proof [104] that in a constant environment extremely small selective advantages will be effective in controlling the spread of genes (p. 182). Genes, he says, will among their pleiotropic effects have some of sufficient selective advantage (or disadvantage) to control their spread.

Even if Fisher's figure for the minimum effective advantage is accepted for the changing environments of nature (p. 183), it does not seem necessary to accept Ford's conclusion as inevitable on the basis of our present knowledge. It is certainly true that the great majority of *macro*-mutations are pleiotropic, and very many of them have effects that will certainly have selective value, even though their most obvious (primary) effects in the phenotype have not. It was noted (p. 71) that in *Drosophila* almost all macro-mutations modify to some extent the period of life; very many also affect viability. Both these types of action are unlikely to be neutral in selection. If micro-evolution was based on macro-mutations, Ford's conclusion might be inevitable. But micro-evolution is largely based on micro- and not macro-mutations, and to apply his argument to micro-evolution as we find it in nature we need to believe that micro-mutations are as certainly pleiotropic as macro-mutations and that their pleiotropic actions are as likely to have selective value. This has not been shown to be true. It cannot be said that we know that a large majority of micro-mutations have other effects of selective value besides their primary effects in the phenotype. If they have not it would still seem open to hold the belief that many of the genetic changes of micro-evolution are wholly non-adaptive.

That the evolution of non-adaptive genes may be possible is an important conclusion for us, for without it drift would have no part to play in evolution. This is not the only condition necessary for drift to be effective. Drift requires not only that some part of evolutionary change be non-adaptive, but also that evolution takes place, in part at least, in populations below an upper limit of size (p. 183). We shall see later (p. 247) that there is reason to believe that populations smaller than this limit are frequent in nature, and that evolution occurs in them. We may conclude that evolution of non-adaptive genes can take place and that they are spread by drift.

The fact that micro-mutation (with recombination) is the most important material for the changes of micro-evolution must not make us forget that macro-mutations also take part in it. This is shown by the large number of macro-mutational differences that are found between differentiated forms (pp. 132 ff.). We have also the example of the recent spread of melanic forms in several species of Lepidoptera (p. 195), and many other examples, to demonstrate that such changes may occur.

As soon as it appears in the phenotype, the expression of a macro-mutation will come under the same system of modification as any character previously present. In the genotype in which it first appears a mutation may be unfavourable, but chance or selective * changes in modification may so alter its adaptive value that the disadvantage is turned into an advantage. If this happens, it will spread and be taken up into the genotype of the population. Huxley ([178,] p. 124) sums up the position thus: "The offer made by a mutation to the species is not necessarily a final offer. It may be merely a preliminary proposal, subject to negotiation. Biologically this negotiation is effected in the first instance by recombination and secondarily by mutation in the residual gene-complex. It can lead to a marked alteration in the effects of the mutation, which may make the proposal acceptable to the organism."

The polygenic character of genetic control implies that the genotype acts much more as a single co-ordinated whole than by the independent actions of its genes (p. 108). This conclusion has further and very important bearings on the process of differentiation. As we have seen (p. 109), selection will maintain the genotype in a condition in which this general action is as

* The objections raised against Fisher's theory of the evolution of dominance (p. 223) seem to apply here also, so far as the action is by selection.

efficient as it can be. The genes will be selected to act together in harmonious co-ordination; groups of genes which would interact to impair viability will be discarded, and any group that leads to higher viability will be preserved and included in the genotype. The value of any group of genes as a harmonious whole may vary as differentiation proceeds—what is harmonious at one stage will not necessarily be so at another—but the action of selection to preserve the harmony of the genotype will continue throughout differentiation. Its success in doing so will greatly increase the animal's chance of survival in competition.

Evolution would proceed even in a completely stable environment; the animal would become more and more perfectly adapted, it would improve its general organisation and efficiency, and it would also change non-adaptively. But mutations are recurrent (p. 98), and after a time most of the favourable macro-mutations will have been included in the genotype. Beyond this point, in so far as macro-mutations are concerned, evolution would be slow, relying only on the rare occurrence of a new mutation. This is what might happen in a stable environment, but natural environments are never stable. Animals in nature are continually exposed to change of environmental conditions, and the selective advantages of mutations change with the conditions. Genotypes will never be stable even so far as adaptive characters based on macro-mutation are concerned. Change in modification will also follow any environmental change, and the animals will continue to change non-adaptively. Evolution should never come to a standstill.

By means of all these types of genetic change, and by the interaction of the principles by which the direction of change is controlled—the principles of selection and drift—the population will gradually alter in character. Given isolation, separated populations will diverge continuously by both adaptive and non-adaptive change, though where the size of the interbreeding population is large non-adaptive change may be insignificant. Further, differentiation may be directional, that is to say it may continue in the same direction for a long time. This follows from the fact that response to adaptational needs cannot be sudden and immediate. For one thing, the response to adaptational need depends on the supply of mutation, and, though micro-mutations may be quickly available for change in any direction, they will not suddenly produce a change of any extent. Selection, too, is a slow process (p. 180) and will need much time to produce its full result. The animal will only slowly approach complete adaptation to any need. There are also other reasons why large and sudden changes are impossible in evolution (p. 294).

The changes of differentiation are cumulative with time, and isolated populations will pass through the various grades of infraspecific differentiation consecutively. In time, provided the isolation is still maintained, they will acquire characters, genetic or other (p. 123), that prevent their interbreeding even though they meet. They will have then become separate biological species and their differentiation will be irretrievable (p. 158). After this, the characters they have evolved can be lost only by extinction of the populations.

These conceptions of the process of micro-evolution are the major contributions of recent genetics to the broad problems of evolutionary theory. Historically, it was the enunciation of Fisher's theory of the evolution of dominance, which we shall discuss immediately, that first broke the apparent deadlock between the results of genetics and those of palæontology and morphology (p. 7). His theory, if it was accepted, removed one of the chief difficulties in the way of a genetic theory of evolution, the difficulty that the great majority of mutations are recessive and therefore, so it seemed, unsuitable material for changes of the largely dominant genotypes of animals (p. 217). But many other difficulties have since been removed by the development of the theory of evolution by micro-mutation and by appreciation of the importance of polygenic control in animal genotypes. These advances will remain whether, as time goes on, Fisher's theory is accepted or not.

ABRUPT CHANGES IN MICRO-EVOLUTION AND THE EVOLUTION OF DOMINANCE

In this section we have to consider further the parts of macro-mutations and large chromosomal re-arrangements in micro-evolution. Large genetic changes, if they do not lead to the death of the animal (p. 75), cause sudden and considerable changes in the phenotype, and many of them, especially chromosomal re-arrangements, often cause sterility with the parent stock. We know from observation of differentiated genotypes (pp. 132, 134) that changes of these types occur commonly during differentiation, and we must consider the circumstances under which a form sterile with the rest of a population may survive after it has arisen and spread. There are other difficulties concerning the part played by large genetic changes in micro-evolution. Most macro-mutations are recessive, and the rate at which even a favourable recessive mutation will spread through a population is very slow, so long as the mutation is rare (p. 180). The rate is in fact so slow that it is doubtful whether it is fast enough to give an effective basis for differentiation even on an evolutionary scale of time. This difficulty is possibly real in all evolution; it is certainly real in the evolution of animals with long life-histories, and therefore long periods between their generations. To some extent this difficulty may be reduced by the fact that mutations occur repeatedly; repeated mutations will certainly spread more rapidly than single mutations. But this does not remove the whole difficulty. There is also the fact, noted above, that animal genotypes are largely dominant, whereas most macro-mutations are recessive. Must we conclude that only the rare dominant mutations are possible raw material for evolution (p. 216)? All these difficulties must be discussed.

We will first consider the rate of spread of recessive mutations. The slowness of their spread is characteristic of bisexual heredity, and results from the fact that a rare mutation will almost always be crossed with the non-mutated form, and cannot then appear in the phenotype (p. 180). Selection in favour of the mutation is therefore only very slightly effective so long as the mutation is rare, and its spread correspondingly slow. The spread would be more rapid in any circumstances in which the rare mutation was more frequently expressed in the phenotype. This will happen in any circumstances in which the mutants meet more frequently than in a population with random mating, the condition for which the rate of spread previously given (p. 180) was calculated. More frequent meeting of mutant forms will also occur in some types of non-sexual reproduction.

8*

The circumstances in which spread of recessive mutations may be rapid are (cf. [167]):

    1. Self-fertilising hermaphroditism. The mutation will occur in both eggs and sperm and homozygotes will be frequent.

    2. Haploid parthenogenesis. If the egg carries the mutation, it will be expressed in the phenotype.

    3. Polyembryony and other types of asexual reproduction. A population bearing the mutation may be formed from a single mutant. The members of this population may mate and give homozygotes.

    4. Epidemics of the same mutation occurring simultaneously or within a short time. The mutants may meet and mate.

    5. Close inbreeding. A mutation is more likely to occur in both of two closely related animals (i.e. individuals having a recent common ancestor) than in two chosen at random from a population.

Some of these conditions, such as hermaphroditism and polyembryony, are rare among animals and are therefore not relevant to the general problems of animal evolution. Parthenogenetic reproduction is much more widely spread and its effects may have modified the evolution of many animals. But it does not occur in any large proportion of bisexual animals. It will not help us to understand the spread of macro-mutations as a general problem in evolution. There is no evidence of epidemics of mutation in normal genes of the extent or frequency that would be needed if it were to be accepted as a general explanation of the spread of macro-mutations (cf. p. 96).

We are left with inbreeding as a possible means of removing our difficulty. We have little accurate knowledge of the amount of inbreeding that occurs in interbreeding populations, or of its closeness when it does occur, but there are some reasons for thinking that it is greater than appears likely at first sight. In some populations, especially those of animals with external fertilisation, it is probably small. But in a typical population, even of animals with external fertilisation, the individuals certainly breed most often with those nearest to them, and the chance of two neighbouring animals being closely related is clearly greater than it is in the population as a whole.* The chance will be still greater when the interbreeding population is small, and in this connection our conclusion (p. 146) that many species are organised into small, partially isolated demes may be important; inbreeding will be more frequent in species so organised. It is also to be remembered that in many species numbers vary rhythmically (p. 173), the populations being reduced to small numbers at certain times. Inbreeding may be frequent at these times.

If it occurs, inbreeding will have large effects on the spread of rare genes [154]; their spread will be very much faster than the rates given in the table on p. 180. It (and all the other reproductive mechanisms listed above) will also allow the survival within a population of a new type that is sterile with the original form, for such an animal can only survive when it mates with another of its type. In both these ways inbreeding, and occasionally others of these mechanisms, may have been effective in evolution. If reproduction is of one of these types, we can understand how a recessive macro-mutation can spread quickly enough to be effective in evolution, even if sterile with the parent stock.

However, rapid spread of a recessive mutation will be of no evolutionary value, unless recessive mutations are able to take their places in the genotype and we know that genes in wild-type genotypes are generally dominant; recessive genes are relatively rare in them. This is a necessary deduction from the fact that the majority of the mutations we encounter, which are allelomorphs of the wild-type genes, are recessive. In *Drosophila* the proportion is 200 recessives to 13 dominants.[80] At first sight this would seem to mean that the great majority of recessive mutations are not accepted—that few new mutations except the rare dominants reach the genotype of the race and are used in differentiation. If so, the supply of macro-mutation for differentiation would be very much less than it would

* This is so whatever the size of the interbreeding population. It implies that the group of complete interbreeding within a population (p. 186) is often very small. In nature this is probably true of many species.

otherwise be. It might, even so, be sufficient; we do not know. Also, if this is the true position our discussion of inbreeding has been unnecessary.

It is, however, not certain that we need accept these conclusions. If it could be shown that a favourable recessive mutation can be altered to dominance before it is taken into the genotype of the race, recessive mutation might still be effective. And, if this can happen, it will make our interpretation of differentiation easier in another way. Not only will any gene, having acquired dominance, be able to take its place in the largely dominant genotype, but its spread will be very much more rapid as soon as it has become dominant (p. 180). In its early recessive stages the spread of a gene may be helped by inbreeding; as a dominant it will in any case spread rapidly. That genes may become dominant under the influence of selection is the conclusion of Fisher's theory of the Evolution of Dominance, which we must now consider.

There is little doubt that the dominance or recessiveness of a gene may vary with the conditions to which the gene is exposed.* Environmental conditions, for instance temperature, may modify a gene's dominance; Goldschmidt [138] was able to modify dominance in "ebony" and "vestigial" mutants of *Drosophila* by treatment with high temperatures (36–7 deg. C.) for short times. In natural races the genetic means by which variation in dominance is brought about is by change in the background of modifying genes. Fisher [102] first brought forward the example of the "crinkled dwarf " mutation of Sea Island cotton, which had been investigated by Harland.[157] This mutation is recessive when bred in its own strain, but when crossed on to other strains may have any condition between full dominance and full recessiveness. Fisher ascribed this variability to change in the background of modifying genes resulting from the cross. Each strain has its own background. When two strains are crossed a large array of hybrid backgrounds is produced, and on these the mutation may perhaps be dominant, recessive or in any intermediate condition. The characters of the Sea Island background that make the mutation recessive are lost in the crossing.

* 101, 105. The first evidence of modification of dominance was given by W. L. Tower.[307]

Later work [158-9] has shown that the position in this example is more complicated. Recessiveness is a character of the mutation not only on the background of the strain in which it commonly arises, Sea Island. It is so on the backgrounds of several other strains, in some of which the mutation is unknown. A background on which the mutation is recessive seems to be a character of a natural race; harmonious backgrounds have this character, hybrid backgrounds, no longer harmonious, lack it. This does not at all detract from the value of the evidence as showing that dominance of a gene can be altered by change in the background of modifying genes.

A later example of experimental work on the subject, concerned with animals and not plants, is that of Ford [110] on the variety *lutea* of the currant-moth, *Abraxas grossulariata*. *Lutea* is normally semi-dominant, the heterozygote being known as the variety *semilutea*. Ford selected the heterozygotes for the yellow colour of *lutea* in one line, and for the wild type in another. He was able in a few generations to separate two lines in one of which the mutation was almost completely dominant and in the other almost recessive. On backcrossing these forms with the wild type he obtained a return nearly to the original condition of the gene. This last result is good evidence for Ford's conclusion that it was not the main gene that was altered by his selection; the changes could only have been due to selection of other, modifying, genes.

From this example, and some others, it seems to be clear that dominance and recessiveness are modifiable (cf. [138]). In view of these facts Fisher put forward his theory. He pointed out that mutations are recurrent and that all the common macro-mutations will have occurred many times in the history of the race. While a gene is rare in a population, its heterozygotes will be commoner than the homozygotes. So, if an originally recessive mutation is advantageous, it would be an advantage to the race that its recessiveness should be changed to dominance, for the gene would then be expressed in the heterozygotes. In the past there will have been selection towards this result and the gene will have become dominant and been included in the genotype. On the other hand, disadvantageous genes will have become recessive. Since most of the favourable mutations will already have been accepted, and must now be in the genotype, the mutations we now meet are almost invariably the allelomorphs of these—mutations which became recessive as their advantageous allelomorphs became dominant. Except for rare new mutations, only those of which the selective advantage has recently been altered by changes in the environment or in the habits of the animal are now likely to be advantageous. These will mostly be recessive when they arise. They will be subject to selection towards dominance, and will be included in the genotype as they become dominant.

Besides accounting for the recessiveness of most of the common mutations and for their being usually disadvantageous, it has been claimed that this theory accounts for some other facts ([178], p. 117; cf. also [193] and [319], pp. 331–2). Thus, there is far less predominance of recessiveness among sex-linked than among autosomal mutations. Fewer sex-linked genes, at least, have been definitely shown to be recessive. Sex-linked recessive genes do not need to wait for expression until they are present in the homozygous condition; they will be expressed in a proportion of the heterozygous sex. Selection against dominance will reduce the expression of a disadvantageous gene much less if it is sex-linked than if it is autosomal, and therefore will be of much less value to the race. The fact that these genes have not in general become recessive suggests that there has been less selection against dominance among them, and, since we can explain its absence, this may be taken as evidence that selective modification of dominance is real in other genes. The exception supports the rule.

The facts of dominance in multiple allelomorphs have also been brought forward in support of the theory.[101-2] In most of these series of allelomorphs, for instance, those of "white" eye-colour in *Drosophila* (p. 97), all the mutations are recessive against the wild type, but they are not so against each other—when two of the allelomorphs are present together in the genotype, the expression is intermediate between them. It is suggested that selection has reduced them to recessiveness against the wild type, but that two of the mutations would not occur together sufficiently often in nature for selection to exert its effect, and most pairs therefore remain in a condition of semi-dominance, the heterozygote being intermediate. Again, it is claimed that the exception supports the rule.

In spite of the evidence which seems to support it, Fisher's theory has been rejected by Wright ([332], cf. also [240]) and Haldane [153] on the ground that there would be no sufficient selective force available, so long as the gene was rare, to modify its dominance appreciably. Fisher [103] has disputed this. Wright and Haldane propose an alternative theory to explain the dominance of wild-type genes. We have seen (p. 83) that genes probably act by control of the amount and activities of the enzymes of the body, and (p. 101) that dominance probably means that the gene produces considerably more than the minimum quantity (or activity) of the enzyme needed to give the full effect, so that reduction of the activity of the gene by one-half—in the heterozygote—has no obvious effect on the condition of the phenotype. Wright and Haldane suggest that it is of advantage to a natural race for the activities of its enzymes to be well above the thresholds for their maximum effects, for, when this is so, small changes in the activities of the genes (and therefore of the enzymes they control) will have little effect on the body—the phenotype will be stable. They suggest that in the evolution of a natural race genes that have this action, i.e. dominant genes, will be selected, and therefore that dominance will be characteristic of the wild-type genotype. In contrast, gene-forms that have not been accepted into the genotype, and now appear as mutations from it, will be mostly recessive.

This theory will account for the dominance of the wild-type genotype, but it does not allow recessive mutations to reach the genotype, and so to be a normal source of differentiation. If it is the true theory, only the rare dominant mutations will normally be used in evolution. If there is no sufficient selective force to cause the evolution of dominance and Fisher's theory must therefore be discarded, as Wright and Haldane (with others) think, their theory is the only one at present in the field, and the common recessive mutations must be regarded as of little significance in evolution. The subject is still disputed. As time goes on the dispute will be settled by accumulation of further evidence on one side or the other.

ISOLATION

Interbreeding forms that are interfertile cannot diverge if

they are able to breed together freely; if two parts of an originally single population are to evolve independently (p. 142), some form of isolation is necessary so long as the parts are completely interfertile. Populations may be prevented from interbreeding by barriers of many kinds, or, without any barrier, by the distance between them (p. 185). We have to consider the relative importance of the various kinds of isolation in micro-evolution.

The chief types of barrier are: (1) geographical—the populations are separated by stretches of land or water that the animals are unable to cross; here may be included any spatial separation, whether the distances are long or short; (2) ecological—the isolation is caused by differences in the habitats of the animals, though they live in the same region—one population may live in grass and the other on trees, one in the soil and the other on plants above it; (3) biological—the populations may be in contact but mating is prevented by biological or psychological differences between them, for instance by differences in the structure of their genital organs or in their mating preferences; (4) genetic—incompatibility between the genotypes of the populations prevents the production of fertile hybrid offspring.

1. GEOGRAPHICAL ISOLATION

There can be no doubt of the importance of this type of isolation in nature. Any area, whether of land or sea, that an animal is unable to cross is a barrier to that animal. It is therefore clear that here, as throughout our discussion of isolation, we must consider the subject in relation to the whole natural history of the animals. What is an absolute barrier to one animal is no barrier to another.

We will next consider a few examples of the geographical barriers that isolate animal populations. To aquatic animals land is always a barrier; the isolation of fresh-water habitats is due to the land between them. The numerous species or subspecies of char (*Salvelinus* spp.) in the lakes of Switzerland, Scandinavia and the British Isles [231] give good examples of differentiation in isolated fresh waters. Almost every lake has a different form. The waters of a river or the sea may be an equally impassable barrier to land animals. The St. Kilda and

Shetland wrens are examples of terrestrial forms that have differentiated as the result of isolation by stretches of water. Mayr ([209], chs. III, IV) gives numerous examples of related species of birds that have differentiated in the isolated islands of the Pacific. In such cases the isolation is largely complete, but geographical isolation may be effective with much less conspicuous barriers. The local races of *Drosophila* investigated by Dobzhansky [83-4] (p. 147 and Fig. 41) are spread over continental areas, being isolated by country unsuitable to the species; they have independently differentiated. The races of the snail *Achatinella* in Hawaii, which Welch described (p. 148), and those of the snail *Partula* in the Society Islands (p. 148) are also separated only by unsuitable land. Geographical isolation is prevalent in every region of the world.

An example of differentiation based on geographical isolation that has been very thoroughly investigated is that of the deer-mice of the genus *Peromyscus* in America.[73, 293] These mice are distributed over wide areas of country and are subdivided into numerous species, subspecies and races. The conclusion was reached that geographical isolation is generally necessary for differentiation, and that each form becomes adapted after isolation to the ecological conditions of its separate habitat. Non-adaptive differentiation was also present, and there was much biological and psychological isolation (mating preferences, etc.), but all these were mostly secondary. The chief interest of the work to us at this point is the emphasis thrown on the importance of geographical isolation in the initiation of differentiation in a wide-ranging group of continental habitats.

At least in the higher animals, geographical isolation has been found to be the most important type of isolation in every well-differentiated group that has been thoroughly examined. If two populations are so isolated, they will differentiate, but by no means always at the same rate. The rate of differentiation varies greatly, and the extent of the differences between local races is very different in the various species (p. 150). Not all fresh-water fish show forms as distinct as those of the char; in many species the forms in different lakes are indistinguishable. Nevertheless, some degree of differentiation between local isolated races is very general. Sometimes genetic differences have been shown to be present between local races that show no distinct structural differences in the phenotype; this is true of many local races of Drosophila (e.g. [91]). It is probable that local populations will always be found to be genetically distinguishable when they are accurately examined.

Geographical isolation being so important in the differentiation of animals, we must consider the conditions under which it may arise. There are many ways in which a population originally single may be divided into isolated parts.

A course of events that would certainly lead to this result would be the development of some climatic or other non-biological change in a part of the range of the population, whereby that part became unsuitable as a habitat for the population, and the range was divided. Probably this is not likely to happen very frequently unless the range of the population is large.

Perhaps more often a sample of the population may be transported by some means to an area suitable for its life but separated from the original range. From this sample a new population might arise and would be able to evolve independently unless the transport was frequent. This is undoubtedly the means by which many land animals have crossed water barriers; many islands have been so colonised—the Galapagos finches (p. 153) are believed to be derived from a single stock that reached the islands in this way. Similarly, it is the usual means by which animals reach isolated pieces of fresh water, the animals often being transported by other animals or by the wind. In migratory animals isolation may arise when in the course of a migration they pass outside their usual range and set up new populations in the habitats they reach. Non-migratory species often spread outwards at times when their populations become crowded after abnormal increase (p. 254), and these occasional wanderings may have the same result.

Spread outside the original range of a species is not a necessary condition for isolation between its populations. We have already seen (p. 142) that very many species live in small habitats in which the conditions are optimal for them, and that these are scattered, often at wide intervals, over the range of the species. In these scattered habitats the populations—demes—are at least partially isolated. The habitats are often first invaded by chance transport by other animals or wind, but among the higher animals—insects as well as mammals and birds—often by active choice, either by a single pair or by small family groups. This "habitat-selection"[94] is an obvious fact of natural history to anyone who has observed animals in the field. An insect will choose a particular plant on which to lay its eggs, and birds a piece of ground such as a wood or a pond that satisfies their preferences as a nesting site. The importance of choice in the selection of habitats is emphasised by many naturalists who have worked with the higher animals. Miller[211] found it important in his studies of birds in California. Lack[189] was impressed by its importance in the birds of the British Isles. He believes that, in association with other factors such as preference for breeding within the flock, it will tend to keep slightly differentiated forms from interbreeding. To what extent habitat selection is important in initiating isolation is a question on which opinions differ. Miller believes that it may be the cause of isolation; Lack doubts whether it is often the primary cause.

As a last means by which geographical isolation may be set up, schismogenesis (p. 172), the principle by which two distinct forms within a single population will drive each other towards the parts of their ranges that do not overlap, may be mentioned. This principle will only apply when a new form that is sterile with the original population has arisen, for if the new form can interbreed with its neighbours of the original population it will be swamped and lost as a distinct form. But if an intersterile form can arise (p. 219), schismogenesis should be effective in separating it from the rest of the population, and should allow it to evolve in freedom from competition with the form from which it arose. These circumstances are theoretically possible, but we have no evidence that they have been of any importance in evolution.

There is then no difficulty in understanding how animal populations may become geographically isolated. Once they are isolated the populations will evolve independently, both in adaptation to the conditions of the environments in which they are living, and non-adaptively by drift and random-sampling (p. 183). Differentiation between the populations will accumulate so long as the isolation is maintained.

2. ECOLOGICAL AND BIOLOGICAL ISOLATION

Other types of isolation almost always occur in association with some degree of geographical or spatial separation. It is therefore impossible to separate the types of isolation into mutually exclusive categories. Huxley ([178], p. 228) makes this point when he says that we must speak of geographical isolation when the *primary* isolating mechanism is spatial separation, ecological when it is primarily a difference in habitat, and biological when the primary factor is some difference in the structure or behaviour of the animals.

We have to consider not three exclusive types of isolation but the relative importance of the different isolating mechanisms in the general facts of isolation between animal populations.

Many examples of isolation which is ecological and biological as well as geographical are given by Huxley ([178], ch. VI). One or two may be mentioned here. There is clear ecological differentiation together with equally clear geographical separation in the climatic zones that succeed one another up the sides of high mountains in the tropics. Related species are often confined to separate zones. A striking example of this was found in the birds of Mounts Roraima and Duida in Venezuela by Chapman.[43] Both of these flat-topped mountains rise about 5000 feet above the surrounding land. Roraima is 8600 feet high and is surrounded by cliffs of 1200 feet; Duida reaches 6800 feet and its slopes are less precipitous. At the tops of both are plateaux with subtropical climate very different from the tropical conditions of the country below them. At least twenty-one species of birds living in the neighbouring districts were found to have evolved distinct forms on the plateaux; some of these forms were present on both mountains (being presumably able to migrate from one to the other), some on one only. Most of the differentiated forms were larger and darker than those of the tropical plains. Their larger size is an example of Bergmann's rule (p. 160), and their darker colour of Gloger's rule, for, although cooler, the plateaux are much more humid than the lower lands.

In examples such as this, the geographical separation is marked, but this is not always so; related forms are often found living in the same habitat, and isolated from each other only by their choice of different parts of the habitat—insects may be found on different species of plant, parasites on different hosts. Here the spatial separation is caused by the biological preferences. Such species are called *sympatric*, in distinction from forms with distinct geographical ranges (*allopatric*) ([209], p. 148, quoting [245]). Sumner and Dice's studies [73] of the deer-mice (*Peromyscus*) of America (p. 225) give numerous examples of this type of distribution. Many of the forms they studied were allopatric, but sympatric species were common.

The sympatric species of *Peromyscus* are examples of the category known to systematists as *sibling species*. These may be defined as closely related species living together in the same environment, but remaining distinct since, being species, they do not interbreed. The two closely related British species of *Parus*, the marsh- and willow-tits (*P. palustris* and *P. atricapillus*), give a good example of a pair of sibling species. They are very alike in structure but have some ecological differences in the types of habitat they prefer, and biological differences in their nesting habits.

Another well-known pair of sibling species are the two banded snails of Britain, *Cepæa* (=*Helix*) *nemoralis* and *C. hortensis*.[76] These are good species; hybridisation between them is prevented by differences in the reproductive apparatus—the dart differs in size on the two species, being larger in *C. nemoralis*, and is discharged with more force in this species. Hybrid copulation is usually unsuccessful. There are also ecological differences between the species—*C. hortensis* is found mainly in banks and hedges, *C. nemoralis* mainly in woods but also on sandbanks. The ranges overlap widely in England, and mixed colonies occur commonly, but the species are also found in separate habitats.

Groups of sibling species may sometimes be large. Crane [51] described a complex group of sibling species in the fiddler crabs (*Uca* spp.) of Central America. As many as 12–15 distinct species were found living on the same stretch of shore, though many differed in the small habitats they preferred. Hybrids were uncommon. Isolation of the species from each other depended on biological differences in recognition marks, courtship behaviour and so on. It was probably an indication of the importance of these differences that courtship was elaborate and prolonged.

Mayr ([209,] p. 200) gives other examples of sibling species. Isolation between these species is at present largely ecological and biological, and not geographical. This is not to say that they arose without geographical isolation; we shall return to the problem of their evolution (p. 237). Even in these species there is usually some spatial separation, though it may be slight.

One other example of sibling species may be mentioned, for it introduces the point that the relations between differentiated forms may vary in different parts of their ranges. Two "species" of whirligig-beetles, *Gyrinus striator* and *G. substriatus*, occur together in England and hybridise freely, producing many intermediates.[46] On the continent of Europe *natator* is a northern and *substriatus* a southern form. Their continental ranges overlap but they do not hybridise.[232] These forms are very near the point of specific distinction, having attained it in some parts of their ranges but not in others.

This last example brings up the whole question of the occurrence of hybrids between sympatric species. An occasional hybrid will not be sufficient to throw doubt on the parent forms being regarded as species (p. 125), but, if they are good species, hybrids will be rare. Hybrids may sometimes result from "mistakes", that is to say from breakdown of the isolating mechanisms in particular individuals. They may also sometimes occur when there is no opportunity for breeding within the species— animals will often cross with another species if they have no opportunity of mating with their own species (p. 125). Crosses due to this cause are sometimes found at the forward edge of an advancing range, where individuals of a species are likely to be isolated. The capercailie (*Tetrao urogallus*) gives an example of this.[64] It has recently spread in the Highlands of Scotland, recovering its range after previous extinction. In the extension of the range the hens lead the way and are often present in an area for a year or two before the cocks reach it. In such a region crosses with the black-cock (*Lyrurus tetrix*) and the pheasant (*Phasianus colchicus*) have been found.

Hybrids such as these are probably never of evolutionary significance. It is true, as we have noted (p. 125), that fertile interspecific hybrids may be formed in some groups of animals ([178,] p. 264) though their occurrence is not usual among animals in general. Even if the hybrid is fully fertile, it is not probable that new forms of evolutionary value will arise by interspecific hybridisation. The hybrids will almost certainly be weaker than the parent forms (p. 235) and will be unable to maintain themselves in competition. Hybridisation is a breakdown of differentiation already achieved, not a source of new differentiation ([209], p. 270).

The *biological race* [301-2] is another type of differentiation between closely related and structurally very similar forms, in which there are clear and distinct differences in ecological and biological characters. There is usually definite spatial isolation between the forms, as there must be if the forms are not distinct species.

A group of biological races that have recently been carefully investigated is the assemblage of forms of mosquitoes formerly included in the species *Anopheles maculipennis*.[16] There are at least six forms in Europe. These have hardly any structural differences in the adults, but differences are present in the eggs and larvæ, and the forms differ in their ability to carry malaria. Where they meet they do not interbreed, so that they must be regarded as species. They are typical biological races that have differentiated far enough to become species.

The *A* and *B* races of *Drosophila pseudo-obscura* (p. 128) are biological races with still smaller structural differences than the mosquitoes, though even in them some structural differences can be recognised (p. 128). As soon as two forms are isolated, they may be expected to begin to differentiate morphologically. It is therefore hardly likely that isolated forms that are completely identical will be found.

Biological isolation is no less important in micro-evolution than ecological. Differences in behaviour between closely related forms are very common and often tend to maintain isolation between the populations. Such differences seem to occur very early in differentiation. A preference for mating within rather than outside the population to which an animal belongs is a character of this type, and even local populations may be distinguished by preferences of this kind. Dice [73] noted that such preferences were common in the various differentiated forms of *Peromyscus*; Lack [189] noted them in British birds; and Stalker [283] in subspecies of *Drosophila virilis*. They are in fact an almost general characteristic of natural races.

We have discussed only some of the many types of ecological and biological differences that occur between closely related forms. There are many other types of these differences. Races of herbivorous species may differ in their food-plants (e.g. the apple-capsid, p. 210), those of parasites in the species of their hosts (e.g. the races of the itch-mite, *Sarcoleptes scabei*, on various mammals) and in other relations to their hosts (e.g. the head and body races of the human louse). All these differences will tend to prevent interbreeding and will therefore take their places among the conditions producing isolation.

It is, then, safe to say that ecological and biological differences are general between closely related animals, that they may occur with any grade of geographical separation and structural differentiation, and that they will always tend to develop and maintain isolation. It may still be asked whether isolation can originate by development of these differences in the absence of geographical separation. Can isolation of the grade required for independent evolution (p. 186) follow the appearance of ecological and biological differences within a population, without division of the population into spatially separated parts? If this can happen, does it in fact often happen in evolution? Opinions differ on these questions. Mayr ([209], p. 199) concludes that divergence without spatial separation is unlikely, at least in the higher vertebrates. It cannot be doubted that many of the animals that today show ecological differentiation with no spatial separation, or very little, did not evolve their differences in the conditions in which they now live. They probably became different while they were geographically isolated, and have later come together (p. 237). Nevertheless, it is not easy to believe this to be true of the many species of *Uca* that live together on the same stretch of shore (p. 229)—so many species could hardly have evolved each in a separate environment and have then come together—and it is almost certainly not true of the races of pests which have recently changed their feeding habits, such as the apple-capsid (p. 210). These examples make it very probable that biological differentiation can sometimes arise within the range of a population, and can initiate isolation. Even in these cases the change of habit may lead to some spatial separation of the races, but it is not likely that there was complete separation of the ranges at any stage of the evolution.

Perhaps the question is not worth much argument. As we have seen, all types of isolation normally occur together in nature. Populations may be separated by long or short distances, but there is usually some element of spatial separation between a pair of differentiated forms, even if, in a parasite, it be only the distance between one part of the host's body and another. We come back to the conclusion that a more important question in each case is the relative importance of the different types of isolation.

3. DISTANCE ISOLATION AND CLINES

Isolation by distance (p. 185) gives a theoretical basis for interpretation of the character gradients that are the typical feature of clines (p. 159). This is true of both the two types of cline—the stepped cline such as that of the Birds of Paradise around the coast of New Guinea (p. 161 and Fig. 45), and the internal cline such as that of the Russian bees (p. 163). If the selective advantages of characters vary in the range over which a population is distributed, and if the distances are large enough to allow distance isolation to be effective, parts of the population will come to differ in adaptive characters. Even if there are no variations in selective advantage, non-adaptive differentiation should occur provided the local populations of total interbreeding (p. 188) are small enough. This last condition implies that non-adaptive differentiation should be greater in species with small powers of locomotion, and in rare as compared with abundant species. There is, however, no reason to suppose that non-adaptive differentiation will be arranged in a gradient along a cline.

It is no more difficult to understand how there come to be two distinct types of cline. A stepped cline is a natural result of adaptation to varying conditions within the range of the cline. Areas where the conditions are relatively constant will be occupied by populations with little variation. The genotype will be similar over such an area, and will become adapted in harmonious co-ordination (p. 109) more strongly than elsewhere. Between two such areas there will be a rapid change from one harmonious genotype to another, and with this a rapid change in structure. The result will be a stepped cline. An internal cline may arise where conditions change gradually over the whole range of the cline, and there are no areas of constant conditions. It is, however, as we noted earlier (p. 162), difficult to understand how such an internal cline can persist. It might be expected to evolve into a stepped cline by development of local populations separated by distance isolation and maintaining their homogeneity by interbreeding. Nevertheless, internal clines do occur.

We have already noted (p. 161) that the organisation of a stepped cline will be indistinguishable, after it has become established, from that of a series of subspecies or other infraspecific groups which have met and interbred after they have differentiated in geographical isolation. When two forms meet, they will be separated by a zone of hybridisation (p. 243), and this will be very similar to the region of rapid change between two areas of constant conditions in a stepped cline. But this need not lead us to doubt that a stepped cline may arise directly. It is not likely that differentiated forms would often meet so as to give a linear gradient of characters through several forms, and stepped clines with this arrangement occur commonly.

We may conclude that clines require no principles for their explanation beyond those that we have needed to explain other types of differentiation. More than any other principle, distance isolation seems to be responsible for their evolution.

Divergence of characters in a cline may be great enough to prevent interbreeding between the most distant forms if they meet. These forms will then, on our definition (p. 126), be biological species. The position here is very similar to that of two lines of subspecies the terminal members of which meet and fail to interbreed (p. 155). In both these situations forms that appear to be distinct species are joined by chains of forms which are no more than subspecifically distinct.

If a cline breaks up as the result of parts of its range becoming unsuitable for the species, the populations in each of its parts will be isolated and will evolve independently. The variation present in the cline at the time it broke up will form the starting point for their further differentiation. This is a possible course of events by which new species might be evolved. We do not know how frequently it has occurred in evolution.

4. GENETIC ISOLATION

Sudden evolution of genetic isolation, though it occurs in nature (as the result of macro-mutation or chromosome re-arrangement), is probably much less frequent than gradual development of isolation by slow accumulation of genetic differences between forms that are isolated in other ways. This gradual evolution of genetic isolation is the basis of the chief part of micro-evolution, and it is this that we must consider here.

The genotypes of isolated forms will begin to differ as soon as isolation between the forms is set up, and their differences will increase so long as the isolation is maintained (p. 179). Long before hybridisation becomes impossible, crossing between the forms will become progressively more difficult, and the hybrids less and less viable. The reasons for this have already been discussed (p. 230), and we shall come back to the subject again (p. 243). Even soon after the start of differentiation, when the differences are small, the two genotypes will differ to some extent in their systems of harmonious co-ordination, and this co-ordination will be reduced when the genotypes are crossed. The reduction of fertility in crosses between differentiating forms is known as *partial biological discontinuity*.

Thus, genetic isolation will continually increase so long as the differentiation proceeds; the two will develop step by step with each other. The gradual development of genetic isolation will be independent of any other type of hybrid sterility that may be evolved, such as that which may be caused by large and abrupt genetic changes or by the evolution of special sterility genes (p. 137). These other types will, if they occur, be added to the genetic isolation gradually evolved.

It may be worth while to note at this point that the reduced viability of hybrids in no way conflicts with the fact that *increased* viability is often found when a closely inbred strain is crossed with another strain of the same biological unit within which differentiation is slight. This "hybrid vigour" is often experienced in domestic animals when extreme inbreeding has been carried on within a herd or flock. The "hybrid" with another flock then often shows increased vigour. The difference between the phenomenon of hybrid vigour and the phenomenon we have been discussing here lies in the fact that the cross that gives rise to hybrid vigour is between strains of a single biological unit, the whole of which is a single interbreeding population in which the genotype will vary little, whereas the reduced viability of hybrids results from crosses between distinct and differentiated populations. An inbred strain has reduced viability because recessive, disadvantageous genes are brought to expression as homozygotes by inbreeding. Crossing outside the strain will make these genes heterozygous again, for they are unlikely to be present in the second strain, and so will restore the viability to that normal to the population. So long as the cross is within a single interbreeding population, there will be little loss of viability due to crossing of differentiated genotypes, for the genotypes will be little differentiated. Hybrid vigour may result when inbred races with very similar genotypes are crossed: loss of viability will occur when the genotypes that are crossed differ.

5. CONCLUSIONS

We may sum up what has been said of isolation and its causes in the following conclusions:

Animal populations may become isolated

1. By geographical changes within the range of the species so that the range becomes divided into isolated parts.

2. By migration to suitable areas outside the species range and by forming new populations in these areas.

3. When the populations of the species live in small, separated areas within the species range, by colonisation of new areas. This may happen either by chance spreading into these areas or by active choice.

4. By changes of habit leading to ecological differences between parts of the population, so that the parts occupy restricted habitats to which the rest of the population does not spread.

5. By development of differences of psychology and behaviour which, in association with other types of isolation, make interbreeding impossible.

6. By distance within a continuous population.

7. By abrupt genetic changes resulting in sterility with the rest of the population, together with close inbreeding or some other means by which these mutations can survive.

These causes of isolation occur much more often in association with each other than separately. In most cases of isolation in which there is ecological or biological isolation there is also some element of geographical separation. The types of isolation are also of very different degrees of importance in the natural history of animals. Geographical separation is by far the most general and important. Abrupt genetic change is probably the rarest in nature, though we know from comparison of the genotypes of related forms that large genetic changes certainly occur. Genetic isolation by gradual differentiation of the genotype will increase progressively so long as isolation continues.

THE MEETING OF DIFFERENTIATED FORMS

In nature today it is perhaps more common to find infraspecific forms of a species in areas that overlap than to find them geographically isolated from each other. In the overlapping areas the forms interbreed, forming zones of hybridisation. These hybrid zones are frequent in the distribution of animals of many groups. Mayr ([209], pp. 263 ff.) gives many examples of them; his results, already quoted, on the distribution of *Paradisea apoda*, for instance, show them (Fig. 45, p. 162). Yet we have concluded (p. 142) that isolation is almost always necessary for independent differentiation, and that geographical separation is by far the most important type of isolation. We have now to discuss how it comes about that so many forms that have differentiated from each other are not today isolated, and how their contact will modify their further differentiation.

There is no difficulty in believing that many related forms that are now in contact differentiated in former times in isolation, and have later come into contact owing to changes in their distribution. We have no direct evidence that this has been the course of events, for we do not know the earlier distribution, but the belief is in general agreement with our knowledge of the process of micro-evolution. Differentiation is slow; even to the subspecific stage it often takes many thousands of years (ch. XI). Changes of environmental conditions are frequent and will occur many times during the evolution of a subspecies. Animals react to environmental change by alterations of their distribution and do so relatively rapidly—we know many instances in which the range of a species has altered within our short experience. Thus, the distribution of an animal form is likely to change many times during its differentiation, and it is to be expected that related forms will often meet as the result of these changes in their distribution.

It is possible that there is another reason for the frequency of contact between related forms at the present time. In part, its frequency may be a result of the abnormal geographical conditions present in the world today. On the geological time-scale, we are living shortly after the end of the last Glacial Period, when large areas that are now temperate were glaciated. The ice finally retreated not more than a few thousand years ago. The climatic changes in the temperate zone that followed the retreat must have caused large changes in the distribution of species and subspecies, and many of the forms in temperate regions that we now find to be in contact may be so as the result of these changes of distribution. Ice Ages have occurred only rarely in the history of the world and, if we lived in a more normal period, it may be that we should not find so many forms with overlapping ranges.

Environmental change is undoubtedly the most frequent cause of the meeting of differentiated forms, but there may be other causes. One of these has been discussed by Sumner.[293] A form that has become successful by differentiation in isolation will tend to extend its range as the result of the advantages of its efficient organisation. In so doing it may come into contact with another form, and, if the two forms have not reached specific distinction, there will be set up a zone of hybridisation where they meet. At the zone of contact there will be what may be called *intergroup pressure* between the two forms; each will tend to extend further and to push the other back. Sumner gives as an example two subspecies of one of the species of deer-mice that he was investigating, *Peromyscus polionotus*. *P. p. albifrons* is a subspecies living on sandy shores on the coast of Florida and is light in colour, apparently in adaptation to the colour of the sand; *P. p. polionotus* is a darker form distributed over the country inland. These two forms meet in a narrow zone of contact, but not at the point where the sand passes over into the darker inland soil. *P. p. albifrons* extends inland some way beyond the border of the sand, and Sumner suggests that this is because *P. p. polionotus* is pressed back from

the border of its possible range by the population pressure of
P. p. albifrons. In many cases situations such as this may be
permanent, but this will not be so if the populations of either
form are subject to large variations in number, as those of
many species are (p. 253). At times of population increase there
is very often outward migration in such species, and this may
bring the population into contact with another. A temporary
zone of contact will then be set up.

It is, then, true that contact between differentiated populations is very common in the world today. We may start our
discussion of the problems raised by this fact by asking what,
on the basis of the knowledge we have so far gained, we should
expect to be the course of events when two forms meet after
isolation and differentiation. The various possibilities are
summed up by Mayr ([209], p. 263) as follows:

" 1. The two populations, during the isolation, developed
to full species which are reproductively isolated and sufficiently distinct in their ecological requirements not to be close
competitors. The lifting of the barrier will generally lead to
a broad mutual overlapping of the ranges.

"2. The two populations have developed to full species,
which are reproductively isolated, but are closely competitive
owing to non-development of sufficient differences in the
ecological requirements. The result is a narrow overlap in
a border zone.

"3. The two populations have acquired habitat preferences
during their isolation, but not reproductive isolation. This
results in a curious interlacing of ranges with hybridisation
at the borders of the habitats.

"4. The two populations have not perfected either different
habitat preferences or biological isolating mechanisms that
would guarantee reproductive isolation, and consequently
will hybridise freely on coming into contact. In this case a
more or less extensive hybrid population, a zone of secondary
intergradation,* will be formed in the area of contact."

Let us consider these four types of interaction in turn.

1. Here the forms that meet are fully evolved species. All

---

* Mayr calls hybridisation between forms that have not been isolated, as
occurs for instance in a stepped cline, primary intergradation, and that between
forms that have differentiated in isolation, and later met, secondary intergradation.

closely related sympatric species, including sibling species (p. 229), belong here. We have seen that closely related species may live together in the same habitat with ranges overlapping widely (pp. 229–30).

2. In overlaps of the first class the species may live together over wide areas because their different ecological needs prevent them coming into active competition with each other. When, as in the second class of overlap, the ecological needs of the species are similar, they will compete where they meet, and we saw (p. 169) that this will usually result in one species driving the other from the environment—if the two species are to live together, their competitive advantages must be very accurately balanced. The balance, perhaps, need not be as accurate as is necessary in experimental cultures, for migration from each side of the zone of contact will maintain a mixed population in the zone. Nevertheless, the zone in which neither species is able to drive out the other will be narrow, for the effects of migration will be less the greater the distance over which the animals have to migrate.

Overlaps of this class will be rarer than those of the first class, for modification of the ecology will generally go with differentiation into new species. Most related species will not compete for exactly the same niche in the environment. But many examples are known. A clear example is described by Herter [165] in the two species of European hedgehog, *Erinaceus europæus* and *roumanicus*. Of these *E. europæus* is the western species and *E. roumanicus* the eastern. Their ranges overlap in narrow zones in northern Germany and to the east of the Alps. In ecological requirements they are little differentiated and the narrowness of the zone of overlap is probably due to this. Being good species, they rarely hybridise in the zone of overlap.

3. We have seen (p. 232) that ecological isolation may often be present between subspecific forms living in the same broad habitat. These belong here. Races of insects living on different host plants, or parasites on different hosts give examples. The forms will interbreed where they meet, since populations of this class have not acquired reproductive isolation and are therefore not good species. The places where they interbreed will occur wherever the habitats of the two races come into contact, and will be irregularly scattered over the ranges.

The two races of the human louse, the head and body lice (*Pediculus humanus capitis* and *P. h. corporis*), have a distribution which is typical of this class. They are morphologically differentiated, though most of the differentiation is phenotypic, since the head louse reared under conditions which are suitable to the body louse loses much of its morphological differentiation. In their natural habitats they do not interbreed freely, being isolated by their distinct locations and habits, but they interbreed freely under experimental conditions and the offspring is fertile.[181]

Numerous examples of this type of distribution are given by Huxley ([178], pp. 298 ff.). The example of the ermine moth (*Hyponomeuta padella*) is typical. There are two races which feed and lay their eggs, the one on apple, the other on hawthorn and blackthorn. They have little morphological differentiation but remain distinct in nature on the basis of their biological characters.

4. In the fourth class are included the great majority of overlaps between subspecies and other infraspecific forms. We must consider this class in more detail.

When two infraspecific forms that are not ecologically or biologically isolated come into contact, it is to be expected that they will hybridise throughout the zone of overlap. At first sight it might seem that, as time goes on, the zone will always spread over the ranges of the two forms, for genes will be carried outwards from the zone of hybridisation by chance migration of the hybrids and by crossing of these with the parent forms. It would seem that there should be a flow of genes from each parent population to the other across the zone of hybridisation. As a result, each population should receive characters from the other, and in time the populations should fuse, the infraspecific differentiation being lost.

This seems at first sight the inevitable course of events, and it is probable that it will be the actual course when the original differentiation between the populations is slight. It will appear shortly that it does not necessarily happen when the forms are more than slightly differentiated. In any case, whether the original differentiation is slight or great, it is clear that the time needed for fusion must be long. If the high frequency of contacts between differentiated forms in temperate regions at the present time is due, at least in part, to changes that followed the

A.E.—9

retreat of the ice at the end of the Ice Age (p. 238), it may be that in many cases the populations have not yet had time to fuse, and are still in the condition of distinct populations with intervening zones of hybridisation.

Though ultimate fusion seems likely when forms that are only slightly differentiated meet and hybridise, it is not easy to find direct evidence of such fusion. Undoubtedly this is at least partly because we have little knowledge of the previous histories of the populations. We therefore cannot tell whether the zone of hybridisation is expanding or not. These zones certainly vary greatly in depth, but this cannot be taken as clear evidence of expansion, and in some cases it appears that a wide zone may be stable. Thus, the carrion and hoodie crows (*Corvix corvix* and *C. corone*), though called species by many systematists, hybridise freely over a depth of 100 km. In this example we have evidence of the previous history, and this indicates that there has been no expansion of the zone of hybridisation in historical times.[210] Reviewing the whole evidence, Mayr ([209], p. 265) comes to the conclusion that zones of hybridisation are characterised by stability rather than expansion. We must not conclude that fusion never takes place, rather that it is by no means an inevitable result of the contact of differentiated forms at all levels of differentiation at the time of meeting, and that we are not able to tell by direct observation how frequent it is.

It is easy to find reasons why fusion should not always occur when infraspecific forms meet and hybridise. It can easily be shown that as the result of the contact tendencies will be set up that will oppose the trend towards fusion. We shall find that these tendencies will be stronger the greater the original differentiation of the forms that meet.

As differentiation proceeds in isolated forms, and their genotypes become increasingly different, the systems of harmonious co-ordination in the genotypes will diverge increasingly (p. 179). There will be set up a partial biological discontinuity between the forms (p. 235), and this will increase as differentiation gets greater. The resulting lack of viability in the hybrids will tend to prevent fusion between the hybridising populations. Its effectiveness in doing so will vary with the extent of the reduction of viability in the hybrid. When the reduction is slight the hybrids may be able to live alongside the parent forms, though, being less efficient, they will not reproduce proportionately. The spread of genes outwards from the zone of hybridisation will be delayed—for the hybrids will be less efficient in carrying them—but it will still occur. There should be a tendency for the populations to fuse, but fusion should be slower in proportion as the viability of the hybrid is reduced. At the other extreme we have the situation in which the hybrid is so largely inviable that it cannot maintain itself in competition with the parent forms in the first of later generations. Then fusion of the populations will be entirely prevented. The two parent forms will live alongside each other, will interbreed and produce hybrids, but will remain distinct. This is the condition we found in the butterfly *Colias chrysotheme* (p. 138). It is probably common.

Between these two extremes we have the situation of contact giving rise to considerably but not completely infertile hybrids. The contact will then have effects on the evolution that differ from the results in either of the extreme situations. First, the lowered viability of the hybrid will tend to keep the zone of hybridisation narrow, for the hybrids will spread less readily into the pure populations on each side of the zone. Secondly, there will be advantage to each population if the number of hybrids is kept small, in the zone of hybridisation as well as elsewhere, for the relatively infertile hybrids will be wasteful to the populations (cf. p. 137). Selection towards development of adaptations preventing hybridisation should be set up. We should expect that all types of reproductive isolating mechanism would be favoured by selection in these conditions. Probably the biological mechanisms—difference in recognition marks, mating reactions, breeding seasons, etc.—not all of which need be genetic (p. 209), would be most rapidly and easily evolved. In fact, these are very often found between infraspecific forms that are in contact; they are, for instance, very important in controlling distribution in the forms of *Peromyscus*.[73] Genetic isolating mechanisms (including sterility genes, p. 137) will follow the non-genetic, and will further reduce the amount of hybridisation. In the end complete cessation of interbreeding between the populations should result, so that the two forms become biological species.

There is still another reason why differentiated forms in

contact at a zone of hybridisation should remain distinct. The forms during isolation will have become adapted to environments which will have differed in some of their conditions. Though the forms meet at the boundary of their ranges and are there exposed to the same conditions, these differences may still hold for the greater parts of the ranges. If the differences in environmental conditions give different selective advantages to characters in which the forms differ, each form will be at a disadvantage in the other's range, and an intermediate form, such as would be produced by fusion, will also be at a disadvantage. There should be selection in favour of the original forms and against any intermediate.

We must conclude that the conditions set up by the meeting of two incompletely inter-fertile forms are complex. Opposing factors will be at work, some working towards fusion and others towards further differentiation of the forms.

The results of the interaction of these opposing tendencies will vary with the special circumstances of each meeting, but always fusion will be slower the greater the original differentiation of the forms. Above a certain level of original differentiation the tendency towards fusion will be overcome, and the forms will not fuse but diverge until they become species. Sometimes, perhaps, the opposing factors may be balanced, and a zone of hybridisation remain stable for long periods. We cannot accurately define the level of differentiation beyond which fusion is prevented, but the fact that we find little direct evidence of fusion as the result of contact in a zone of hybridisation may mean that the level is lower than would at first sight seem probable. It is certainly true that hybrids between differentiated forms, however slight the differentiation, may be expected to show some degree of lowered viability. The question that remains is how much the viability of the hybrid must be lowered to prevent fusion.

These conclusions are in general agreement with other results of observation. Subspecies and, indeed, all well-differentiated forms are usually distinct in the greater part of their ranges although they meet in zones of hybridisation, and these zones are often narrow. Some at least of the frequency of the contacts that we find between differentiated forms may be due to slowness of change in the zones of contact.

THE DEME IN MICRO-EVOLUTION

The part played in micro-evolution by organisation of the species into partially-isolated interbreeding populations—demes —must be further considered. At first sight it might seem that demes could not be of any importance in evolution unless they were permanent enough to give rise to new forms that might differentiate into new subspecies or species, that is to say, unless the deme continued its differentiation in isolation throughout the evolution of these new forms. Undoubtedly it is rare for a deme to be as permanent as this; the great majority of demes will sooner or later become extinct or will fuse with other demes. We must, indeed, think of the evolution of the species as consisting of frequent formation of new demes, and of their equally frequent fusion with other demes.* The history of the evolution may be represented as a plexus or reticulum of fusing and subdividing demes.

Nevertheless, in parenthesis, it may be remarked that it is not clear that demes can *never* be permanent enough to give rise to independent new forms. Islands and mountains are the habitats in which demes are most likely to be permanent for indefinite periods, but even in less extreme forms of isolation it may be that a deme sometimes remains isolated until it becomes a species or subspecies. Here the great variability of the time required for the evolution of a species should be remembered. The evolution of new systematic species often takes hundreds of thousands of years. Even where the evolution is rapid, it will take a few thousand years (ch. XI). But these periods refer to the evolution of the morphological differences of systematic species; biological species may be evolved in much shorter periods. Indeed, a macro-mutation causing reproductive isolation from the rest of the species may occur at any time after isolation, and the population will have become a new biological species as soon as the mutation is fixed. Also, we have seen (p. 219) that a new form intersterile with the population surrounding it may, perhaps, sometimes survive if aided by inbreeding. Here again we shall have an almost sudden evolution of a biological species. It is certainly true that only a very

---

* If the deme dies out, its differentiations are lost. All such demes are clearly of no evolutionary value. Some, however, will fuse with other demes, for unless this is so the species will become extinct. It is only these that we need consider.

small minority of demes will give rise to new species, either systematic or biological, or to subspecies, but differentiation of new permanent forms is itself a rare phenomenon on our time-scale. It seems not unlikely that their evolution may be significantly aided by organisation of the species into demes. This would be so even if there were no other grounds for thinking this organisation of importance in evolution.

It is, however, still more important for the theory of micro-evolution that organisation into demes may have evolutionary value even when the demes are not permanent enough to give rise to new forms. We have seen (p. 147) that in some species (e.g. *Drosophila* spp.) the demes are in fact differentiated from each other, though their differentiations may be slight. So far as our present evidence goes, it is justifiable to assume that the demes of species which have not been investigated are similarly differentiated. Certainly it is true that in many species differentiation of the deme may be no more than genetic; they may not show clearly visible morphological differences from each other. But no species has yet been found in which the genotypes of the demes are not differentiated, and it is at least probable that such differentiation is a general character of demes. Since species are normally organised into demes, we may conclude that, whether the differentiation of the demes is slight or considerable, it is in the small partially isolated populations of the demes that differentiation is in general proceeding and not in the species as single wholes. In these demes evolution will be rapid (p. 189), and if the demes are small enough the non-adaptive changes of drift will take part in their differentiation.

Demes, then, become differentiated, but this differentiation will have no value in evolution if it is lost when the isolation of the deme breaks down and it fuses with another deme. If that is so, only the rare permanent demes are of evolutionary significance. But it must be remembered that a deme which loses its identity will in general do so by fusing with another deme and not by submergence in the whole population of the species. The second deme will on the average be of the same size as the first, and the characters of the fused population will be intermediate between those of the two demes that fused to form it. Advantageous characters in either deme should be retained, and the characters that have been evolved in their differentiation will not be wholly lost. After fusion the population will continue to evolve, and if its size is still below the maximum size for drift, it may still evolve non-adaptively.

In the course of repeated fusions characters may spread across the range of the species. By the fusions—and also by migration between the demes—the genotype of the species will be kept more or less similar in the different parts of its range. But gradual alteration of the specific genotype will occur, built up from the differentiations acquired in the demes during their isolation. The alteration of the specific genotype should be continuous and cumulative. Only if some part of the species becomes permanently isolated, so that interchange of genes between it and the rest of the species is prevented, will that part evolve independently. It will then in time form a new subspecies or species.

It must, however, be admitted that these views are not accepted by all biologists interested in evolution. Thus, Fisher and Ford [107] believe that no demes small enough to allow the action of drift (for which they give an upper population limit of 1000) are sufficiently permanent to have any evolutionary value. They add that therefore drift is unimportant in evolution.

Before considering their argument it must be said that, without question, demes with populations below this limit of size occur in many natural species. Small demes may be commoner in the higher animals than in invertebrates, though even in such invertebrates as insects it is probable that the deme is often below this limit of size in the rarer if not in the commoner species. (And not only the common species are of value in evolution; a rare species may at any time become abundant and at any time give rise to new evolutionary forms.) In many small habitats—for instance, isolated pieces of fresh-water such as ponds—many species will have less than 1000 individuals. In the vertebrates there is definite evidence that the population of the deme may be less than 1000. Miller [212] finds demes of some American birds to vary from 50 to 500 individuals (wren-tit, *Chamœa fasciata*, 500; song-sparrow, *Melospiza melodia*, 150; some rarer species, about 50). Wright's results on populations that vary in numbers (p. 175) should also be remembered here. He found that the effective size is near that of the minimum numbers. Demes may be large at maximum numbers and yet evolve as small populations.

Thus, small demes exist, and if Fisher and Ford's views are to be accepted it must be shown that they are never permanent enough to be of value in evolution. It is probably true that the smaller a deme the shorter time it is likely to persist. The permanence of a deme depends on the nature of the environmental conditions to which it is exposed, and of the changes that occur in them, and not directly on its size. Nevertheless, small demes usually occupy small habitats, and in general small habitats are likely to be less permanent than larger. It may be admitted, then, that in general small demes are likely to persist for a shorter time than larger demes of the same species. This is probably true as a general rule, though it would be rash to say that it is always true. Where it is true, the differentiation of small demes at the time that they fuse with other demes will be less than that of larger demes.

This, however, does not prove that small demes are unimportant in evolution. If our conception of the course of micro-evolution is correct—namely, that it proceeds by reticulated fusions of demes with their neighbours, alternating with equally frequent subdivisions—the fact that the demes are very slightly differentiated at the time of fusion would not prevent the progress of micro-evolution, nor would it make it difficult to believe that their differentiations form the material from which the evolution of the species is built up. If fusions are frequent and the differentiations of the fusing demes slight, the evolutionary change at each fusion will be small, and the evolution of the species will be built up from a larger number of these changes. The reticulum will be closer the shorter the time the demes persist in isolation, but its nature will be the same however close or open it may be. These conclusions would seem avoidable only if the demes persisted for so short a time that they did not evolve *any* differentiations between them. But differentiation commences as soon as isolation is established. Recombination will commence at the next generation, and differentiation due to micro-mutation will commence within at most a few generations. It can hardly be maintained that even the smallest demes do not normally persist for longer than a few generations. Also, we know that in fact demes *are* differentiated in nature.

We may then accept the conclusion that organisation of the species into demes is fundamental to the progress of micro-evolution, and that this is so whatever the size of the deme. The earliest stages of differentiation take place in these partially isolated local populations, and from these beginnings the whole of micro-evolution is built up. Where the deme is small, non-adaptive change spread by drift will play a part in the differentiation.

THE COURSE OF MICRO-EVOLUTION: SUMMARY

We may now shortly summarise our conclusions concerning the course of micro-evolution.

As soon as the isolation of a deme is established, differentiation will commence between it and other demes. The characters of the differentiation will vary with those of the population—its size, the extent of migration between it and neighbouring populations of the species, any rhythmic changes in numbers, the extent of inbreeding, and many other characters. The differentiation will also vary with characters of the environment. In the course of the differentiation it is the mean characters of the whole interbreeding population that change. So long as interbreeding is maintained, independent evolution of smaller units within the population is impossible.

Where there are environmental differences between the habitat of the deme and those of other demes of the species—and there are bound to be differences of this kind, however slight they may be—the deme will become adapted to the conditions of its own habitat.

The first changes of differentiation will be phenotypic, without any genetic basis. These phenotypic changes will occur within a generation and will improve the chance of survival as soon as they have occurred.

The earliest type of genetic change will be recombination, which will occur at each fertilisation. It also will result in better adaptation as the more valuable combinations of genes are selected. Much of the material of the recombination will be the small genetic differences of micro-mutations—differences in modifying genes, position effects, etc. By recombination of these the population will be altered in the quantitative relations of its metrical characters. Any macro-mutational differences

9*

that were present between the individuals of the population before isolation will also take part in the recombination. Applied to these differences, recombination will alter the proportion of individuals in the population that carry a character.

Recombination leads to selection among the genes already present in the genotype; it adds nothing new. As time goes on new mutations will arise in the diverging populations. These also will come under the action of selection, which will be determined by the conditions of the environment of the moment and may differ from the selection before isolation. Some genes that were previously discarded may now be favoured. The effects of selection of these new mutational characters will be added to those of recombination. As in recombination, by far the majority of the new genetic characters will be micro-mutations and will take their place in the polygenic control of metrical characters that is so typical of natural races. Occasional macro-mutations may arise in the populations and will also be selected, often after modification by recombination of the micro-mutational background.

At any time during the differentiation of a population, its isolation may break down and it will fuse—provided its differentiation has not already gone too far—with a neighbouring population. By repeated fusions and subdivisions of the populations, the differentiations originally evolved in the isolated populations will spread through all parts of the species in which fusion of the populations is possible, and the genotype of the species will continuously evolve.

This will be the course of events where the isolation of the populations is relatively impermanent and fusion frequent. Where the populations are able to evolve greater differentiation before they lose their isolation, the course of events may be very different.

As divergent micro-evolution proceeds in separated parts of a species—whether the parts are demes or larger units, groups of demes—the result will be to set up increasing incompatibility between the genotypes, and hybrids between the separated forms will increasingly lack viability. This effect will commence very soon after the parts are isolated, for the systems of harmonious co-ordination in the genotypes will diverge from the start of independent evolution, and the hybrid between any two such systems will necessarily be less viable than either parent stock. So long as isolation is maintained, the inviability of the hybrids will increase. To it will be added any inviability that may be directly caused by macro-mutations that occur in the populations. These may at any stage cause hybrid sterility, or even if they do not do this, they may lead to cessation of interbreeding between the populations. They will increase isolation, facilitate divergence, and sometimes raise it rapidly to the specific level. By all these means the separated parts of the species will differentiate until they become distinct species.

With increasing divergence the organisation of the populations of the species often becomes more complicated. The demes may become arranged in groups, within which migration is easier than between the groups. The organisation of these groups depends on the characters of the environment and is therefore not the same in all species.

Sometimes the environmental conditions may be arranged along gradients. The groups of demes are then not clearly distinct from each other; one merges into the next along the gradient. The gradient may be regular as well as continuous—an intragroup cline; or there may be regions where the characters of the populations change rapidly and others where the change is slow—a stepped cline. In other species there may be no gradients, but the range, though continuous, is large enough to allow distance isolation to cause divergence between groups of genes in distant parts.

Neither of these types of organisation occurs in the majority of species. More often, groups of demes become geographically isolated from the rest of the species, and evolve in isolation. Within each group divergence will be less owing to greater similarity of conditions in the smaller area of the group and greater migration between the demes within the group. In time divergence between the groups will be sufficient for them to be called subspecies—the species has become polytypic—and with further evolution the groups will lose their power of interbreeding and become biological species.

Many species, however, so far as our present observations go, remain monotypic, and in them evolution is entirely successional so far as the whole species is concerned. But even in these species differentiation will in fact be carried on in the isolated populations of the demes, and the evolution of the species will accumulate by characters brought in at the repeated fusions of the demes and by migration between them.

We have discussed the results to be expected from breakdown of isolation between differentiated forms of the species, and the discussion need not be repeated here. When the differentiation is slight, this may lead to fusion of the forms; when it is greater, it is likely to lead to accelerated divergence.

Thus, it is clear that, even in the generalised form in which we have discussed it, micro-evolution is a very complex and variable process. The progress of evolution in each species varies with the special circumstances of its natural history and distribution, its genetics, its reproductive mechanisms, and so on. Though we have been able to draw some general conclusions which will be true of the evolution of the majority of species, it will never be easy to foretell the course of evolution in any particular species.

A very striking feature of micro-evolution, and one that is responsible for much of its variability, is that it is often controlled by balance between opposing tendencies. We have found this more than once in our discussion. In the genetic mechanism variation is increased by mutation and recombination, and is reduced by linkage; selection reduces variation, drift and random sampling increase it. The resultant variation, the raw material used in evolution, is controlled by balance between all these factors. Again, we have found that hybridisation between differentiated forms tends towards fusion in some circumstances, and greater divergence in others. Which of these tendencies prevails is determined by the relative strengths of the opposing tendencies in each case.

Into this general scheme of micro-evolution must be fitted the action of the many biological characters of the animals that we have not been able to discuss. Some of these lead to special types of evolution that occur in comparatively few animals. We shall discuss two of these in the following sections of this chapter. There are others that we cannot discuss. It would be of interest to consider the evolutionary effects of the various types of parthenogenesis and asexual reproduction, of alternation between asexual and sexual generations, of parasitism and symbiosis, and so on. One other character of animal populations that may modify the course and nature of their evolution may be mentioned here. The process of evolution will not be identical in rare and common species. Rare species are generally confined to narrow ranges of conditions and distributed in small populations. Isolation between their popultions will be more complete than between those of commoner species. In these small, well-isolated populations evolution will probably be slow (p. 185) and a greater proportion of the changes will be non-adaptive. Further, as Haldane [154] has pointed out, the nature of selection changes with the abundance of the species. In rare species it is largely the conditions of the environment that act selectively on the animals; in the more abundant species selection is rather between the individuals for viability. In the one selection will lead to an animal better adapted to the environment; in the other to a generally stronger animal.

FLUCTUATIONS IN NUMBERS AND MIGRATION

Few animal populations are constant in numbers for any long period; much more often their numbers change continually.

These variations in numbers are the result of various causes. The most familiar are seasonal rhythms; many species survive the winter in small numbers and multiply to large populations in the warmer months. Not only insects, such as the house-fly, aphids and many others, but also other invertebrates, especially those living in fresh waters, vary seasonally in numbers. In the vertebrates life-histories are longer, and these seasonal rhythms much less frequent. It is not always in the cold season that numbers decrease. In deserts and other tropical climates the hotter and drier months are often the season of scarcity.

Another type of rhythmical variation in population density is that investigated by Elton [93] in the mammals and birds of temperate and arctic climates. These are of longer period, 3–4 or 9–10 years from one maximum to another, and have been shown to persist for more than a century in some species. Examples of the species showing these rhythms are: in Canada, the lemming, *Lemmus richardsoni* and *L. trimucronatus*; the varying hare, *Lepus americanus*; the arctic fox, *Alopex lagopus*; the Canadian lynx, *Lynx canadensis*; in Norway, the lemming, *Lemmus lemmus*; in Britain, the field-mouse, *Microtus hirtus*.

Similar fluctuations in numbers are probably the cause of the occasional migrations that various species of birds and insects make into regions where they are normally rare. Birds such as the sand-grouse (*Pterocles exustus*) and the crossbill (*Loxia curvirostra*) and insects such as the clouded-yellow butterfly (*Colias croceus*) invade Great Britain. The migrations that cause these invasions are probably the result of unusually great increase of the species in their normal habitats. The invasions often occur at more or less regular intervals, but this is not true of all of them. The outward migrations of locusts, by which they become pests in many parts of the world, are due to irregular rhythms of population increase.

More general than any of these types of rhythm are the fluctuations of smaller amplitude to which almost every animal population is subject. These are caused by variations of many kinds in the physical and biological conditions of the environment. An abnormal spell of weather, invasion of the animal's habitat by some new species, an epidemic, and events of many other kinds, may alter the balance between a species and its environment, and result in change in the number of its population. We may conclude with Elton ([94], p. 19) that unbalance is much more characteristic of populations in nature than persistent balance.

We have seen (p. 172) that in experiments with competing populations rhythmical changes in the numbers of the populations may occur as the result of the inherent conditions of the competition, and without change in the environment. It is possible that such inherent rhythms may be present in nature, but it is certain that the great majority of the rhythms we observe are not of this kind. Most of the natural rhythms are correlated with environmental change and are caused by these changes.

There can be no question that seasonal rhythms are caused by environmental change. This is equally true of many of the irregular fluctuations we observe in natural populations. The long-period rhythms in mammals and birds, described by Elton, are, also, almost certainly controlled by environmental change. Correlated rhythms of this type occur in far distant regions, in Scandinavia and in Canada. Their cause certainly cannot be local, and is therefore not the inherent conditions of competition within local populations. It can only be a rhythm of some kind in the environment, and a rhythm in some widespread condition. The rhythms extend over food-chains; those in populations of the later members of the chains—the carnivorous animals (e.g. in Canada the lynx and arctic fox) are undoubtedly caused by rhythms in the earlier members— herbivores (in Canada, the varying hare and other rodents)— which form their prey. We can in this way trace back the rhythms, but, so far, it has not been possible to find a cause for the initiation of the rhythm in the earliest members of the chains. For some time it seemed probable that the rhythms of longest period (10 years) might be correlated with the sunspot cycle, but comparison of the two types of rhythm over long periods has shown that this is not so.[96] The control is almost certainly environmental, but we cannot say what is the controlling environmental condition.

Our knowledge of many other natural rhythms, such as those in populations of locusts and various species of birds and insects, is in much the same state. They also are almost certainly under the control of the environment, but our knowledge of the nature of the control is incomplete.

We have to consider what will be the effects of these rhythms on the course of evolution in the species in which they occur. A rhythm consists of phases of decrease, minimum numbers, increase, and maximum numbers, and these phases succeed each other in this order. We may discuss some points concerning this succession.

1. During the phase of decreasing numbers, selection will be active and powerful, for it is the high death-rate produced by selection that causes the decrease in numbers. Selection continues to be active during the period of minimum numbers.

Thus, the population that survives the decrease of numbers will be a selected, and not a random, sample of that at the preceding maximum. Only the better adapted are likely to survive, and an advantageous mutation will be present in a much larger proportion of the population after the decrease than before it—its spread will have been greatly facilitated. It follows from this that adaptive evolution will be accelerated at the time of decrease.

This is an example of a more general principle. Any environment in which the fauna occasionally has to meet conditions so unfavourable that only a small proportion survive should be characterised by more rapid and closer adaptation than an environment of stable and favourable conditions. In a dangerous environment we may expect to find rapid evolution and close adaptation in any animals that are able to survive the conditions and live in the environment.

2. We have next Wright's conclusion (p. 175) that the effective size of the population as an interbreeding unit is largely determined by the minimum size. Where the fluctuation in numbers is large, this effect is very striking; if a population fluctuates from N_0 to $10^6 N_0$, the effective size is not larger than $6 \cdot 3 N_0$. This implies that the amount of non-adaptive change that occurs in the population will be almost entirely controlled by the minimum population size. So long as the minimum numbers are small, a population may reach numbers of almost any size at its maximum and still show much non-adaptive change.

3. While the numbers of a population are increasing, selection will be weak. This is obvious, for at that time a larger proportion of the individuals are able to survive than when the numbers are constant; variants that at other times would be unable to maintain themselves will then survive. Thus, an increasing population should be more than normally variable and the surviving variants less closely adapted than at other times. When the population again approaches constant numbers, it will be this variable population that will be subjected to selection. Any variations that happen to be advantageous will be accepted into the genotype, and non-adaptive variation that was able to spread at the time of weak selection may also be perpetuated, if it is not positively disadvantageous. The effects of rapid increase in numbers, like those of decrease, will be change in the genotype and rapid evolution, but during population increase the change should be less closely adaptive.

A series of observations on a colony of a butterfly, the marsh fritillary (*Euphydryas aurinia*), recorded by Ford and Ford ([112], cf. also [113]) confirms the truth of some of these conclusions. This butterfly occurs widely in England, but in scattered colonies. An isolated colony was observed for 54 years, from 1881 to

1935. For the first 13 years, 1881–1894, the colony increased in numbers; from 1897 to 1906 it decreased; from 1906 to 1912 the numbers were small and between 1913 and 1919 still smaller, so that individuals were rare; from 1920 to 1926 the numbers again increased rapidly until in 1926 the colony was as large as its earlier maximum. It remained in this condition until the observations ceased in 1935.

The cause of these fluctuations in numbers is unknown, but this is immaterial to us. To us the interesting point is that during the fluctuations the butterfly showed structural changes that confirm some of the conclusions that have just been stated. Before 1919 the structure varied only slightly among the individuals of the colony, but during the period of rapid increase (1920–1926) the population was very variable—"so that hardly two individuals were alike". When the numbers again became constant, this outburst of variability ceased, but the new form was recognisably different from that before the period of increasing numbers. It seems that we have here clear evidence of abnormal variability in a population that is increasing; this confirms our conclusion that selection must then be weak. The conclusion that the characters of the population may be permanently altered as the result of the variation during the phase of increase, i.e. that rapid evolution may occur then, is also confirmed.

4. In a rhythm of fluctuation in population numbers, the phase of increasing numbers, if not stopped earlier by some other change, is continued until the population is overcrowded. Conditions then become unfavourable.

It is at this point in the cycle that outward migration from the area in which the population is crowded so often occurs. The migrations of lemmings in Norway, of locusts and of butterflies [327] in many parts of the world are typical examples of these migrations.

Migration is a large subject. Here we need only discuss its relation to fluctuations in numbers; we can leave aside the many types of migration that are not associated with these fluctuations—for instance, those of strongly locomotory animals in search of prey, e.g. the migrations of the snowy owl in America, [94] the seasonal migrations of the many birds that pass the two halves of the year in different countries, and migrations associated with the breeding cycle in fishes such as the eel and salmon.

Some of the effects of outward migration from a crowded population are clear. First, it will reduce the population density, and thus decrease the chance of epidemics, or check them if they have already started. Secondly, it will facilitate spread of the species into new habitats, where new populations may be set up. It is true that, as a means of doing this, outward migration is very often an extravagant process. New habitats will only occasionally be found, and in some migrations very rarely —practically every lemming that takes part in the seaward migration dies, and so do almost all the individuals of a swarm of locusts; it is not usual for new populations to be set up in the migrations of these animals. Many biologists have found it difficult to believe that migration can be of selective value to the species for this reason alone. We must remember that these migrations have the other function of reducing the density of a crowded population. Together these two functions may perhaps account for their persistence. But, even so, it must be admitted that the migrations are surprising phenomena, and we may suspect that there are other reasons for their persistence.

We may, perhaps, be able to understand the biological reasons for the migrations more fully if we consider them in relation to the whole cycle of population numbers with which they are associated. Rhythmic fluctuations in numbers are a means by which animal populations are adjusted to periodic changes in environmental conditions. In order that quick advantage may be taken of improving conditions during such a cycle, rapid reproduction is clearly of advantage to a population. But usually the only checks to increase when the population has reached and passed the maximum density that the habitat can support are those of starvation, epidemics and, for many species, increased predation. Until these come into play all the members of the population will reproduce at the maximum rate. The population must therefore become overcrowded, and when this happens, the increase will be checked by these factors acting upon all its members. Starvation and epidemics at least will weaken them all. It may be better for the species that a part of the crowded population should migrate and allow those that are left to form a healthy but less numerous population. If so, migration is the price that a species with fluctuating numbers pays for the rapid rate of reproduction that allows it to take full and quick advantage of improvement in the environment.

On the subject of rhythmic fluctuations in numbers we may conclude in general that these have two main advantages to a species. They allow it to correlate its numbers with changes in the conditions of the environment, and they also allow evolutionary change to be more rapid than it would be in a species with constant numbers. Probably the main reason why migration occurs during these rhythms is that it has an important function in the organisation of the rhythm. It may also in some cases tend to widen distribution.

POLYMORPHISM

A polymorphic species may be defined (Ford [111]) as one in which two or more distinct forms occur together in the same habitat in such proportions that the rarest of them cannot be maintained by recurrent mutation. As Ford says, this definition excludes seasonal and geographic variation, since the variants in polymorphism occur at the same time and in the same habitat. It excludes continuous variation, since this does not give rise to distinct forms; in continuous variation the forms grade into each other. The term is often used in wider senses,* but it is convenient to restrict it to this meaning.

Since interbreeding is general within a population, only characters that do not blend on crossing can be polymorphic, i.e. those controlled by single genes, or at least by closely linked groups of genes.

When it is so defined, three types of polymorphism may be distinguished—transient, neutral and balanced polymorphism (Ford).

A population is in a condition of transient polymorphism when some distinct mutational form is spreading through it under selection. It is polymorphic while the spread continues, but ceases to be so as the mutation becomes fixed in the population. The spread of melanic forms in European Lepidoptera (p. 195) is a typical example of this condition. So also is that of the hamster in Russia (p. 196 and Fig. 53).

* For instance, butterflies in which seasonal forms differ are often called polymorphic. These differences are caused by action of environmental conditions that differ with the seasons. We are not concerned with this phenomenon.

Both the other types of polymorphism may continue indefinitely. Balanced polymorphism arises when a variant has a selective advantage so long as it forms less than a certain proportion of the population, but loses the advantage and becomes disadvantageous when it is more widespread. This state of affairs may be due to either genetic or biological conditions. A typical genetic example is given by a semi-dominant mutant that is advantageous as a heterozygote but disadvantageous as a homozygote. We have already noted that such mutants are common (p. 71); often the homozygote is lethal. Ford ([112], pp. 79–80) quotes from Gerould [129], [130] the example of the butterfly *Colias philodice* in New Hampshire. A pale variety (*alba*) of the female was present in a locality at the town of Hanover (U.S.A.) forming 16 per cent. of the population both in 1911 and 1940. The polymorphism was thus stable although the proportion fluctuated at intermediate dates. The variety was shown to be caused by a dominant sex-controlled gene which was linked with a recessive lethal, so that only the heterozygotes survive. Presumably the dominant gene has some selective advantage. The advantage will appear in heterozygotes, but in the homozygotic mutant the lethal character of the recessive gene will be expressed and the combination will be highly disadvantageous. Ford gives many other examples.

In all cases of this class few homozygotes will be formed when the mutation is present in a small proportion of the population (p. 180), and their disadvantage will not greatly affect the conditions. The spread of the gene will then be controlled by the advantage of the heterozygote. But as the gene becomes frequent, its spread will be checked at some point by homozygotic expression of the mutation in sufficient numbers. Equilibrium will be reached when the advantage of the heterozygote and the disadvantage of the homozygote are balanced. The population will then be polymorphic, with individuals showing the mutation, and others without it. This balance may continue indefinitely. It is likely to be modified, but not necessarily destroyed, when conditions change. So long as the conditions remain the same, it should be unaltered.

It is not rare to find a small but definite proportion of a variant among the populations of a species. The proportion is often much too large to be caused directly by recurrent mutation, which does not normally occur in more than $1/10^5$ of the population (p. 97). Many of these cases may be examples of transient polymorphism, in which, as in the melanic European Lepidoptera, one form will in time spread through the whole population. In many of the remainder it is probable that the condition is one of genetic balanced polymorphism.

Well-known examples of balanced polymorphism in which the balance is controlled by the biological conditions of the animal's life are given by mimetic species. One sex, usually the female, of a mimetic butterfly is polymorphic, some of the individuals being normal, others mimics of one or more distasteful models. The value of a mimetic resemblance will decrease with increase in the proportion of mimics, for, as the mimic becomes commoner in comparison with the models, predators will more often take it and, finding it not distasteful, will lose their distaste for specimens with the appearance of the model. We have here the same condition of advantage with small numbers and reduced advantage with larger numbers that occurs in genetic polymorphism. Here again a balance will be set up, the proportion of the mimetic form being controlled to give the greatest advantage to the resemblance. The balance will be permanent so long as the conditions remain constant. Where more than one species is mimicked, a balance of this kind should be set up for each mimetic form.

Lastly, we have to consider the third, neutral, type of polymorphism. In this type the characters on which the polymorphic forms are distinguished are selectively neutral, that is to say, they are without selective value, non-adaptive. There will be no force of selection to spread such characters through the population, or to remove them. In these circumstances it would seem that the species might remain permanently polymorphic, unless the non-adaptive changes of drift (p. 183) bring it about that one character is fixed and the other lost.

Species are often polymorphic in characters that appear to be non-adaptive. The banded snails, *Cepæa nemoralis* and *C. hortensis* (p. 148), give a good example. In both these species the bands on the shell are extremely variable in expression. There is a maximum of five bands and they occur among the individuals of a population in almost every combination. The species are thus polymorphic to an extreme degree. If this polymorphism is not neutral, it must be either transient or balanced. It is not transient, for Diver [74] has shown that prehistoric populations were in very much the same condition as those alive today; there has been little change in the distribution of the characters in several thousand years. If it is balanced, there must be differences between the selective advantages of the arrangements of the bands, for their distributions in the populations cannot be held in balance—in the manner we have just discussed—unless some, at least, have selective advantage. There is no evidence that any of the arrangements have adaptive value; none of them are cryptic and it is difficult to suggest any other adaptive use that they could serve. It is, of course, possible to assume that they are correlated genetically with underlying characters that are not visible, and that the selective advantages belong in reality to these underlying characters. There is no evidence of such correlation.

It would be justifiable to make the assumption of correlation with underlying adaptive characters if, and only if, neutral polymorphism is impossible. If it is possible, the simplest view is that the polymorphism is truly neutral—that there is no effective selection and that the populations are therefore able to remain permanently polymorphic. But the possibility of neutral polymorphism has been denied by Ford [111] on the basis of Fisher's proof [104] that if a genetic mutation has selective value the advantage (or disadvantage) will be effective—in a constant environment—even though it is extremely small—so small that he concludes that neutral mutations are of no significance in nature. We have already discussed this argument (p. 213), and seen reason to doubt its force against the evolution of non-adaptive genetic changes in the changing environments of nature, if the evolution is based on micro-mutation. If non-adaptive genetic changes may be evolved, neutral polymorphism will be possible. Examples such as that of the banded snails are much more easily explained as neutral than balanced polymorphism, and seem to support the belief that it is a real phenomenon. Mayr ([209], p. 75) gives other examples of what appears to be neutral polymorphism. At the present time, it seems to be unnecessary to deny that polymorphism can be neutral.

There is no reason to think that polymorphism will have

any very striking effects on micro-evolution in animals. It is a form of intraspecific differentiation, a form in which the differentiations occur within a single population. It could lead to the evolution of new species only if the population divided into reproductively isolated groups correlated with the polymorphism, but we have no evidence that this occurs in nature. Polymorphic forms, if isolated from each other, might serve as a starting point for further differentiation. This is perhaps most likely to happen when, as in some species of mimetic butterflies, different models are mimicked in different parts of the range of the species, so that the various mimetic forms are already separated from each other.

CHAPTER VII

MACRO- AND MEGA-EVOLUTION:
INTRODUCTION

WE now pass from the small part of evolution that we can observe in the world of animals alive today to the larger evolutionary changes observable in palæontology. These we have called (p. 22) macro- and mega-evolution. As soon as we leave living animals, the methods of investigation open to us are much more limited. Since we cannot directly observe the faunas of past ages, their hereditary mechanisms, their behaviour and to a large extent their ecology and organisation into species and smaller units are outside our knowledge. From the structures preserved in fossils and the rocks in which they are found, we must deduce as much as we can of the animals' biology. Except in the rare series of strata in which we can observe the micro-evolution of the past, we have only occasional fossils preserved at long intervals of time, and must try to link these by hypothetical intermediates. For these reasons it is not to be expected that we should be able to reach so complete an understanding of macro- and mega-evolution as of micro-evolution. Nevertheless we must push our interpretation of these larger evolutionary changes as far as it will go if we are to reach any broad view of animal evolution as a whole.

The first question for us to ask is how far we can regard the whole of evolution as simply an extrapolation of micro-evolution. Is there no more to be said of macro- and mega-evolution than that they are the results of micro-evolution continued over long periods of time?

There can be no doubt that evolution throughout its course is a process of the same general nature as that we observe in the micro-evolution of today. Throughout palæontological time, as today, animals have been undergoing micro-evolution, and there is no reason to think that the process has been greatly different in past times. Divided into small enough units all evolution becomes micro-evolution. Species were always distributed in partially isolated populations which diverged so long as they were isolated. Differentiated forms have often met, and adaptive and non-adaptive changes played roughly the same parts in the micro-evolution of the past as they do today.

There has, then, always been a basis of micro-evolution in the evolution of animals. But this does not mean that we have no more to do in interpretation of the larger changes of evolution than to regard them as extended micro-evolution. There are many aspects of evolutionary change which have not so far appeared in our discussions because the periods of micro-evolution are not long enough to allow them to become evident. Either they are rare—though they may still be important in the long-period evolution of animals—or they need a long time to develop. It is these aspects of evolution that we must discuss in the following chapters. But before doing so we must consider somewhat further the general nature of the changes of macro- and mega-evolution. Let us first recall the conclusions regarding their nature that we reached when we discussed the results of palæontology (ch. II).

We found that there are two distinct types of change to be recognised in palæontological evolution. There is first allometric change (pp. 37 ff.) in the relative size of organs or parts of organs, arising by differential growth during development and correlated with change in the size of the body as a whole. This is responsible for a large part of the less fundamental changes in structure. We called these changes (after Osborn) allometrons. Distinct from these are various other types of change in the organisation of the body, to which we gave Osborn's name of aristogenesis. They, like allometrons, occur very generally throughout evolution and are essential to progress. They are more evident in the larger evolutionary changes and therefore more evident in mega- than in macro-evolution.

Much of aristogenesis is due to modification of the elements of pattern already present in the body. But it is impossible to deny that pattern may also arise *de novo* in the course of evolution, that differentiations may appear where there was no earlier differentiation to be modified into them. The major changes of evolution would be impossible without such novelties.

As an example of aristogenesis we took the evolution of the teeth in mastodonts and elephants (p. 42). Much here is modification of previous pattern—e.g. the reduplication of the cusps, which is multiplication of the pattern of these organs—but there is also formation of new pattern in, for instance, the development of cement. In the evolution of the horns of the titanotheres (p. 39) there must at some time have been a new formation of a more active growth-rate at the point on the skull where the horns were later borne. When it arose, this must have been a new element of pattern. We saw (p. 94) that we have at present no experience of mutations of the kind needed to produce these novelties of pattern. They seem to arise as changes of, at first, very small, hardly recognisable, expression in the body, and to grow to larger sizes in the course of evolution by allometric change. It is easy to postulate mutations that would give rise to them; it is indeed easy to imagine mutations that will act in any way we choose. But that is of no real value. We must admit the reality of aristogenes of this type, and also admit that we know nothing of the manner in which they arise. If this is the position, we shall not advance our interpretation of evolution by discussing them further.

All other evolutionary changes consist in modification of the organisation already present in the body. The simplest of these changes are the allometrons, which are directly correlated with change in body size. The only evolutionary change needed to account for them is an alteration in the size of the body; the organs would reach the proportions they have in the later animal if the earlier animal grew to the size of the later.

All other types of modification of pattern are included in aristogenesis. Some categories of aristogenetic modification of pattern already present in the body are: alterations in the relative growth-rates of the parts, that is to say of the allometry of the body, as in the initiation of hypsodontism in the horses (p. 41); reduplication of parts as in the teeth of the elephants (p. 42); disappearance of organs in the course of evolution; and many others. To these should probably be added many of the effects that we observe to result from mutation in living animals, though they do not appear in fossils—changes of colour pattern; changes in the histology of the tissues; possibly, of the place in the body at which an organ is formed, as in aristopedia and proboscipedia (p. 93); and others.

These are the types of change that have taken part in the macro- and mega-evolution. We know nothing of the means by which new pattern arises, but we may ask whether the others of these types of change are to be expected from long-continued micro-evolution. Here it should first be said that *any* type of change in the patterns present in the body may be produced in living animals by mutation. Mutation may alter the length of development, it may alter an animal's size, and cause any other type of alteration in the arrangement of the patterns of the body (p. 94). Thus, there is no necessity to ask for any evolutionary mechanisms to explain these larger changes other than those we have needed in our discussions of micro-evolution. But we may ask whether the different kinds of mutation have played the same relative parts in these larger changes that we found them to play in micro-evolution. We found that the greater part of micro-evolutionary change was due to alteration in modification as the result of micro-mutation. How much of macro- and mega-evolution can be due to micro-mutation?

The most characteristic features of the changes based on micro-mutation, as contrasted with those due to larger mutations, are that they are gradual and may be directional (p. 212). We have seen (p. 48) that the changes of palæontological evolution are as clearly characterised by their gradualness and directiveness as those of micro-evolution. Sudden changes are at least rare in palæontology. These features, at any rate, give us no reason to doubt that micro-mutation plays as large a part in macro- and mega-evolution as in micro-evolution.

In other ways the changes of macro and mega-evolution are of types that we should expect from micro-mutation. Allometric change may be due to change in the length of development. In discussing the mode of action of micro-mutational changes in genes, we concluded that it is precisely such characters as this that they affect—by altering the efficiency of enzymes. Allometric changes are gradual and small alterations in these characters may very easily be caused by the modifying action of micro-mutations. There is then every reason to think that at least the allometric changes of palæontology may be based on micro-mutation. Is this equally true of the alterations of pattern that occur in aristogenesis? It is when change is sudden that we are forced to postulate macro-mutation as its cause. Though by far the greater part of the changes of aristogenesis in palæontology are clearly gradual, some changes that can hardly be other than sudden do occur in it. Increase in the number of similar organs in the body, for instance increased number of segments in the body of a vertebrate, is a character of this kind. Also, there is no evidence that change of a growth constant, such as occurred in the evolution of hypsodontism in the horses (Fig. 18, p. 41), is not sudden, though the palæontological evidence may not be detailed enough to allow us to be sure on the point. However this may be, there is no doubt that sudden changes occur in evolution and for them macro-mutations are required. It would seem that the evolutionary changes of macro- and mega-evolution (always excepting the formation of new pattern) may be brought about by much the same genetic changes as those of micro-evolution—the greater part by micro-mutation but some part by mutations of larger effect.

So, then, we must think of evolution on the large scale—the whole course of evolution in the horses, for instance—as being caused in the main by gradual alteration of the genotype of the race by micro-mutation, but with the occasional addition of a macro-mutation that spreads through the race and becomes fixed in it. This view is very different from that held some years ago, when the evolutionary changes were thought of as being produced by a succession of macro-mutations. It is, however, in much better agreement with recent views of the structure of the genotype and of its action. It also accords much better with the facts of palæontology, not only with the gradualness of its changes, but also with the fact that they are often directional. It does not imply that we shall find in macro- and mega-evolution only the phenomena we have discussed in dealing with micro-evolution. In the following chapters we must discuss some of these phenomena that have not previously been considered.

CHAPTER VIII

PRE-ADAPTATION

IF the argument of the last two chapters is accepted we can broadly understand the natural processes by which evolutionary change arises in a population of animals and is built up to specific and higher levels. In the main, the population responds to the conditions of the environment by adaptation under selection, though non-adaptive change also plays a part in the evolution.

So far, then, we have seen how animals evolve continually closer adaptation to their habitats and habits of life. As adaptation becomes closer, it is to be expected that the range of conditions to which the animal is adapted will become narrower, and the niche in which it lives smaller. The species may be expected to become specialised. This is, in fact, a very frequent result of evolution—we find narrow specialisation to be common among living animals, and fossils also give much evidence of it. But it does not occur universally and inevitably; species may be able to live in wide ranges of conditions. Some, even among such highly evolved animals as birds (the barn-owl, *Tyto alba*, and the osprey, *Pandion haliaëtus*) and insects (house-fly), are cosmopolitan or nearly so, and many others have wide ranges of conditions. We shall discuss this subject in ch. XI. Here we need only note that these species are exceptional and that adaptation very generally leads to specialisation.

Specialisation is necessarily in the long run a danger to survival, for the conditions to which an animal is specialised may cease to exist, and this is in general more likely the narrower the specialisation. If environmental change occurs too rapidly to allow the animal to re-adapt, so that it may continue its old life in the new conditions, we should expect that it would die out. But this, again, does not inevitably happen. Specialised animals sometimes succeed in surviving large changes in their

environments by changing their modes of life to others suitable
to the changed environment. In this chapter we have to discuss
how it is possible for them to do this.

First, we must consider the evidence that such changes in
mode of life occur. There is plenty of palæontological evidence
for this. We have seen that vertebrates throughout their evolution frequently invaded new environments and passed to new
modes of life (p. 16). Each time this happened, animals that
had been adapted to one life gave up that life and became
adapted in a different direction. A clear example is found in the
evolution of the horses.[275] *

From their origin at the beginning of the Eocene until the
Miocene, all the Equidæ were browsing animals, feeding on
leaves and probably for the most part living in wooded country.
During this period they underwent considerable adaptation to
the browsing habit. Their size increased (p. 35), the crown of
their teeth became slowly but continuously higher (p. 41), the
shape of the skull changed by relative elongation of the face
(p. 36), reduction of the outer digits commenced, and changes
took place in other parts of the body. This evolution may be
regarded as directly adaptive to browsing life. We shall see
that increase of size is adaptive in many mammalian groups
(p. 293); the heightening of the crown of the teeth may have
been in response to the need for a relatively greater food-supply
in the larger animals (Simpson [275], p. 162), and to maintenance
of the efficiency of the teeth in a longer life; reduction of the
digits was adaptive to rapid running on hard ground whether in
woods or elsewhere. In general, the horses became closely
adapted and specialised to their browsing habit.

In the Miocene some lines of equine descent (but not all)
gave up the browsing habit and took to eating grass, probably
on open downs. With this change the whole course of their
evolution altered. We saw earlier (p. 41) that the development
of hypsodontism became suddenly much more rapid at this
time, but this was by no means the only change. Simpson
([275], p. 90) says of the other changes: "the tooth-crown
pattern is more complicated in grazers, the occlusion † is
different from that of browsers, jaw musculature and move-

* For general accounts of equine evolution, see R. S. Lull,[200] W. B. Scott.[271]
† I.e. the contact of the surfaces of the upper and lower teeth as they meet.

ment are somewhat modified, the digestive tract is undoubtedly different, although what the digestive tract of browsing horses was is not known, since they are extinct. Less directly, there are modifications in feet and limbs and throughout the skeleton that are more or less correlated with different habitats." In fact, the whole organisation of the body was modified, though some of the changes that had begun earlier, such as increase in size, development of hypsodontism and reduction of the outer digits, were continued.

Large and far-reaching examples of similar changes in habit occurred in the migration of fishes from the water to the land (pp. 279–283), and in the evolution of aerial life in birds and mammals. These large changes are always accompanied by re-organisation of the whole body. They are undoubtedly complex and take place in many steps through long periods of time. From them a series of decreasing magnitude could be quoted until we reach the changes of habit that we can observe in living animals. These do not usually require any considerable structural modification, being mainly changes of behaviour. Typical are the changes of feeding habit by which animals have become pests by feeding on crops cultivated by man. As an example we have the apple capsid, *Plesiocoris rugicollis*, already mentioned (p. 210), which originally fed, so far as is known, only on willows, but took to feeding on apple and became a pest.[119] Similarly, the potato-beetle, *Leptinotarsa decemlineata*, changed its food from the buffalo bur (*Solanum rostratum*), on which it fed in its original habitat in the Rocky Mountains, to the potato, when potatoes reached its habitat ([182], p. 219).

In a single evolutionary line large changes of habitat are not frequent, though in some lines they have probably occurred more than once. In the elephants, for instance, the tusks have reached large size several times. They are believed to have been used for digging and rooting up food from the ground, and their repeated evolution to large size was probably associated with repeated acquisition of this habit. On the other hand, if we had more knowledge, we should probably realise that small changes of habit are much more frequent in evolution than they now appear to be. This would be in accord with our experience of living animals in which such changes appear to take place without much difficulty. As evidence that the larger changes that require general reorganisation of the body are infrequent, we have the facts that horses have only once changed from a browsing to a grazing habit and never in the reverse direction, and that vertebrates have only once successfully left the water for the land.

We have to explain how these changes of habit and habitat come about. We have seen how animals become more closely adapted to the conditions of their environments under the pressure of selection; we have now to explain how it is possible for a group of animals to escape from selection pressure in the original direction, and pass to a new life where the pressure of selection is in a different direction.

It may perhaps be contended that there is here no problem. At any time, it may be said, some individuals may be forced out of the normal range of the species by some such cause as pressure of numbers or destruction of the normal habitat, and finding themselves in new conditions will adapt to them. Where the change of habit is small and does not require structural modification, this is a possible, and indeed probable, view. Some specimens of the apple capsid probably found themselves on apple, and, since the food was suitable, fed there and gave rise to the new race. Adaptation to the new conditions would follow, and the new race would differentiate from the original. This has happened in the case of the capsid. There is no more difficulty in understanding the change of food plant of the potato-beetle.

But this explanation will not account for the larger changes which demand widespread reorganisation of the body. A browsing horse could not suddenly take to grazing. It would almost certainly die if prevented from reaching its normal food—animals do not readily change their habits at need as a man would do. If the conservatism of the animal's habits was broken, and it attempted to browse, it would still find itself in competition with the fauna of the new habitat, which would be better adapted to life in that environment. It is true that some ecologists believe that animal environments are by no means always full to capacity.[95] But even if our animal happened on an empty environment at the time of its migration, it would in time meet competition, long before it had time by the slow processes of structural evolution to re-adapt to the new conditions. It would inevitably perish in the competition. This at least is what we should expect unless there were exceptional reasons for its survival.

The argument is not greatly weakened though we take account of the theory called "Organic Selection", which has been recently revived and supported by some Russian authors.[125] As we noted earlier (p. 209), an animal in an environment in which the conditions differ from those to which it has been adapted will first, and rapidly, react, so far as possible, by phenotypic modification, i.e. by non-hereditary change of structure and function in the body. Later these modifications will be replaced by hereditary variations based on recombination and mutation. There is therefore no need, these authors say, for genetic mutation to be available when the animal passes to a new mode of life.

There can be no doubt that there is some truth in this view. Undoubtedly, the immediate reaction of an animal in a strange environment will be non-hereditary, phenotypic, modification, and if it is able to survive in the new conditions these modifications may be later replaced by hereditary variation. But there are very definite limits to the amount of phenotypic modification that can occur in the body of an animal. The fact that an animal's bodily structure is to some extent modifiable in response to the conditions of its environment extends the range of conditions in which it can live. But, if the change of habit is large, phenotypic modification will not account for survival in the new life. What we are considering is not how the range of conditions that are viable for an animal is as large as it often is, but how the animal is able on occasion to pass beyond that range and to undertake a new manner of life outside it. By phenotypic modification the range may be extended beyond what it would be were the body not so modifiable. Phenotypic modification does not help us to understand how the range itself can be altered.

Again, interpretation of these changes is not made much easier if we agree, as we must, that the larger changes of habit were often gradual rather than sudden. It is true that it is easy to imagine a course of events by which a large change of structure and habit could arise gradually, and to do so without

A.E.—10

postulating any evolutionary principles beyond those discussed in the last two chapters. In the example of the change from browsing to grazing in the horses, we may suppose that a population of browsing horses became divided by geographical isolation between two separate habitats of the original type. In both habitats the horses would be adapted to the conditions and would survive. If one of the habitats changed gradually after its isolation from woodland to grassy down, and if the change was slow enough, it is possible that the horse stock isolated in this environment would be gradually forced to a grazing habit, and might adapt itself to this habit, evolving into a line of grazing horses. It would either do so or die out.

This is a possible course of events, but there are serious objections to it as a general explanation of the success of the large changes that we are discussing. First, it assumes accurate correlation between the rate of change of the environment and the evolutionary changes in the organism. If the changes of structure necessitated by the alteration of habit were large enough to require any considerable reorganisation of the body, the environmental change would have to be extremely slow. For structural modification in animals always requires much time, especially when much correlation in different parts of the body is needed, as it would be in the circumstances we are considering. Unless this time were available, we should expect the isolated line to die out rather than to evolve. Also, this explanation gives no reason why major changes of habit are so rare in evolution. Environments are always changing, and, if the correlation between environment and evolutionary change were usual, we should expect the habits of animals often to undergo large changes in the changing environments. Stocks of horses must often have been isolated in environments in which the conditions later changed. Why have their feeding habits altered only once?

We must, then, find some other explanation for the success of these large changes of habit.

All changes of habit, even relatively small changes such as those of feeding habit in living animals, require something in the animals before the change, if the change is to be possible. They require that the animal should be so constituted before the change that it is able to take on the new manner of life; the animal must have originally possessed characters that made it capable of living the altered life. It may be laid down as a general proposition that whenever an animal meets an environment that is not fully populated it will spread into this environment if it is capable of living in it. But its ability to invade will always be determined by the characters it possesses as the result of adaptation in its original environment. This is equally true when the change is not the invasion of a new environment but a change of habit—when the adoption of a new habit gives opportunity for wider distribution in the original environment. At the time of change the new conditions will act as a filter allowing only those animals capable of life under the new conditions to pass; all others will be unable to undertake this life.

Cuénot [59] discusses this aspect of the problem at length. For the property in an animal of suitability for some change in its habit or habitat, he uses the term *pre-adaptation*.* In distinction the term *post-adaptation* may be used for direct adaptation of an animal to the conditions in which it is living while the adaptation is proceeding.

Before we go further, it should be noted that pre-adaptation is a more general phenomenon than the form of it we are here discussing. In its most general sense pre-adaptation implies merely the possession of characters suitable for use in some situation, and the possession of these characters before the situation arises, before there is any opportunity for the use to which they are pre-adapted. In all adaptation the animal must to some extent be pre-adapted in this sense; it must always possess characters that can be modified to give the adapted character. We used the term in this sense in speaking (p. 47) of the pre-adaptation of the ancestral mammal for the use of the quadrate and articular to form bones in the ear. Here the pre-adaptation is especially obvious because the two bones had lost their previous functions and, being functionless, were available for modification to a new use. But pre-adaptation may be present in organs that have not lost their functions. No adaptation is possible without some grade of pre-adaptation in the structure to be adapted.

* According to Cuénot the term was first used by C. B. Davenport.[67]

The sense in which the term is used by Cuénot is more restricted. By pre-adaptation he means a correlation between the characters acquired while the animal is leading one type of life and those that it needs after a change in its habits. These characters will have been evolved for certain purposes in the earlier life, and, if pre-adaptation is present, will be found adaptive to *different* needs in the altered life. An organ that merely serves the same purpose after a change of habit as before it, is not pre-adaptive in his sense. We must accept that there is this correlation in very many of the examples of change of habit that we know to have occurred in living animals, and indeed that they would be impossible without it. Pre-adaptation of this kind is most easily demonstrated in the many cases where the biology of animals has been altered after contact with men, for the change in environment is recent and sudden in these cases. Many other pests besides the apple capsid and the potato beetle have taken to feeding on man's crops within recent years and might be mentioned; in all pre-adaptation for the sudden change of food must have been present. Not only pests show pre-adaptation. The vinegar eel must certainly have been adapted to life in a very acid medium before it could have come to live in its present unnatural habitat. In all these examples organs evolved in one environment are adaptive to the different needs of another environment. If such pre-adaptation is evident when the opportunity of change is provided by man, there can be little doubt that it is equally important when such opportunities occur in nature without his interference.

Pre-adaptation may also be found in the animals that succeeded in the larger, palæontological, changes of habit. In the change from browsing to grazing in the horses pre-adaptation is very clear. The slow and continuous heightening of the crown of the teeth in browsing horses was pre-adaptive to the hypsodontism required by a grazing habit; the reduction of the outer digits was pre-adaptive to running on open downs; and the elongation of the facial region pre-adaptive to providing the larger space needed for hypsodont teeth. In all these characters, and others, evolved as they were while the horses still browsed and for the needs of that life, we find pre-adaptation to a grazing life. We shall see (p. 279) that other palæontological examples of large changes of habit show pre-adaptation.

There is then no doubt that the existence of pre-adaptation is frequent and perhaps general in successful examples of these changes of habit or habitat. But we need to know more than this. If pre-adaptation is necessary for the success of these changes, we need to know how it comes about that animals possess pre-adaptive characters.

When the change is small and one solely of behaviour, there is little difficulty in understanding how the pre-adaptation arises. The pre-adaptive characters are presumably possessed by the whole population before the change. It is not difficult to believe that the digestive system of the apple capsid was fitted to a diet of apple by characters evolved while it fed on willow; or that the potato-beetle was similarly fitted to feed on the potato. The pre-adaptive characters are here physiological rather than structural, and not very complex—it is not so very unlikely that a willow-feeding animal should be able to digest apple. Beyond this, all that is needed is a change of behaviour. But the larger changes of habit cannot be so easily accounted for. As we have seen, grazing requires characteristics different from those needed for browsing and requires them in many of the organs of the body, structural as well as physiological characteristics, and structure at least does not alter suddenly. Why should browsing horses have evolved so many characters pre-adaptive to grazing while they still browsed leaves?

The essential point here is that the pre-adaptive characters are used for different purposes before and after the change. This correlation between the characters of the organs evolved in one environment for one purpose and their use in another environment for a different purpose can only be due to chance. It may seem surprising that such correlation should occur. Yet, as we have seen, it certainly does occur.

Since this correlation can only be due to chance, it will undoubtedly be rare, but this need not deter us from discussing it as a possible explanation of the pre-adaptation, for the larger changes of habit are, as we have seen, themselves rare. If a large change of habit were successful only once in a thousand times, this would be enough to account for their occurrence in palæontology. There is an increasing body of evidence, much of it recently accumulated, in favour of the view that many large changes of habit have required this chance correlation (e.g. [275]).

Examples from living and fossil animals in which the correlation appears to have been present will illustrate the nature of this evidence.

The adhesive pads of the feet of tree-frogs [228] give a clear example. The genera *Hyla* and *Polypedates* are both arboreal, but belong to different and distantly related families. In the two genera the pads are very similar in structure, though they have been independently evolved. The structure of the pad of *Hyla* is shown in Fig. 54. In both genera the adhesive surface

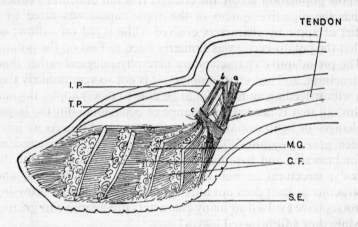

Figure 54. Diagrammatic sagittal section of the adhesive pad of *Hyla*. C.F., collagen fibres; I.P., intercalary phalynx; M.G., mucus glands; S.E., corrugated epithelium; T.P., terminal phalynx; a, b, c, terminations of the collagen fibres. (After G. K. Noble and M. E. Jaeckle)

of the pad is covered with corrugated epithelium. Within this are mucous glands, opening through the epithelium. Between and around the glands are numerous strong collagen fibres. These are attached to the epithelium at the distal end of the pad and to the terminal phalanges at the proximal end. They are pulled when the weight of the animal is thrown on the phalanges, which happens when the pads are used in climbing. As they are pulled, the fibres squeeze out the mucous secretion from the glands. The pads adhere by friction between their corrugated epithelium and the surface on which it is pressed, but the mucus is also adhesive. There is a further elaboration of the apparatus in both genera. Between the terminal phalanx and that originally next to it, there has been introduced an intercalary phalanx. This increases the efficiency of the pad by allowing more movement of the leg without raising the surface of the pad and so losing its adhesion (Fig. 54). Adhesive pads are present in other genera of tree-frogs besides these two, but in many of them the intercalary phalanx is not present.

The point of special interest to us here is that various other frogs, which do not climb trees and which are shown by the phylogeny of the group to have no arboreal ancestry, possess adhesive pads similar in structure to those of the arboreal forms but smaller and without the intercalary phalanx. It seems clear that adhesive pads were not evolved as an adaptation to climbing, but were first developed in ground-living frogs, presumably in adaptation to the habit of jumping—they would tend to prevent the frog slipping at the end of its jump. They were pre-adaptive to arboreal life, and in forms that became arboreal were further elaborated and specialised (by post-adaptation)—they became larger and the intercalary phalanx was added in some forms as a final specialisation.

For another example we will take the evolution of aerial from aquatic respiration in the vertebrates, at the time when the fish emerged from the water to become an amphibian. It is generally agreed by palæontologists that the crossopterygian fishes from which the amphibians evolved lived in fresh waters and that their migration to the land took place on the fresh-water shore. Further, the geological evidence is that the fresh waters in which this occurred were shallow and under a warm climate—what we should today describe as a tropical climate. Study of present-day waters of this type [35, 39] shows that the physical and chemical conditions of such waters are very different from those in outwardly similar temperate waters. Very often shallow and stagnant tropical waters are undisturbed by wind owing to thick growth of vegetation above them; they are stratified with a steep gradient of temperature from top to bottom owing to great heating of the surface in daytime; there is much bacterial decay in them, which is active because of the high temperature; and, being heavily shaded and often highly coloured, the waters are poorly lighted, so that little oxygen is produced in them by photosynthesis. As a result of all these conditions, the oxygen content of the water is often and for long periods negligible except very near the surface, and the carbon dioxide content is considerable—up to 30 c.c. per litre or even more.

We can get some idea of how the crossopterygian fish must have reacted to these conditions by studying the present-day fish of these waters. These show two different types of adaptation towards satisfying their respiratory need for oxygen. Some, mostly small, fishes use for their gill-current the very thin surface layer, which is better aerated by diffusion from the air above it. They come to the surface and, so it seems, nibble at it, but do not break the surface; they do not take in air. Other fishes of these waters possess internal accessory organs of aerial respiration. They take air from above the water and pass it into these "lungs". The "lungs" are of many kinds; the epithelia of the mouth, the gill-chamber, the air-bladder, the stomach, the intestine, and perhaps in a few cases the gills themselves, may each be modified for aerial respiration.[36] These organs must always be internal; an external organ of respiration would be useless in the deoxygenated medium.

This study of the ecology of present-day tropical waters makes it difficult to avoid the conclusion that the lung was evolved, in the similar waters in which the fish ancestors of the Amphibia lived, in response to the same needs as those which have caused the evolution of these accessory respiratory organs in living fishes. The crossopterygian (or earlier) ancestor evolved a lung in its aquatic environment as a respiratory organ for the satisfaction of its needs in that environment. It evolved the lung because it lived in a deoxygenated environment, and used it for breathing while it was still a purely aquatic animal.

The analysis can be carried one step further back. It has been mentioned that tropical stagnant waters, besides lacking dissolved oxygen, contain a considerable concentration of carbon dioxide. Now the bloods of typical fresh-water and marine fish are far more sensitive than the bloods of terrestrial vertebrates to carbon dioxide, which greatly reduces the power of the blood to take up oxygen.[258] So great is this effect in many fish bloods that at carbon dioxide pressures below those found in stagnant tropical waters they will not combine fully with oxygen even at atmospheric pressure, i.e. in water fully saturated with oxygen. Such a blood in a fish living in a stagnant tropical water would clearly be entirely useless as a means of transporting oxygen, for, as we have seen, the oxygen content of these waters is far below saturation. Before it could live in such an environment, the fish must have evolved a blood far less sensitive to carbon dioxide than the bloods of most fishes, and, in fact, a blood much more like that of a terrestrial vertebrate so far as the carbon-dioxide effect is concerned.

Willmer [328] investigated the bloods of fresh-water fishes in British Guiana, and found that those living in stagnant waters have the expected carbon dioxide-insensitive blood (Fig. 55). In this they contrast with the fish of the rivers and to a less extent with those of the streams, which have bloods of the same type as those of normal fresh-water fishes, sensitive to carbon dioxide. This was to be expected, for in the rivers and streams the water is disturbed by currents; it contains little carbon dioxide and, relatively, much oxygen. On the other hand, the bloods of the swamp fishes were as insensitive to carbon dioxide as the bloods of the higher vertebrates are.

We may conclude that before the crossopterygian fish could live in a stagnant tropical swamp it must have evolved a blood insensitive to carbon dioxide. Here another consideration enters the argument. In an internal organ of aerial respiration there is always a considerable concentration of carbon dioxide. This is inevitable since carbon dioxide is leaving the respiratory epithelium, and exchange between the contained air and that outside the body is never complete. In our own lung the exchange is about 70 per cent., and the carbon-dioxide content of the alveolar air is about 7 per cent.; fish "lungs" may contain 3 per cent. of carbon dioxide. Thus, in an internal air-breathing organ the blood takes up oxygen from a medium containing as high a pressure of carbon dioxide as the water of a tropical stagnant swamp, and a blood sensitive to carbon dioxide would be as ineffective in a lung as in the swamp. An insensitive blood is as essential to the evolution of an internal air-breathing organ as it is to invasion of stagnant tropical waters.

We may picture the evolution of aerial respiration in the ancestral terrestrial vertebrate thus.[36] The fish breathing by gills had to evolve a blood insensitive to carbon dioxide before

10*

it could live in tropical stagnant waters. This would be the
first step in the evolution, for the pressures of carbon dioxide
at which typical fish bloods are ineffective occur in water in

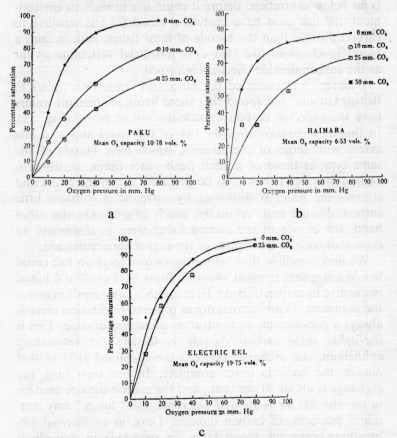

Figure 55. Dissociation curves of river, stream and swamp fishes
from Guiana in the absence and presence of carbon dioxide.
a—A river fish, *Myleus setiger*, paku; b—a stream fish, *Hoplias
malabaricus*, haimara; c—a swamp fish which breathes air,
Electrophorus electricus, electric eel. (After Wilmer)

which the condition of stagnancy is not so extreme as to result
in great shortage of oxygen. With such a blood it could have
lived in the less swampy waters, and could approach those of
more extreme conditions. Having evolved a blood of this type,

the evolution of a lung would follow, in adaptation to the conditions in the water during periods of drought when the water would become deoxygenated. With a lung it could invade even the most swampy waters. All this occurred in fish which were still purely aquatic animals and before they had started on any course of evolution towards leaving the water and taking on amphibian life. But the possession of a lung would have been of great value when the fish was forced to live inactively in mud, as it might often have to do to survive periods of drought when its swamp dried. From such æstivation the passage to an active mud-living life, in fact to amphibian life, is direct.

At each stage of this evolution we find pre-adaptation. An insensitive blood is pre-adaptive for the evolution of a lung, and a lung for mud-living life. At each stage characters evolved for one purpose in the earlier life are useful for another purpose in the later life. Throughout, there is a *chance* correlation between the characters evolved in the first environment and the characters it needs in the second environment. Here we seem to see most clearly the pre-adaptive correlation serving as a bridge which enables the animal to change its habits of life and to invade a new environment.

We have so far spoken of the pre-adaptive characters as evolved in direct, post-adaptive, adaptation to the needs of the animal's life before the change in habit, and in the examples we have considered there is evidence that they did arise in that way. It should, however, be asked whether there is any other way in which they might arise. It is sometimes suggested, by those who do not believe in chance correlation between the needs of the two environments as the general explanation of pre-adaptation, that the pre-adaptation is due to mutations that happen to be pre-adaptive to the changed life. It is supposed that these mutations arise by chance at the time when the animal needs to change its habits, and that the individuals that bear these mutations are those that take on the new life. This is the view supported by Goldschmidt.[142] His views of evolutionary change in general are unusual in that he believes that specific and higher differentiation is due to macro-mutation (and mainly to chromosomal re-arrangement) rather than to gene mutation. It would not be easy to maintain his views of pre-adaptation on the theory of evolution by micro-mutation to which we have been led in the previous chapters. If the evolution of structure is gradual, as it must be on our view, the pre-adaptive characters would be removed by selection during their evolution, unless they were of selective value in the original environment—and to suppose they were of selective value would be to assume the pre-adaptive correlation that we are hoping to interpret; the theory would not at all help us to interpret it. Only if the characters were non-adaptive and spread by drift, would their gradual evolution without selective advantage be possible. However, if, as Goldschmidt believes, these pre-adaptive characters arose by single macro-mutations at the time of the change in habit, these difficulties would not arise.

Goldschmidt calls animals bearing macro-mutations such as he believes may be a probable origin for pre-adaptations "hopeful monsters". Of them he says: "A Manx cat, with a hereditary concrescence of the tail vertebræ, or a comparable rat or mouse mutant, is just a monster. But a mutant of *Archæopteryx* producing the same monstrosity was a hopeful monster because the resulting fanlike arrangement of the tail feathers was a great improvement in the mechanics of flying. A fish undergoing a mutation which made for a distortion of the skull carrying both eyes to one side of the body is a monster. The same mutant in a much compressed form of fish living near the bottom of the sea produced a hopeful monster, as it enabled the species to take to the life upon the sandy bottom of the ocean, as exemplified by the flounders." ([142,] p. 490.)

It is not easy to accept this theory as a *general* explanation of pre-adaptation, even if we accept Goldschmidt's theory of evolution by macro-mutation. Here, again, the difficulties are much greater when we consider the larger changes of habit and structure. It is not unlikely that some small changes may result from chance mutation. It is, indeed, well known that mutations occur which alter within certain limits the range of conditions in which an animal is able to live. A clear example is given by the mutant race of *Daphnia longispina* investigated by Wood and Banta.[329] The normal form of this species thrives at 20 deg. C., and lives less successfully at 27 deg.; the mutant race cannot survive at 20 deg., but thrives at 27 deg. It is adapted to life in warmer conditions, and, if it arose when such conditions were available, would be pre-adaptive to them. Many other mutations similarly altering the viable range of conditions might be quoted. Many are known in *Drosophila*.

Such mutants might, perhaps, be called "hopeful monsters", though Goldschmidt seems to be thinking of much larger changes of structure or habit when he uses the term; he certainly does not wish to restrict his theory to small changes of habit. When large changes are considered, the theory meets many difficulties. An obvious difficulty is that it assumes that a mutant appropriate to the new life would be available at the time and place at which it was needed. This would very rarely be so. It is true that large changes of habit are rare, and, presumably, successful only on exceptional occasions. It may perhaps be maintained that it is on these rare occasions that the mutant is available. This might be accepted if it could be shown that a "hopeful monster" appropriate to a large change is *ever* likely to appear. But these large changes require reorganisation in many parts of the body, if the animal is to compete successfully in the new way of life. We have seen, for instance, how various were the changes required in the horses when they took to grazing. It is impossible to imagine that a chance mutation would combine all the alterations needed. By an appropriate mutation an animal might gain some advantage towards adaptation to a new way of life. A mutation giving greater height to the crown of the teeth would make grazing easier for a brachyodont horse, but that alone would not make it capable of efficient life on grassy plains. Merely because its teeth enabled it to graze, it would not necessarily be able to compete successfully with other members of the fauna of the plains; many other changes would be necessary before it would have much chance of doing so.

There is still another objection to this theory of the origin of these changes by macro-mutation. Large mutations are mostly recessive at their first appearance (p. 217) and the chance of a recessive mutation being expressed in the phenotype soon after its appearance is, in a random-breeding population, almost infinitesimal (p. 180). Unless the mutation were advantageous in the original environment, it would not be spread by selection, though it might be retained as a rare recessive and expressed only on the excessively rare occasions on which it occurred as a homozygote. The chance that such a homozygote would be available when it was needed would be so small as to be negligible. There is one way by which these difficulties could be avoided (p. 218). This is by close inbreeding in the original environment (p. 219); if that was usual, there would be a very much greater chance of the mutation being expressed as a homozygote. It is true that some degree of close inbreeding probably occurs in many natural populations (p. 219), and it is possible that with close inbreeding a suitable macro-mutation might be expressed when it was needed.

However this may be, on the evidence taken as a whole, it is impossible to accept Goldschmidt's theory as a *general* explanation of pre-adaptation. Where change of habit is small, and does not require any considerable reorganisation of many parts of the body, it might result from a single mutation, and probably sometimes does. It is very difficult to believe that a macro-mutation could give rise to any large change that requires widespread reorganisation.

If we cannot accept chance macro-mutations as the general origin of pre-adaptation, only one explanation remains open. These characters must have been evolved in adaptation to the conditions to which the animal was exposed before the change in its habits and habitat—their origin was by post-adaptation in the original environment. This implies that there must be real but chance correlation between the organs required to satisfy the animal's needs in the two environments.

Simpson ([275,] p. 92) has expressed diagrammatically (Fig. 56) the course of evolution from browsing to grazing in the horses in a manner that makes clear the part that pre-adaptation has played in it. He is here using a form of diagram originally suggested by Wright.[333] In this diagram differences in adaptation are represented as a two-dimensional extension in the plane of the paper. It is necessary to realise this, and not to interpret the diagram as in any sense a geographical map; points on it represent not localities but adaptational states. One point will represent browsing adaptation and another grazing, and the distances between these points is a measure of the differences in adaptive characters between the animals occupying the points, i.e. the differences between browsing and grazing adaptation. Elevation above the plane is shown by the contours and represents selection towards the adaptive states, i.e. towards the points of the diagram. The force of selection is expressed by the gradients towards the points, i.e. by the closeness of the contours. Any adaptive state, such as those of browsing and grazing, will therefore be represented by a peak or hillock above the plane, the slope towards the peak being steeper the stronger the selection towards it.

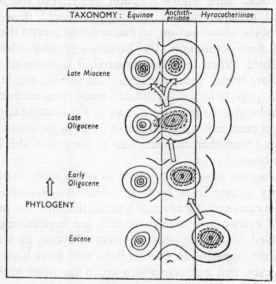

Figure 56. Diagram of the evolution of the grazing horses.
(After Simpson)

At the beginning of the evolutionary history of the horses, in the Eocene, there were two distinct peaks, those of browsing (*B*) and grazing (*G*) habit. Only the browsing peak was occupied by the early horses. The population of these horses would, owing to the variation natural to all animal populations, vary around this peak. The range of this variation is represented by the shaded area. During the Oligocene this peak came nearer to the grazing peak by the evolution of characters that were also adaptational to the grazing peak—the characters that were later to be pre-adaptive to the change of habit—heightening of the crown of the teeth, reduction of the digits, elongation of the face, etc. (p. 270). By the late Oligocene this movement resulted in the two peaks overlapping, i.e. they became connected by a saddle. The slopes on the saddle side of the browsing peak being less steep than those on other sides, i.e. the force of selection being weaker on that side, the population varied further in this direction than in others, and sooner or later extended on to the saddle. Any individual that varied so much from the browsing peak as to pass the lowest point of the saddle would come under selection away from the browsing peak and towards that of grazing. It would then become adapted in the new direction, so that it would ascend the grazing peak. A new population, the Equinæ—grazing horses—had been evolved. When this had occurred, it is probable that the intermediate forms, those occupying the saddle, would die out as the two populations differentiated away from each other and ceased to be able to interbreed, and as the intermediate forms themselves became adapted to one or other of the peaks. Browsing horses (Anchitheriinæ) persisted to the end of the Tertiary, but then became extinct.

This diagram must not be taken as doing more than stating the theory clearly in a form in which its assumptions are evident. It does nothing towards a proof that this was the actual course of events, and indeed its data are hypothetical rather than proved fact. It suggests a course of events by which the change from browsing to grazing habit may have been evolved in the horses, and a course which seems the most probable in the light of the facts discussed in this chapter. It is a course that requires approximation of the adaptational needs of the two modes of life, and thus pre-adaptation in the population before the change. That the two peaks of browsing and grazing should come close together is a necessary preliminary to the change.

In general summary of our discussion of pre-adaptation, we may conclude that changes in animals from one way of life to another very often depend, if they are to be successful, on pre-adaptive correlation between the evolved characters of the animal and the new needs it meets after the change. When the change is no more, or little more, than altered behaviour and does not require any large structural modifications, as in the example of an altered feeding habit such as that of the apple capsid or the potato-beetle, the change may happen rapidly and often, so it seems, easily. Animal behaviour is conservative but changes in it do occasionally occur, and when they occur they seem to be sudden. Even in these small changes of habit, the success of the animal in its new life is the result of pre-adaptation in the characters it possesses before the change. Always, the animal will adapt after the change, by post-adaptation, to the new conditions to which it is then exposed.

Large changes of habit and habitats are relatively rare and it is probable that their evolution is only occasionally successful. For several reasons it is difficult to believe that changes that require complicated re-organisation of structure are often, if ever, due to the appearance by chance mutation of the characters needed in the new life—"hopeful monsters"—but some smaller changes that do not require much general re-organisation may originate thus. Success in the change depends on the possession of pre-adaptive characters, and if these are not due to chance mutation they can only have been evolved in adaptation to the conditions of the animal's life before the change. This means that characters evolved in satisfaction of the needs of the animal's previous life are suitable for the different needs of its life after the change. That can only be due to chance correlation, which will occur only rarely in the history of the species. Yet we have evidence that it was present in some examples of large changes of habit, and especially in some of which we know most. Where the re-organisation is very large, as in the migration of vertebrates from aquatic to terrestrial life, it must have taken place in many steps. We have, in at least one instance, the evolution of aerial respiration, evidence of pre-adaptive correlation at more than one of the steps. That the correlation should occur repeatedly will be still rarer, but a chance correlation such as this is to be expected now and again in the long stretches of palæontological time. Its rareness is indeed in its favour as an interpretation of the means by which these large changes of habit are evolved, for it accounts for their rarity, which would otherwise be difficult to understand. Without pre-adaptation of this kind, large changes of habit must always be very difficult. Animals in an environment that is strange to them, however they may have been forced into it— by pressure of numbers, by destruction of their old environment, or by some other cause—will not in general immediately alter their behaviour to suit the new conditions. Almost always they will attempt to follow their old life in the new conditions. In rare cases changes of habit and behaviour may take place, but even if this occurs, the animals will not be adapted to the new conditions, and in competition with the native fauna they will inevitably die out. The new environment might be only partially filled before the animals invaded it, but even so it is unlikely that the strange species would survive. Some bridge seems to be required that will make transference from one way of life to another easier, and this is provided by pre-adaptation in the characters evolved before the change.

CHAPTER IX

EVOLUTIONARY TRENDS

THE fact that much of evolution is directional, that it consists of trends of change continuing in the same direction for long periods, has already been mentioned (p. 48). We have also noted (p. 182) that accepted genetic theory gives a basis for some directional element in evolution. Here we have to ask whether this character of the genetic background will account for all the directional trends to be found in evolution; if not, whether our general views of the evolutionary process offer any other explanation; and, if all such explanations fail, whether we must conclude that there are inherent tendencies in animals to evolve in certain directions and not in others, and to continue these "straight-line" courses of evolution for long periods independently of selection. This last proposition is the postulate of the theory of *orthogenesis*, a term that has been used in many senses but is best restricted to this meaning. An orthogenetic interpretation of evolution is often thought to be inconsistent with a naturalistic theory; it is thought to have mystical implications, to imply some control outside the phenomena of nature to direct the course of evolution. This is not necessarily so. A tendency to evolve continuously in certain directions, even if caused by inherent characters of the animal and not due to interaction with the environment, might well result from some purely material property either of the genetic mechanism or of some other part of the animal's organisation. Indeed, we already know one such character, the fact that some forms of mutation—macro-mutations—are to some extent restricted in direction, and this may very possibly also be true of the origin of new pattern in aristogenesis. Any restriction of the direction of hereditary change must control the direction of evolution to some extent, and this control is true orthogenesis in the sense in which we have defined the term. There may be other causes of orthogenesis, at present undefined but not necessarily undefinable or any less material than other properties of the organism. We must ask how far the facts of evolution require control of its direction by characters such as these, and how far they are intelligible without it. We need not concern ourselves with the possibility of control by non-material interference.

There are some other subjects that are naturally associated with that of evolutionary trends, and come up for discussion here. One is the interpretation of characters that appear to us disadvantageous to the life of the organism, usually because they have been evolved beyond the point at which they cease to be valuable. Such characters certainly occur, or seem to occur, as, for instance, the excessive size of the horns of the elk. Can these characters be over-evolved by the normal processes of evolution, in spite of selective disadvantage? A second subject is the question whether evolutionary lines pass through changes comparable to those of the individual life-history. In particular, can we speak of a line as being in a condition of senility, when it is no longer capable of active evolution and tends to degenerate? A third subject is the belief, widely held, that evolution is irreversible. This is a deduction from the facts of evolution. We must ask how far it is true, and, if true, why it should be so.

Let us first examine some typical examples of evolutionary trends, and see how far they are directly explicable on our general theory of evolution. We may take as a typical example of evolution in which these trends occur the history of the horses, which we have already discussed from other points of view. Simpson ([275], pp. 159 ff.) makes a list of several characters in which the structure of horses changed in the same direction for long periods. These trends are:

1. General increase of the size of the body (p. 35). This trend is present in most lines but not in all. In a few lines (*Nannippus, Archæohippus*) the trend is in the opposite direction.

2. Skull proportions, see p. 36.

3. Brain. A trend towards improved organisation of the brain occurred between the Eocene and the Oligocene.

4. Limb proportions. Gradual elongation of the distal segments.

5. Foot mechanism. A trend towards improvement for running.

6. Reduction of the outer digits of the feet.

7. Molarisation of the premolars. This was complete in the Oligocene.

8. Hypsodonty and cement. There were here true trends, but a sudden alteration in the trend towards hypsodonty occurred in the Oligocene (p. 41).

9. Molar pattern. A trend towards lophodonty and complication of the pattern was general, but it was variable in speed and in the details of the changes.

We will first take the trend towards increase in body size, one of the most definite of these trends, and discuss its course and the nature of its progress.

The trend was widespread and extended over long periods. Its speed was variable. It was always a gradual and continuous change, and was always accompanied by changes in other characters.

If we are to attribute this trend to the action of natural selection, we should be able to find reasons why increased size is of advantage to the animal. There is no difficulty in doing this. It should be noted that this trend is a feature chiefly of land animals (p. 36). Defence against enemies and escape from them, choice of suitable habitats, physiological regulation, as in maintenance of the body temperature, will all be easier for the larger animal. There may be other advantages. Haldane (154, p. 124) suggests one that may be valuable in many mammals, though the advantage is not to the adult. In any mammal that gives birth to multiple litters, the embryos will compete in the uterus and the advantage is likely to go to the larger embryo, which will be the one with the fastest growth-rate. The capacity for rapid growth is likely to persist through the life-history,[41] and large size in the adult will result from selection for this character in the embryo. We do not know whether early horses gave birth to more than one young at a time; most primitive mammals do, and it is probable that at some stage horses did. If so, this advantage may have been effective in their evolution. However this may be, there is no difficulty in attributing selective advantage to larger size—so long, as we shall see immediately, as the size does not exceed a maximum limit.

We may next ask in what way we should expect such a mammalian group as the horses to respond in normal evolution to the need for increased size.

First, we may be sure that the change in size would be gradual. The most conclusive reason for this is not that the supply of mutation may be insufficient for a sudden change. That is very probably true (p. 212); micro-mutations may be numerous enough to allow change in any direction, but not necessarily at any speed. A more impressive reason is that any sudden and large change in size is certain to be non-adaptive, and selection will prevent the survival of any animal in which it occurs. Altered size requires change in almost every other feature of the animal's organisation, if viability is to be maintained (p. 36). The animal can react phenotypically, and at once, to small changes; it will so react and remain fully viable. It cannot react to sudden and large changes. Correlated genetic change cannot be rapid.

Though the change in size will necessarily be gradual, it may perhaps be surprising that it should be so slow as to extend over millions of generations, as in fact it did in the horses— we know that some evolutionary changes may be much more rapid (ch. XI). But this is not enough reason to make us demand some other cause than selection as the basis of the change. Its slowness may be due, probably among other causes, to the complexity of the correlation required to maintain viability.

Secondly, we should not expect the trend to be equally marked and rapid in all the evolutionary lines of the group. Each line will be adapted in detail to its own manner of life, and the selective advantage of increased size will vary among the lines. It is not surprising even to find that some lines show the trend reversed, size decreasing in them. This may occur if the life of these horses differed in important features from that usual in the group as a whole.

A third consideration follows from the fact that increase of size brings with it other effects besides the advantages we have considered. For instance, the large animal must be more heavily built and relatively less rapid in locomotion (p. 36). This and other disadvantages will set a limit to the profitable increase in size. At some point the advantages and disadvantages will be balanced, and further increase will have no selective advantage. We may expect that, though the animal may grow larger for long periods of evolution, a time will come when the increase slows down and finally stops. In fact, in the horses, the growth in size was much slower in the later stages of the evolution than in the earlier. This is not the only reason why trends should cease to operate. Some, such as the molarisation of the premolars in the horses, may cease because they have become complete.

In all these ways the palæontological facts fit very well with what we should expect to find on the assumption that the trend in body size is due to long-continued selection, and to this alone. There seems no reason to ask for any other cause.

Selection continuing in the same direction for long periods has been called *orthoselection*.

Most of the other trends in the evolution of the horses can be accounted for without demanding any orthogenetic tendencies in the animals. Some of these trends, e.g. the changes in the proportions of the skull (p. 37), are correlated allometrically with body size, and will follow increase in size without any change in the genotype beyond that needed for the size-increase. These may be called secondary trends. Others, not so correlated with size, are primary, but most of them were clearly advantageous and, so far as we can see, the results of orthoselection.

There are other arguments against an orthogenetic interpretation of trends such as these. Some trends, for instance that towards larger size, are widespread; increase of size during evolution is to be found not only in many groups of mammals but also in reptiles. It is indeed very general in the terrestrial vertebrates, though certainly not universal. If it is due to an inherent tendency unrelated to the conditions of the environment, the tendency must be a character of many distantly related animals in the higher vertebrate groups. Yet we should have to suppose it absent, for no apparent reason, in numerous groups that did not become larger but even decreased in size. In another way the evolutionary distribution of these trends is against their being orthogenetic. If they were due to inherent tendencies, we should not expect their occurrence to show correlation with the type of evolution that the animal was

undergoing. But we find that these trends are much more prevalent in animals evolving actively in adaptive radiation (when
they are adapting always more closely to the environmental
conditions) than in those evolving in other ways ([275,] p. 153).
Indeed, the trends are almost restricted to that type of evolution. This alone would show that their origin is in some way
related to adaptive differentiation in the animals, i.e. to the
animal's reaction to environmental conditions.

Trends of the same kind as those in the horses may be found
in almost every group of animals in adaptive radiation. We
may take one other well-investigated example, the increase of
coiling of the shell in oysters that gave rise to the form known
as *Gryphœa* (p. 27). It has already been suggested that the
adaptational reason for the trend was the need to raise the
body above the surface of the soft mud on which the animal
lived.

The increase in the coiling has been investigated [308] in samples
large enough to bring out another of its characters. The progress can be measured by the angle through which the shell
twists spirally (Fig. 10, p. 29). In one series it was found that
the angle increased from a range of 10–130 deg. in the earliest
forms to 270–540 deg. in the latest. At each level there was overlap with the condition at higher and lower levels (p. 29), but
the change in the mean of the population was continuous. In
this character as in so many others the trends behave exactly like
adaptive changes in general (p. 30). The population evolved as a
whole, its means form altering continuously and directionally.

So far we have found little difficulty in attributing the
directional characters of the trends to orthoselection. There
are some features in them that are less easily accounted for on
these lines.

First, there is the very detailed parallelism that is often found
in trends in many distinct lines within a single group of animals.
We found good examples of this in the pads of tree-frogs
(pp. 278–9), as well as in increase of size, and in the coiling
of *Gryphœa*. Osborn ([234,] p. 816) says of the results of his
studies of the titanotheres: "One of the most significant
discoveries made concerning the titanotheres is that their horn
rudiments arise long after the phyla * have been separated

---

* This term is here used for any distinct evolutionary line.

from one another, earlier in some phyla, later in others, but always on substantially the same part of the skull. This is probably true in general of the horns in mammalian families." The horns arise in almost exactly the same way and at the same place on the head in the various lines, but independently in each line and at different stages of the evolution.

This parallelism, which is present in very many other trends, has often been thought to be evidence for some orthogenetic interpretation of the trends, and to require some evolutionary principle not included in the theory we have developed. The facts may require orthogenesis as we have defined it, but there seems no need for any new principle; the facts may probably be explained on the basis of restricted mutation. Related animals leading similar lives are likely to have similar adaptational needs, and, since their genotypes will be related, the mutations that occur in them may be expected to be similar. There is no doubt that restriction of mutation causes some restriction of change of structure in animals. Man has been able to produce many variations of form in his domestic animals, but by no means every conceivable form. We have no reason to suppose that the changes that can be evolved in natural evolution are any less restricted, and, if they are restricted, those that occur in related animals are likely to be similar.

Nevertheless, it may seem something of a strain on our credulity to believe that the detailed parallelism that is found in many lines of such a group as the titanotheres is entirely due to similarity of adaptational need and restricted supply of heredity change. Some further points may be mentioned. In some trends the difficulty does not arise, for the changes that were evolved were the only changes that could satisfy the adaptational need. This is certainly true of the trend in body size, and may also be true of the coiling of the shell in *Gryphæa*, for with a soft substratum, such as that on which this mollusc is believed to have lived, it is difficult to suggest any adaptation except the coiling that would raise the body above the surface of the mud—a stalk or similar device would have been inefficient in the soft mud. If there is only one solution of an adaptational need, the animal is bound to take that solution or fail to satisfy the need; parallelism in the adaptations is inevitable.

We must also remember that animals so distantly related

that it is difficult to believe them to have the same orthogenetic tendencies sometimes show very detailed parallel evolution. A classical example of this is the reduction of the outer digits in the horses (Perissodactyla) and the Litopterna, a group of

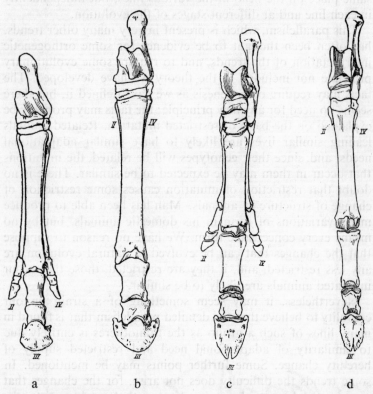

Figure 57. Left pes in three-toed and single-toed horses (Perisso-dactyla) and Litopterna. a—Three-toed horse (*Protohippus*); b—single-toed horse (*Equus*); c—three-toed litopternan (*Diadia-phorus*); d—single-toed litopternan (*Thoatherium*). (After Scott)

South American ungulates (Notoungulata). These groups were separate from an early division of the mammalian stock in the middle Palæocene. Reduction of the digits occurred in the horses between the Eocene and the Pliocene, and in the Litopterna in the Miocene and Pliocene. The close parallelism in the two groups is shown in Fig. 57. If distantly related animals such as these can show this detailed parallelism in evolution, why should not the closely related lines of a single group?

Lastly, our ignorance (p. 94) of the mode of origin of aristogenes of new pattern must be mentioned again. We know nothing of the mode of origin of such a character as the horns of the titanotheres though we can to some extent explain their development after they have originated. There may be restriction here, only certain characters of this kind being able to arise in an animal's body. This—like restriction of the supply of mutation —would be a true orthogenetic tendency, for it would be a tendency inherent in the animal and resulting in evolution in certain directions but not others. But, even if it is real, we have no reason to believe that it is not a material property of the animal's organisation, just as are the many other properties which we are able to define.

There are other features of the evolutionary trends that have been thought to make their origin by selection difficult to credit. One is that we are often unable to find the adaptational reasons for them. Thus Watson [321] in studying the early Amphibia found two primary trends in many lines, one towards reduction in the height of the skull and the other towards reduction of cartilage bones. He was unable to find an adaptive reason for either of these trends. Other examples could be given. But it may be objected to the use of such conclusions as evidence for orthogenesis that we are largely ignorant of the natural history in these palæontological examples, and that correlation of the characters that show the trends with other, possibly adaptive, characters is not excluded. The evidence does not seem strong enough to serve as a basis for a theory of orthogenesis.

It is clear that for reliable evidence of orthogenesis (whether due to restricted mutation or some other cause) we need to find trends in characters that can be accepted as non-adaptive. For, first, the evolution of non-adaptive characters cannot be controlled by selection, since they have no selective value. We can therefore exclude orthoselection as the cause of their evolution. Secondly, the process that causes the evolution of these characters—drift (pp. 180, 213)—depends on chance for fixation of a gene, and therefore should not lead to fixation of the same gene in several distinct lines. If we can show that there is real parallelism of these characters in separate lines, this can only be due to some orthogenetic tendency, whether it is caused by restricted mutation or otherwise.

The characters that most clearly appear to be non-adaptive are many of the small specific and subspecific differences of micro-evolution. Most observers believe that very many of these characters have no adaptive value (p. 47), and it is difficult to believe that they are all correlated with underlying adaptive characters (p. 213).

In micro-evolution parallel variation is almost everywhere to be found (cf. [314]). Of many cases that have been recorded, one described by Rubtzov [260] in grassshoppers may be taken as an example. He found similar varieties of colour pattern and other characters in several related species. If the range of variation in one species was defined, that in others could be predicted with considerable assurance. This is not unusual in the micro-evolution of insects. Balfour Browne [13] gives a closely investigated example of parallel variation in the structure of the proventriculus of the Coleoptera, and another [12] in the wing-venation. We must conclude that there is here real orthogenesis, but there is no reason to think that it is due to any other cause than identical mutation in related evolving lines.

A palæontological example of micro-evolution that is often thought to require orthogenesis is that of the Devonian brachiopods studied by Fenton.[98] In following evolutionary lines through long series of strata, Fenton found trends in many characters besides those in the form of the shell that we have discussed earlier (p. 23). The characters of interest to us here are the small details of the sculpture of the surface of the shell. In many lines this sculpturing showed parallel changes in the course of the evolution.

The earliest form of the sculpture consisted of straight ridges obliquely radiating from the grooves of the shell (Fig. 58, a). These ridges varied in strength and straightness in different lines, but were always arranged in more or less the same way. As the evolution proceeded, the regularity of the arrangement of the ridges broke down, and the course of the changes was similar in many lines. The ridges became divided into short lengths much less regularly arranged (b), and these subdivisions of the ridges swelled in some places to form pustules. In some

a

b   c

Figure 58. Sculpturing of the shell in brachiopods. a—The primitive type; b—the later, modified type; c—an example in which the sculpture is of the primitive type on the earlier-formed (inner) part of the shell, and of the later type nearer the edge. (After Fenton)

specimens (c) the more primitive ornamentation was present on the parts of the shell formed in the young animal, and the modified type on the later-formed parts.

There can hardly be any doubt that this minute sculpturing was non-adaptive—we cannot imagine how its details can have seriously affected the viability of the animal, and there is no evidence that its characters were correlated with other, adaptive, characters. It would seem at first sight that we have here excellent evidence of parallelism in the non-adaptive characters of micro-evolution. But there is another feature of the evolution to be considered. Soon after the period of the strata that Fenton examined, this brachiopod fauna died out, and shortly before this the animals showed clear symptoms of degeneration—in malformations of the shell and slowness in repair of injuries. The later forms of the ornamentation also suggest degenerative changes—in their loss of regularity in the arrangement of their details. May not this course of modification in the details of the ornamentation be due to the progress of some degenerative process in a senescent group shortly before its extinction, rather than to normal micro-evolution?

To answer this question we must consider what we mean by degeneration and senescence in an evolutionary line, and how far they are likely to be real. It has often been suggested that evolving groups of animals undergo changes comparable to those of the individual life-history, that a group that has recently separated from a parent group will be "youthful" and evolve actively; that it then passes through an "adult" stage, when its evolution is still active though perhaps less so than in the first stage; and that it finally becomes "senescent", when it is no longer able to evolve new adaptations and may show degeneration.

Many groups have been thought to show this cycle of change.[21] A classical example, which was also one of the earliest to be investigated, is that of the ammonites of palæozoic and secondary times. Hyatt [179, 180] thought that he could recognise in their evolution a cycle from "youthful" straight forms in the Devonian through the tightly coiled, typical ammonites of the Lias to many "degenerate" forms, some of them again uncoiled, in the Cretaceous. He found a similar cycle in the sutures—the septa that separate the air-chambers of the shell. These were straight and simple in the earliest forms, became elaborately twisted in many of the "adult" forms, and were often again simplified in the final "degenerate" forms. His conclusions have not been accepted by most of the more recent authors. Their factual basis has been questioned by Spath,[278] who maintains that all Hyatt's types were present throughout large parts of the evolution, and that there was no clear succession from one to another. Simpson ([275,] pp. 214 ff.) concludes that there is no real evidence of a racial life-history, but that there is often an outburst of variation towards the end of the evolutionary history of a group and that ill-adapted and simplified forms may appear then. In fact, the reality of any evolutionary cycle comparable to the individual life-history is discredited, or at least regarded as unproved, by the majority of contemporary biologists.

There is, however, no doubt that animals may become unhealthy and show signs of degeneration when they are living in an unfavourable environment to which they are unable to adapt completely. In such conditions, even the whole structural organisation of the body may break down, and the body dedifferentiate to a formless mass of cells. These phenomena are examples of the wider principle that the organisation of the body is determined not solely by its hereditary characters, but by a balance between their effects and those of the environmental conditions.[37] Among reactions of this type degenerative changes in animals living in unfavourable conditions certainly have a place.

The conditions in which a group is living shortly before its extinction are likely to be unfavourable, for otherwise there would be no reason for the extinction. Degenerative forms are likely to appear at that time.

On these grounds it seems possible that the changes in the ornamentation of the shells of Fenton's brachiopods were the result of a gradual breakdown of the animals' organisation in an unfavourable environment. If this were so, the changes would not be evolutionary in any real sense; they would be phenotypic modifications of the body form. This view is to some extent supported by the observation that the less degenerate forms of ornamentation sometimes occur on the younger parts of a shell, the older parts of which show degenerate

ornamentation (Fig. 58, c); the younger animal is likely to be
the more healthy.

Fenton's brachiopods have been discussed in some detail
because they are often thought to give conclusive evidence of
orthogenetic evolution in non-adaptive characters. We must
conclude that their evidence is not as conclusive as it appears
at first sight. But, whatever the decision in this case, there can
be no doubt that enough other evidence is available to show
that parallel evolution is common in the non-adaptive characters
of micro-evolution. This parallelism can only be due to

Figure 59. The horns of the Irish elk, *Cervus megaceras*.

orthogenetic tendencies, but these tendencies require no other
explanation than that of parallel mutation in related lines.

There is in palæontology and in living animals one other
class of phenomena that has been thought to imply orthogenesis
of a kind that cannot be due to orthoselection or restricted
mutation. This is the occurrence in animals of characters that
appear to us disadvantageous to the animal's life. Most of these
characters might be useful at a smaller size, but they seem to
become "over-developed" and to reach a size so great that
they must be disadvantageous, and even dangerous to the life
of the animal. The antlers of the Irish elk provide a very well-
known example (Fig. 59). Antlers are typical secondary sexual
characters; they are used in sexual combat, and at a normal
size they are so familiar that their occurrence is not a cause of
surprise. But the enormous size of the antlers of the elk makes
it difficult to believe that they were evolved by the processes of

natural selection. At this size they must have interfered seriously with the activity of the animal, and therefore, one would have thought, have been disadvantageous and removed by selection. Similarly, in *Gryphœa* the coiling of the shell may have been useful in its earlier stages, since it raised the body above the surface of the mud, but in the most coiled forms the coiling had reached a stage at which it prevented the valves from opening by more than a very small angle. Any further coiling must have resulted in the death of the animal, and it would seem that the coiling that does occur must have restricted the animal's feeding. In fact, these highly coiled lines did not evolve further. And, again, it has often been suggested that increase in body-size has sometimes been carried beyond the point at which it ceased to be advantageous. The great size of some of the secondary reptiles has been thought to have been a cause of their extinction.

Many characters in living animals that seem fantastically over-developed fall into the same category. As Simpson ([275], ch. V) says, the enormous development of secondary sexual characters in birds, such as the plumage of the birds of paradise or the tail of the peacock, and of excrescences, such as the horns of some beetles or the teeth of the babirussa, is so great that it is hard to believe that they are not disadvantageous to the animals.

In all these cases the easiest explanation would be that there is in evolution a "momentum" ([275], p. 150), by which development of a character that has been evolved for some useful purpose may be carried beyond the optimum, with the result that the character becomes over-developed and disadvantageous. Such a momentum would clearly be orthogenetic. This would be an easy explanation, but it cannot be accepted unless it can be shown that overstepping of the optimum is impossible in evolution governed by the normal processes of natural selection. If this is not possible, it would certainly seem that the facts require some orthogenetic tendency which forces evolution to continue by its momentum after selection in favour of a character has ceased or been reversed.

In considering the possibility of over-development in normal evolution, we must first recall that mathematical analysis has shown that in certain circumstances selection may result in a character overstepping the optimum development (p. 182). No orthogenetic principle is needed for this; the overstepping is caused by the normal processes of selection working on the accepted genetic basis. But it is hardly possible that this is the whole cause of these "over-developed" characters. They persist for long periods of evolution, and if they were really disadvantageous we should expect them to be soon removed by spread of new mutation. The effect may have played some part in their origin; it could not cause them to be permanent.

There are several other points to be noted here:

1. As Simpson remarks ([275], p. 214), we cannot justifiably assume that a character is highly disadvantageous because it seems to us fantastic. The fantastic characters of living animals, if they are disadvantageous, are certainly not so much so as to cause the extinction of the animals. In fact, these organs have their uses in the lives of the animals, and our surprise at their extreme development is largely due to lack of realisation of their importance to the animals. We take too narrow a view of animal natural history. We are apt to think that conflict with other animals for food is always the dominant influence in controlling the life of animals, but continuance of a species demands more than this. One other need is certainty of reproduction, and recent study of animal behaviour has shown the importance of secondary sexual characters, which many of these fantastic characters are, in ensuring reproduction— in sexual displays, combat, etc. (pp. 123–5). In some of its activities the animal might be more efficient if these characters were simpler. Unless we know all the details of the animal's natural history, we cannot say that the species would necessarily be more likely to survive without these organs, and therefore that they have negative selective value.

We must not, then, be too ready to assume that an organ in a fossil animal that appears over-developed was disadvantageous, and certainly not that it was so highly disadvantageous as to endanger the survival of the animal. Nevertheless, it is at least possible, and in many cases it may seem likely, that these organs were over-developed for their immediate functions; and the question remains whether development of an organ beyond its selective optimum is possible in evolution under the action of selection and without orthogenesis.

2. We may understand the evolution of these organs beyond

the point at which their selective value ceases without calling in any orthogenetic process if the development of the organ is correlated with that of another, advantageous character. There is good evidence of correlation of this kind in the examples of the antlers of the elk and the horns of beetles; both these characters have positive allometric correlation with body size ([176,] pp. 42, 54). Increase of body size—up to a limit (p. 294)—has positive selective value, and relative increase in the sizes of the organs will go with larger body size.

In these circumstances we should expect, so long as the correlation cannot be broken, that selection would establish a balance between the advantages and disadvantages of the two characters considered together. At the position of balance, which would be the selective optimum, the advantageous character would be less developed than would give its optimum if it had been evolving in isolation, but the correlated character would be evolved beyond its own optimum; it would be "overdeveloped". We should observe an apparent "momentum" effect in the evolution of the latter character.

This has probably been the cause of over-development in many other seemingly fantastic characters besides the elk's antlers and the horns of beetles. It can be used to explain the origin of most of these organs. But probably not all. It will not easily explain the excessive size of the secondary reptiles.

3. Simpson ([275,] p. 174) suggests two other ways in which over-developed organs might be evolved.

1. If mutation pressure (p. 177) towards over-development is present, and continues after the organ has reached its optimum under selection, development of the organ will continue beyond the optimum. This effect would be greater if, as is likely, selection had given rise to a high mutation rate while the character was evolving. Mutation rates are, however, small (p. 97) and it seems unlikely that the optimum would be largely overstepped. Presumably, selection would soon act to bring the organ back to the optimum, if the variability of the stock allowed it; the over-developed condition would be temporary.

2. If a change in environmental conditions occurs, an organ that has evolved to the optimum under the earlier conditions may be in an over-developed state after the change. It was probably too rapid a change of conditions that caused the

extinction of the large reptiles at the end of the secondary epoch.* The sizes of the larger of these animals may not have been excessive for amphibian life, and yet may have been the cause of their extinction after a change of conditions to which they were not able to react with sufficient speed. Here, again, selection should soon bring the organ back to the new optimum.

These three possible causes of the over-development of an organ are illustrated diagrammatically in Fig. 60. Only the first of these causes can account for permanent over-development. We may, however, conclude that these over-developed organs may be sufficiently explained on the theory of evolution by natural selection, and that recourse to orthogenesis is not necessary.

The supposed irreversibility of evolution may be considered here, for, if it is in general true, it implies that evolutionary trends, being irreversible, cannot be produced by selection, which can certainly act in both directions. Belief in the irreversibility of evolution is based on the work of Dollo,[89] who stated his conclusions in what is known as Dollo's Law. But this "law" is often mis-stated. It is often supposed that Dollo maintained that all evolution is irreversible. That would be clearly untrue; there is no doubt that organs that have been evolved may be later lost. This occurs in evolution of every type, perhaps nowhere more obviously than in parasitic adaptation; in very many parasites organs adapted to the needs of a free-living life may be lost. As clear an example as any is given by the parasitic copepods, which are certainly derived from free-living Crustacea with the typical crustacean organisation. In many of the parasitic forms the body is reduced to an almost formless sac in which only the genital organs and the organs for attachment to the host are fully developed.[270] Many organs required for free life are lost.

Dollo did not maintain that all evolution is irreversible. His conclusion was that the *loss* of an organ in evolution is irreversible, that an organ that has been lost will not be evolved a second time in the same form. Another organ of similar function may be evolved in place of the lost organ, if the need arises again, but it will not be identical with the lost organ.

* But see Swinton [298] for other views.

This is a much more restricted statement. The subject has been often discussed since Dollo's time.[1, 145, 219, 224, 230]

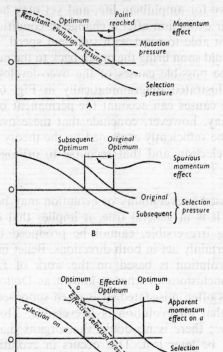

Figure 60. Three possible causes of over-development of an organ. Abscissæ, measurement of an evolutionary character of the organ, e.g. its size. Ordinates, tendency for the character to change; *o*, line of equilibrium, at which there is no tendency to change. A—mutation pressure added to selection pressure raises the equilibrium point of the character beyond the measure given by selection alone. B—a reduction of selection pressure may leave the organ (temporarily) beyond the equilibrium point of the new selection pressure. C—correlation between two characters a, b, may lead to equilibrium at a point intermediate between their separate optima; one is then over-developed so far as its own optimum is concerned. (From Simpson)

On the basis of our present knowledge of genetics it is clear that the chance of a lost organ or character being evolved a second time will differ according as the genetic factors on which it is based are few or many. A single mutation may be reversed and occur again repeatedly; its effects in the phenotype are clearly reversible and may be evolved many times. The same is true of a quantitative change in a metrical character (p. 182). But if numerous macro-mutations are necessary for the evolution of an organ or character, the chance of their occurring together a second time is very small. For the occurrence of mutations is individual, and there is no reason to believe that distinct mutations are correlated in their occurrence. It would be very unlikely that a combination of many mutations would occur twice, and therefore unlikely that an organ based on many mutations would be evolved a second time. Almost every organ in the animal body has a complex genetic basis, in which many genes take part, and therefore Dollo's "law" is very generally true. If a need arose again after the organ needed to satisfy it had been lost, it is probable that an organ differing from the lost organ both in its genetic basis and in its structure would be evolved to serve the same function.

Thus, Dollo's law is no more than a statement of results to be expected from the hereditary mechanism as we now know it. The "law" should, however, be modified in the light of modern knowledge. We may conclude with Huxley ([178], p. 503): "Dollo's law should in the first place be restated in more general form, and in the second place it should be regarded as a mere rule and not erected into a principle. It is true that the more complicated an organ is, and the more completely it is lost, the less likely it is to be regained in its original form, but this depends on no absolute 'principle of irreversibility'—only on the high degree of improbability of reversal in all of the many factors involved."

Looking back on the whole of our discussion of evolutionary trends, we must conclude that they are a characteristic and general feature of animal evolution, but they do not require any new evolutionary principles to account for them. In large part they are the result of long-continued orthoselection. The only real evidence of orthogenesis that they give comes from the evolution of similar characters in parallel evolving lines. This parallelism can mostly be accounted for as the result of occurrence of the same mutations and aristogenes in the related lines. Restriction of the course of evolution by restriction of the possible hereditary changes is true orthogenesis, but it requires no addition to the theory of evolution developed in the earlier chapters. It is a property of the genotype no less material and definable than any of its other characters.

CHAPTER X

EVOLUTION AND THE LIFE-HISTORY

THE most fundamental truth about the life-history in animals is that it is a continuous sequence of change extending through the whole period between fertilisation and death. It should be regarded as a single whole, for its progress is never-ceasing and continuous throughout its course. Change is, of course, much more rapid during the early, developmental stages of the life-history, but it does not cease so long as the animal is alive—the adult body is continually changing in its structure and physiology.

The course of the life-history is determined for each animal form, and is never identical in any two distinct forms. A species should not be defined by the form of the body at a single stage of the life-history; rather it should be defined by the whole sequence of forms that make up the life-history. Still more accurately, it should be defined not by the forms of the body during the life-history, but by the sequence of change within the body that underlies the change of form. But such a definition would be impracticable. We define a species by its form because we are not able to describe the internal changes that underlie change of form. We use the adult form for our definition because form is more stable at that stage than in the rest of the life-history, and because in many animals and in almost all fossils we have only the adult form to study. The truth remains, however, that it is the sequence of change constituting the life-history that truly defines an animal.

Development is the part of the life-history in which the complexity of the body is increasing towards the condition of the adult. Very often one of the last changes of development is the functioning of the gonad, and in general this may be taken to indicate the end of development and the beginning of adult life. During development elaboration of structure proceeds from broader to finer detail; in the early stages organisation is broadly sketched, detail is added in the later stages. One of the characteristics of development is that it is by no means always direct. The young animal often differs from the adult in its habitat and habits. It must remain viable throughout development and to provide for its life in its special habitat larval organs are often developed. Later these will be lost or modified into the different organs of the adult. In the formation of these larval organs development necessarily deviates from the direct course towards the adult condition; their occurrence is itself sufficient to make it clear that development is not a direct modelling of the body into the adult form. Development, and indeed the whole of the life-history, is a sequence of phases in which the organisation of the body continually changes, and its course is determined for each species. This is as close a definition as we can give. We know practically nothing of the means by which the general plan of the life-history is caused to proceed, and is maintained through the generations of the species. We therefore cannot define the life-history more accurately than this.

The means by which the details of developmental change are brought about are rather better known. During the life-history the substances of the body are produced by chemical reactions, each at its own point of time, under the control of intracellular enzymes, themselves each controlled by genes. These reactions are often organised into series or chains, in which the products of the earlier reactions are used as the substrates of later reactions (pp. 82–3). The emergence of pattern is an essential part of development, and it, as well as the production of chemical material, may be controlled by the progress of enzymatic reactions (p. 86). Developmental change may also be controlled by influences, probably chemical, originating in parts of the body near the part influenced—as in evocation. There are probably many other means by which it is controlled.

This is the broad picture of the life-history that we get from the study of living animals. Since the characters of an animal species are developed in the course of its life-history, evolution, the process by which the characters of species change, must essentially be change in the progress of the life-history.

We must consider whether our present knowledge of genetic

change gives us a sufficient basis for understanding the changes in the life-history that have occurred in evolution. We found that the genotypes of animals may change by mutations of various kinds (pp. 64 ff.), and that we were forced also to postulate initiation of new elements of pattern by aristogenesis (p. 43). Can we interpret the evolution that has occurred in animal life-histories as the result of hereditary changes of these types?

Before we can answer this question we must know what kinds of change in the life-history have occurred in evolution. The first feature of this evolution to be noted is that it is not evenly distributed through the life-history. New organisation may occur at any stage—larvæ as well as adults may change in their adaptations—but there is no doubt that evolutionary change is greater and more frequent in the later stages of the life-history than in the earlier. Larvæ resemble each other more closely than the corresponding adults do, and the earliest stages of development—segmentation stages, blastulæ, etc.—very often alter little in long periods of evolution. These are general conclusions; they are not true of every example of evolution. Large larval changes occasionally occur in relatively short evolutionary periods, but this is in general only when some large alteration in the manner of the larval life has taken place. One of the clearest examples of this is the change in development that occurs when the embryonic period is prolonged and the larva feeds inactively for a long time within the coverings of the egg on stores of yolk provided for it. With this change in the habit of the larva, go great changes in segmentation and other parts of the development. This assumption of a meroblastic form of development is one of the most frequent types of larval change; it has occurred four times independently in the evolution of the vertebrates—in the Myxinoids, Chondrichthyes, Teleostei and reptiles—and many times in the invertebrates. In meroblastic development and in some other conditions, change in the larval habit of life may lead to larval modifications greater than the simultaneous change in adult structure. Sometimes, indeed, there may be large changes in a larva with no considerable simultaneous change in the adult. The species of *Peripatus* give an example of this. Some of the species have large and yolky eggs which are laid and later hatch into free-living

11*

young. Others have much smaller eggs carrying little yolk which develop within the parent's body and may be fed from the parent's tissues. These are viviparous, being born as small worms. There are no large differences in the adult to correspond with these differences in the development. This is an example of what de Beer [70] calls *clandestine evolution*, for it will not be noticed if only the adult stage is studied.

In circumstances such as these larval change may be greater than the change in the adult. But these cases are exceptional, and there is no doubt that in general the earlier stages of the life-history evolve more slowly than later stages. The facts may be stated in another way by saying that early stages retain the characters of their ancestors in more detail than later stages; tadpoles are more like fish than frogs are.

These facts are exactly what we should expect from our knowledge of the nature of the genetic changes that occur in animals, and of the ways in which they produce their effects in the body. Mutations act by altering the efficiency of enzymes in the body, and do so at all times in the life-history (pp. 82, 84 ff.). There is then no difficulty in attributing change at any stage of the life-history to mutation. There is no more difficulty in understanding why evolutionary change should be greater in the adult than in young stages. The primary action (p. 68) of a mutation is very often on some process of development, but its secondary effects may result in altered organisation at any later stage. We have seen examples of this in the wing-pattern of *Ephestia* (p. 86), and in the secondary effects of Little and Bagg's mutation in mice (p. 88). Allometric change gives equally clear examples. A change in the relative growth-rates of an organ may take place early in development, but it results in alteration of the organ's size at all later stages of the life-history, and the change in relative size is greater the larger the animal grows. It is, in fact, true that the effects of many mutations, both those controlling allometry and others, do not appear until long after the time of their primary actions.

From the fact that mutations may alter any period of the life-history after, but not before, their primary actions, it necessarily follows that the later periods of the life-history are altered by more mutations than the earlier.

In view of these facts it is inevitable that the effects of genetic change should be concentrated in the later parts of the life-history. Evolution, since it is built up of the effects of mutation, should produce greater and more rapid change in the adult than in the larva. Evolution is very largely a process of change in development, but its effects in the body are most evident in the adult.

So far we have considered only the distribution in the life-history of evolutionary novelties in the structure or physiology of the body. There is another type of modification of the life-history that has been very important in evolution. This is alteration of the time-relations of the processes that take place during the life-history.

Comparative study of animals allows us to distinguish the following categories of evolutionary change in the life-history as a progress in time [70]:

1. Whole parts of the life-history may be shortened as compared with the rest (tachygenesis), or lengthened (brady-genesis).

2. Stages of the life-history may be dropped out, so that they are unrepresented in the life-history of the descendant (lipogenesis).

3. An individual organ may develop earlier or later in the descendant than in the ancestor. This implies that the period of the life-history at which certain developmental processes occur may be altered in either direction without corresponding change in other processes of the development (hetero-chrony).

Tachygenesis is frequent in evolution. A larval stage is often hurried through in a later development as compared with an earlier. In the arthropods, for instance, the stage corresponding to the unsegmented trochophore larva of the annelids, which are undoubtedly ancestral to the arthropods, is compressed into the embryonic period; and in the higher arthropods still later stages are similarly compressed, so that the animal hatches at a fully segmented stage. Similar reduction of free-living larval stages occurs in many types of meroblastic development (e.g. Cephalopoda, some Echinodermata). Bradygenesis is less common. de Beer ([70,] p. 19) quotes from Huxley the example of metamorphosis in three species of frog. *Rana temporaria* metamorphoses in the late summer of the first year; *R. clamitans* in the second season and *R. catesbeiana* in the third season. Metamorphosis in a single season is usual in the frogs and there can be little doubt that the longer larval life of the last species is due to bradygenesis. Metamorphosis in the Amphibia is controlled by the coming into activity of the thyroid, and a mutation that delayed its activity would lengthen the larval period.

It is difficult to draw a clear distinction between lipogenesis and tachygenesis, for the disappearance of a stage from the life-history may be regarded as an extreme form of its shortening or compression. It is doubtful whether lipogenesis is ever more than an extreme form of tachygenesis. Examples can be found in which traces of the lost developmental stages are very slight. For instance, some frogs (*Eleutherodactylus* and some other genera [202]) lay large, heavily yolked eggs, on land and not in the water, and in these the embryonic development continues until the animal hatches as a young frog. The tadpole stage is omitted. The absence in the terrestrial vertebrates of an aquatic stage comparable to the amphibian tadpole may be regarded as another example. Traces of these lost stages may remain as vestigial organs. The embryonic gill-slits or pouches of mammals or birds may be regarded as the last trace of an aquatic stage. It should, however, be emphasised that in these and other examples we have no proof that the disappearance of a stage is due to shortening of the development rather than to modification of the structure of the stage that seems to be lost. By such modification this stage might come to resemble and finally to be indistinguishable from an earlier or later stage. There is here no certain evidence of the loss of a stage from the life-history, i.e. of lipogenesis.

Heterochrony, a quickening or slowing of the development of a part and not of the whole body, is the most widespread and varied of the types of change in the time-relations of the life-history. It is found everywhere in evolution and is of more than one kind. A heterochronic change may arise either by alteration of the time at which a structure is first formed in development, or by change in its growth-rate after it has been formed.

Quickened development may be called *acceleration*, slowed development *retardation*.

Acceleration is often found in organs which must function early in development if the animal is to survive. The heart in reptile and bird embryos is such an organ. Absorption of the yolk, on which the growth of the embryo depends, requires efficient and early functioning of the heart, and we find that the structural condition of the embryonic heart is in advance of that of other organs in the embryo. There can be no doubt that its development has been accelerated in the evolution of the closed egg. The development of man gives many examples of acceleration. The grasping power of the hand in the baby, strong enough to support the weight of the body, and the early development of the brain, reaching almost its adult size in a young child, are examples.

Neoteny (or pædogenesis) is a well-known phenomenon that involves heterochrony. In neoteny development of the reproductive organs is accelerated, so that they become functional before the structure of the other organs is adult, and the animal reproduces in the larval condition. The axolotl is the classical example but the phenomenon occurs in several insects and a few other animals. Among the insects [326] the best-known examples are in the Cecidomyidæ, the gall-midges. Larvæ in *Miastor metroloas* and pupæ in *Tanytarsus grammi*, both belonging to this family, are able to reproduce. A hemipteran, *Hesperoctenes*, and a beetle, *Micromalthus*, also reproduce before reaching the adult condition. In the trematode *Polystomum integerrimum*, which is parasitic in the frog, reproduction is neotenic if the parasite is located in the lung, but not if it is in the bladder.

These neotenic forms are able to complete the life-history by becoming adult, and the adult as well as the larva may reproduce. But it is easy to suppose that the adult stage of a neotenic life-history might be lost after the larva had become reproductive. There is no reason why the axolotl should not survive as a species although the power of metamorphosing into the adult had been lost. It would not then be possible to recognise the life-history as neotenic by direct observation, for we should have no evidence of the lost adult stage. It has been suggested that this has happened in the evolution of more than one group of animals, and in some instances evidence from comparative morphology has been brought forward to support the suggestion. Thus, the perennibranchiate Amphibia (*Proteus, Necturus, Siren,* etc.) are newt-like forms that have several larval characters. They have, for instance, external gills throughout life, and some of the gill-slits remain open. It has been suggested that they are neotenic larvæ, the adult stages of which have been lost. Similarly, de Beer ([70], p. 54) points out that the segmentation of the insect body is very like that of some larval millipedes. He suggests that the insects may have been derived from a form similar to the millipedes by loss of the development to a many segmented body, that is to say that the insects are neotenic members of this line of descent. And, again, Garstang [121] suggests that the Euchordata (*Amphioxus* and the vertebrates) arose from an early protochordate group in which the adults were sessile, as the modern tunicates are, and that the Euchordata evolved by loss of the metamorphosis into the sessile adult and by retention of many larval characters in their adults, characters similar to those now present in the tadpole larva of the tunicate.

Most of these suppositions are very speculative. If we are to accept them, we need to be sure that the characters in which the supposedly neotenic forms resemble larvæ of related forms are not merely primitive characters retained in the adult of the "neotenic" form, but lost in the adult of the other form and occurring only in its larva. May not the insect and the millipede be both derived from a stock which had not yet evolved a many-segmented condition, and multiplication of the segments have occurred only in the millipedes? May not tunicates and *Amphioxus* be both derived from an early stock in which the adult was not sessile, and only the tunicates evolved the sessile adult, *Amphioxus* retaining the more primitive life-history? In some instances there is evidence against such suggestions as these. Thus, the perennibranchiate Amphibia are probably descended from forms which had already become terrestrial; they are secondarily aquatic. It is not probable that such aquatic features as external gills would have been retained in a terrestrial animal. The gills are therefore not primitive adult characters; they must be present in the adult of the perennibranchiates for some other reason, and the most likely reason would seem to be that this adult is a neotenic larva. Similarly, Garstang gives reasons for thinking that an early protochordate stock from which *Amphioxus* and the vertebrates could have arisen must have been sessile in the adult. But whether we accept the evidence of permanent neoteny in cases such as these, or reject it, it is undeniable that neoteny in living animals, such as the axolotl, is a real phenomenon. Its origin necessarily requires heterochrony.

It is possible that neoteny might have large and more or less sudden effects in evolution ([70], p. 24). If a larva became reproductive and the adult was lost, a new evolutionary line would be started which would be very different from any previous line. This is, in fact, what was suggested by de Beer for the insects and by Garstang for the vertebrates. If the new line was successful, it might result in a rapid change in the fauna of the world, for the new successful line might radiate to occupy widespread habitats. We have no direct evidence that evolution has proceeded in this way, and we must regard the suggestion as no more than a speculation of a possible course of events.

Retardation is almost as frequent in evolution as acceleration. Whenever an organ is not used in the early stages of the life-history, it is liable to be retarded and to develop only after those stages. The larvæ of the social Hymenoptera are provided with food by the parents; those of many flies and beetles live in masses of decaying organic matter or dung which they use as food. These larvæ have no need to go in search of their food, and their organs of locomotion are retarded; they are often legless in the feeding stages. Often the retardation of an organ may be so great that it is lost completely from the life-history. In the vertebrates the legs have been so lost in most snakes, many lizards and the cœcilians (Amphibia). The development of man shows retardation in many organs (cf. [70], pp. 48 ff., [178], p. 526). In his lack of a complete covering of hair, in the late closure of the sutures of the skull, and in some other characters, man resembles the embryos rather than the adults of other mammals. The condition is therefore fœtalisation brought about by retardation rather than neoteny, as it is often called. The comparison is particularly clear in the form of the face and the angle of the cranial flexure (Fig. 61). In these features the adult man contrasts with the adult dog and resembles the embryo.

Frequently an organ that has been strongly retarded does not disappear completely from the body but remains in a vestigial condition. A vestigial organ may be defined as one that is present in the body but is small compared with the homologous organs of related animals, and is functionless. The small size of these organs is due to their slow growth after they are first

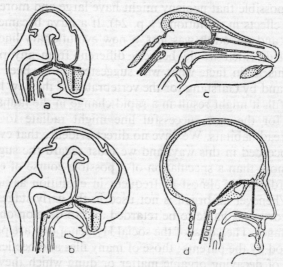

Figure 61. Sagittal sections of the head of an embryo and adult dog (a, c), and an embryo and adult man (b, d); to show the similarity of the angle between the head and the trunk in the adult man and the embryos, and the difference in this respect between adult man and adult dog. (From de Beer after Bolk)

formed in development—their growth is retarded. The pelvis in whales, the legs of pythons, and the tail in man are typical examples. Many vestigial organs are recognisable only in the early stages of development shortly after they have been formed. Later their growth may be so slow that they are unrecognisable in the larger body, or they may be completely resorbed. Gill-clefts or pouches are formed in the development of birds and mammals, but in later development they cannot be recognised as such.

The reduced and non-functional condition of some secondary sexual organs in one sex in vertebrates may be compared with the condition of vestigial organs. The nipples of male mammals may be looked upon as vestigial. Their growth is so retarded that they remain functionless throughout life.

It is sometimes thought to be surprising that organs should persist in the body after they have become reduced to a vestigial condition and have lost their function. Why should not the process of reduction be carried to completion, and the organ disappear entirely? We have seen that this sometimes happens, as in the case of the legs of some vertebrates, but not always; the legs are retained as vestiges in the python. Retention of organs that have been reduced to a vestigial condition is frequent. There seems to be a tendency for reduction to cease when a reduced organ has become small and lost its function.

In considering why this should be so, we must distinguish the first formation of an organ from its later growth. Vestigial organs are formed but later grow slowly; if an organ is to disappear completely from the life-history, its formation as well as its growth must be inhibited. It is probable that the genetic control of these two processes will often be distinct. There is no reason to suppose that the mutations required to inhibit the formation of an organ will necessarily occur because those inhibiting its growth have occurred. It is possible that many of these organs are still formed because the mutations inhibiting their formation have not been available.

This may explain why some vestigial organs are still formed in early development, but it does not explain why so many organs that have become functionless have not disappeared, like the gill-pouches or slits of mammals and birds, from the later parts of the life-history. This problem is discussed by Haldane.[155] He concludes that the retention of these vestigial organs is probably because an organ that has been so far reduced as to become vestigial will have no selective value. The pelvis of a whale or the legs of a python will not be removed by selection because at their present size they will not in any way affect the life of the animals. Organs that are functionless will be reduced by selection to the size at which they are selectively neutral; further reduction might occur by non-adaptive change (p. 183), but there is no reason to expect that this will always occur. This argument assumes that organs *can* be selectively neutral. We have seen (p. 212) that this is disputed, but we saw reason to think that many characters in animals are neutral. If characters can be neutral, none are more likely to be so than the reduced vestigial organs.

All the changes in the time-relations of the life-history that we have so far considered are of kinds that might readily be caused by mutations of the types that we know. As we have seen (p. 84), mutation may alter the time during the life-history of any process. Changes in which the rate of progress of the whole life-history is altered will require many correlated mutational changes, and may therefore be rare. But there is no theoretical difficulty in ascribing them to mutational change. Heterochrony may also be brought about by mutation. Indeed, in one type of reduction, that of the secondary sexual characters in one sex in the vertebrate, we know the mechanism by which the reduction is produced (p. 80). It is well known that growth in these organs is controlled by the concentrations of the genital hormones in the internal medium, and that the concentrations of these hormones are ultimately controlled by the sexual differences of the genotype. The genes determining sex therefore act, indirectly, as rate genes controlling the growth of these organs.

Retardation and acceleration of growth are no more than alterations in the allometry of the organs concerned. Huxley ([178], p. 529; [176], p. 235) has pointed out that small changes in relative growth-rates may cause large changes in the sizes of the organs. He suggests that the variability in size that is characteristic of many vestigial organs is to be expected, since their size will necessarily be sensitive to small variations in the allometry.

There is one possible type of change in the life-history that we have not so far considered. This is prolongation of the development by addition of stages at its end. Such a lengthening of development has been called *hypermorphosis*. It is the opposite of the shortening of development that occurs in neoteny if the adult stages are lost.

As animals became more complex, their development necessarily became longer; it takes longer for the more complex animal to reach the complexity of the adult condition. But this need not imply hypermorphosis. The life-history may elongate by expansion at any or all its stages, and not necessarily by addition of new stages to the end of development. We must ask whether hypermorphosis occurs in nature, and if it does how frequent it is. The question is important from the point of view of evolutionary theory, for belief in hypermorphosis as the general mode of evolution of the life-history was until recently commonly accepted by the majority of zoologists. On this belief Haeckel's theory of *recapitulation* [149] * was based. He maintained that the young stages of later animals represent the adults of their ancestors, the later adult stages having been added to the life-history by hypermorphosis. Ontogeny is, according to him, a recapitulation of the animal's phylogeny, though it may be a recapitulation shortened and otherwise modified in adaptation to the animal's habits.

This theory is based on the assumption that hypermorphosis occurs widely in evolution, and before estimating the likelihood of its truth we must know whether this is so. What evidence is there for the frequent occurrence of this type of change in the evolution of the life-history? It may be said at once that conclusive evidence for the occurrence of hypermorphosis is slight and hard to find. Haeckel based his theory largely on the undoubted truths that developmental stages resemble each other more closely than the corresponding adults, and often resemble more closely the structure of animals believed to be ancestral to the group to which they belong. A tadpole is more fish-like than a frog; a human embryo is like a fish in possessing gill-pouches and in other ways. But these resemblances cannot be accepted as conclusive evidence for hypermorphosis. The facts would be as readily accounted for if (1) the early developmental stage of the descendant represents not the adult ancestor but a developmental stage of the ancestor—and there is no reason to reject this, for young stages are as much like the young as the adult of the ancestor; a tadpole is as much like a larval as an adult fish—and (2) evolutionary change has been greater in adult than in developmental stages of the life-history (p. 313), so that adults have altered more, i.e. the life-history evolved by changes at all its stages, but the change has been greater in the adult. This interpretation of the greater resemblances of early stages of the life history is generally accepted today

* Haeckel did not originate the theory, but was its chief exponent. For the history, see [261], ch. XIV.

(37, ch. XXIII). It does not require the occurrence of hypermorphosis. The theory that hypermorphosis is general cannot be accepted on the evidence that Haeckel brought forward.

Some other evidence that has been used to support belief in hypermorphosis is no more convincing. At one time the facts of metamorphosis in the Amphibia were thought to be explicable only on the basis of hypermorphosis. When it was shown that metamorphosis in these animals is stimulated by increased activity of the thyroid, this was thought to imply that this mechanism of metamorphosis arose as a new evolution in a life-history in which the present adult stages were not represented, and that these stages were added as a result of the evolution of the thyroid mechanism. That would be hypermorphosis in a very extreme form, but there is no evidence that amphibian metamorphosis arose in this way, and it is unlikely that it did. It is much more likely that it arose as a modification of a more direct life-history which already contained stages representing the modern adult stages, and that metamorphosis has been gradually introduced into this life-history. We cannot say what the earlier life-history was like, but that is unnecessary to the argument. In any case, metamorphosis is always a highly modified type of life-history, and it would be rash to use the facts of amphibian or other form of metamorphosis as the basis for our interpretation of the normal evolution of animal life-histories.

The increase of size that so often occurs in the evolution of groups of the terrestrial vertebrates is sometimes regarded as evidence for hypermorphosis (70, ch. XII). Certainly, in these groups, the young of later forms resemble the earlier adults in size, but this result does not without further evidence imply hypermorphosis. The increase in size might be produced by a general acceleration of growth during the life-history and not by a lengthening of the period of growth beyond the end of the earlier life-history. We need proof that the growth-rates have not altered in evolution before we could accept this evidence as conclusive for hypermorphosis. In many other animals the young of later forms resemble the earlier adults. This is true of *Gryphœa* in lines in which the coiling of the shell increased, and it has been found, among other instances, many times in ammonites. Here, again, it is as easy to interpret the facts as due to change occurring throughout the life-history as to lengthening of the period of development. In *Gryphæa* the young as well as the adult became more coiled as evolution proceeded; the evolutionary change may have been an increase in the rate of coiling, not a lengthening of the time during which the coiling proceeded.

In one instance it seemed until recently that there was good evidence of hypermorphosis in a life-history. Robb ([255], cf. Fig. 16, p. 38) concluded that het relative growth-rate of the facial region in the horse was the same in the development of the living animal and in the phylogeny of tertiary horses (as shown by correlation with the total size of the skull). This would certainly fit with the assumption that as horses became larger they did so by continuous lengthening of the period of growth, i.e. by hypermorphosis. Robb's conclusions have, however, been criticised by Reeve and Murray,[251] who believe that the relative growth-rate was not constant throughout the evolution of the horses, and that the rate in the ontogeny of modern horses is not identical with that of the phylogeny. It cannot be said that this evidence is conclusive in favour of hypermorphosis.

Not all the evidence that has been thought to support belief in hypermorphosis has been mentioned, but the rest is not much stronger. At least it is clear that reliable evidence in favour of its occurrence is not easily found. This, however, is no proof that hypermorphosis never occurs. It may be that our inability to find clear evidence of it is due to the nature of the phenomenon and to the limitations of our methods of investigation. It is certainly true that there are so many ways in which change may arise in the life-history that it is hard to show conclusively that any example of change is due to hypermorphosis. It is also true that hypermorphosis is a type of change in the life-history that is by no means impossible or even unlikely on the basis of our present knowledge of evolution. Retardation of developmental processes might readily result in their being continued into the adult period, which would then become a part of development. New changes might also be evolved in the adult, and might result in the original adult stage ceasing to be the final stage of development. In either case we should have hypermorphosis.

Thus, hypermorphosis is a possible evolutionary change and may have occurred. But at least we can say that the facts as they are known today do not support belief that it is the usual mode of evolution of the life-history, and certainly give no ground for believing that it is the cause of the resemblances that we find between the young stages of animals. Recapitulation in Haeckel's sense is not a basic phenomenon in the evolution of animals. It is at least doubtful whether hypermorphosis has played any significant part in evolution.

Our discussion of the evolution of the life-history leads to the following conclusions. The life-history evolves by change at all its stages, as the result of mutations which may have their primary action at any point of time in the life-history. But the structural change is greater in the later than the earlier parts of the life-history, because a mutation may produce secondary effects at any time after (but not before) its primary action. Change in the time-relations of the processes of development are frequent in evolution. Whole parts of the life-history may be shortened or lengthened. Sometimes, perhaps, a stage may be entirely lost, though very often traces of its organisation remain as vestigial organs. The rates at which individual structures in the body develop may be quickened or slowed, and the point of time in development at which a process takes place may be altered in either direction. There is also, as evolution proceeds and the animal becomes more complex, a gradual elongation of the whole development, but this is not in general by the addition of new developmental stages at its end. It results rather from modification of the whole course of development. There is no reason to doubt that all the changes that have occurred in animal life-histories are of kinds that may be caused by hereditary changes of the types that we know to occur in the genotypes of animals. Our present knowledge of the evolution of the life-history does not conflict with our knowledge of the action of hereditary change.

CHAPTER XI

RATES OF EVOLUTION

THROUGHOUT this book we have been concerned with the progressive evolution of successful groups of animals, of which the vertebrates have been our most frequent example, almost to the exclusion of other types of evolution. Specialisation, that is to say continually closer adaptation to the conditions to which the animal is exposed, is the common result of this progressive evolution. This is true even though, on occasion, the direction of specialisation may be altered, as we saw in our discussion of pre-adaptation. Specialisation typically leads to more complex structure and more efficient organisation of the body as a living mechanism, but it need not do so. When organs are no longer needed, they may degenerate. This often occurs (pp. 21, 307) in the course of specialisation to habits different from those in response to which the organs were evolved.

It must, however, be remembered that not all evolution is of this type. Not all animals become increasingly specialised as evolution goes on. We noted (p. 269) that some species, even in groups in which the majority of species are highly specialised, for instance the birds and the insects, may be cosmopolitan in distribution and seem to be adapted rather to live in a wide range of conditions than in the narrow range of a specialised habitat. The account of evolution so far given would seem to lead to the conclusion that the tendency to specialisation should be inevitable. We must ask how it comes about that some species are able to resist this tendency.

Again, not all groups of animals have been successful in evolution in the same sense as that in which the vertebrates have been successful. There are some groups of which only a few species survive, and which seem to have been incapable of further evolution. The smaller animal phyla are typical examples of these groups (Gastrotricha, Chætognatha, Phoronidea).

Some of these forms are highly specialised and may be regarded as having got into blind alleys of specialisation from which they have been unable to escape. But this is not true of all; the arrow-worms, *Sagitta*, are widespread and abundant animals, and by no means specialised to a narrow range of conditions. Can we point to any characteristics of the conditions which control evolution in these forms and, perhaps, may have resulted in the stagnancy of their evolution? Why are some groups success-ful and others not?

Finally, as we have already seen (p. 21), evolution, even among animals belonging to successful groups, and, as it seems, evolving according to the principles discussed in earlier chapters, is extremely variable in rate.

It is not possible at present to say much of value about most of these questions. But some reasons can be given for the fact that evolutionary rates are so highly variable, and we will now discuss this question. If we can understand why evolution may be slow in some animals and fast in others, we may be able to extend our interpretation to the cases of apparently complete stagnancy of evolution in animals such as those of the small phyla. The subject of evolutionary rates has been recently discussed by Simpson.[275]

It is very difficult to compare accurately and quantitatively the rates of structural change in the evolution of distantly related groups of animals. To do so we should need some unit of evolutionary change that could be applied to animal evolu-tion in general. We have no means of defining such a unit. It is hardly possible to determine by direct observation whether changes in animals of different structure are or are not of equal extent; and we cannot take the systematists' supraspecific categories as defining the units, for, as we saw (p. 113), sys-tematists working on different groups disagree widely on the appropriate sizes of the categories. Within a single, relatively restricted group of animals, such as the birds or the mammals, the size of the genus or family may be more or less constant, but it would be rash to assume that this is so throughout larger groups, and certainly unsound to assume it of the animal kingdom in general.

In any event, it is doubtful whether comparison of the rates of structural change in the evolution of the various groups of animals would be of any great value. We have noted more than once in our discussions that the process of evolution varies in many of its characters in different animals. This is so whether the animals are closely or distantly related. The rate may be expected to vary as much as any other of the characters of the evolution. Only the mean rates in the various groups could be compared, and it is doubtful whether such comparison, with the questionable means of making the comparison that are all we have, would tell us much about the process of evolution.

It does not follow from this that nothing of interest can be said about the rates of structural evolution. Not all the facts about the rates can easily be explained by their variation with the animals' biology. The chief fact that cannot be so explained is the enormous extent of the range of variation in evolutionary rate. Let us examine the extent of its range.

It is certainly true that in some animals evolutionary change of structure is extremely slow and indeed hardly progresses at all. This is true of the archaic forms that still survive from groups which have long ceased to be dominant. Some animals, such as the brachiopod *Lingula*, are generically the same today as they were in the early Cambrian some 400 million years ago, since which time the whole evolution of the vertebrates has taken place (Ordovician to Recent). Among the vertebrates, the lampreys and hagfishes (Cyclostomata) still have the fundamental structure of the earliest vertebrate group, the Agnatha, and have retained that structure throughout the whole of vertebrate evolution. There is also alive today *Latimeria*, a representative of a group of fishes (the cœlocanths) that originated in the Devonian. Examples in the higher vertebrate groups are not much less striking. *Sphenodon* is a living reptile that has preserved with little change the structure of its ancestors of the Trias, and the opossums that of the mammals of the Cretaceous.

In contrast to these examples of slow evolution we have the whole radiation of the reptiles in the 100 million years between the Permian and the Cretaceous, and that of the mammals in the 60–80 million years of the Tertiary.

These differences in rate of evolution are great, but even in them we have not the full range of evolutionary rates. In microevolution rates may be much more rapid than those general in the adaptive radiation of the reptiles and mammals. The species and subspecies of char found in the lakes of Northern Europe ([231] and p. 224) must have differentiated since the last retreat of the ice at the end of the Ice Age, for these lakes were covered with ice-sheets during the glaciation. The ice retreated not more than 20,000 and probably not more than 12,000 years ago; subspecific and even specific differentiation in structure is therefore possible in a few thousand years. The cichlid fishes of the lakes of East Africa tell the same story. Worthington [330-1] believes that those of Lakes Victoria and Kioga have differentiated into many species since the last Pluvial Period, which was simultaneous with the last extension of the ice in northern regions. With this rapid evolution we may compare Zeuner's estimate [340] of the normal rate of evolution in the adaptive radiation of the mammals. He finds on palæontological evidence that the time normally required for the evolution of a species is not less than 500,000 years. Again, the differences are great. To give the whole range of the variability of evolutionary rates, they must be added to the differences of rate between the evolution of *Lingula* and that of the majority of mammals and reptiles.

It may be noted that we found that species may become biologically distinct in still shorter periods (p. 245). But that is not relevant here, for we are here discussing evolutionary change of structure, and the differences between biological species are not necessarily structural.

We have to discuss the causes of these very large differences in evolutionary rate of structural change. The question that arises at once is whether there are differences of kind in the evolution of slowly and quickly evolving animals. Can we regard the rates as all variations about a mean, some slower than the mean and some quicker, but all produced by essentially the same kind of evolution? If they may be so regarded, it should be possible to plot them all on a curve of variability with a single apex (pp. 27, 117). Can this be done? If it cannot, it will mean that the whole array of rates is divisible into smaller groups, and these groups will presumably correspond to differences in the type of evolution that the animals are undergoing.

First, we will compare the very slow evolution of such

animals as *Lingula* and *Latimeria* with the normal rates of
adaptive radiation. Simpson ([275,] pp. 126 ff.) gives an analysis
of the periods of survival of fossil general to the Lamelli-
branchiata and the Carnivora. The period of survival is the
time before the genus either dies out or is sufficiently altered by
evolutionary change to lead the systematist to set up a new
generic name. If we may assume that genera are of approximately the same size in relatively restricted groups such as both

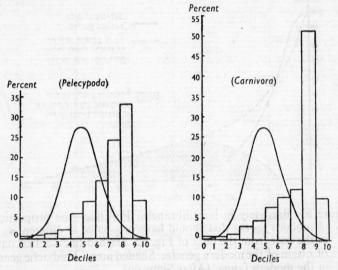

Figure 62. Survival curves for genera of lamellibranchs (Pelecypoda)
and carnivores. The histograms give the proportions of genera
surviving to each period of time (abscissa). A normal curve of
error is superimposed. (After Simpson)

these are, the period of survival will be correlated with the
rate of structural change in the group, though it may not give
an accurate measure of the rate. Simpson finds that the majority
of the genera in each group have periods of survival that fit on
to a curve of variation about a mean (Fig. 62). The distribution
is not symmetrical on the two sides of the mean; fewer of the
genera survived for an abnormally long period than for less
than the average period. Also, the mean rate of evolution is not
the same in the two groups. It is not to be expected that it
should be, and without doubt it varies even more in other

groups. A rate that would be slow in some groups would be fast in others.

Nevertheless, the curves given by the periods of survival in these genera are typical curves of variation, and there is no evidence in the curves that the evolution is of more than one type. These genera were evolving in typical adaptive radiation, and their evolution is the type associated with that process, which will probably be found in all radiating groups of animals.

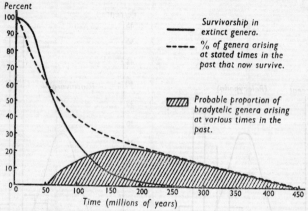

Figure 63. Bradytely in lamellibranchs. Full line—the proportions of modern genera that should have originated at different dates in the past from the data of Fig. 62. Dashed line—actual dates of origin of the modern genera. Shaded area—bradytelic genera in the modern fauna. (After Simpson)

Not all the genera of these groups give rates of evolution that fit on to the curves. A certain number survived for periods far outside the range of the curve. Among the lamellibranchs several genera—*Lima, Ostrea, Nucula* and others—have survived from Palæozoic times to the present day and show no signs of dying out or of evolutionary change of generic grade. These genera are too numerous and have survived too long to be regarded as extreme examples of the groups that fit the curve of variation. They cannot be members of these groups that have survived for an abnormally long time; they clearly form a distinct group of their own.

Simpson analyses the modern lamellibranch fauna with the results summarised in Fig. 63. He calculates, from the results given in Fig. 62, the percentages of the modern genera that should be present in the faunas of the past. These percentages are given by the full line. The dotted line gives the actual percentages of the modern genera present in past faunas. The area between these curves, the shaded area, gives the number of genera of abnormally long survival that have arisen. It is not possible to say to which category the genera that arose less than 50 million years ago belong; they have not survived long enough to allow us to say that any of them belong to the long-lived category.

Simpson calls the class of genera with abnormally long survival, and slow evolution, *bradytelic*, and those with normal survival periods *horotelic*. Bradytelic lines certainly occur in many other groups of animals, probably in almost all groups. The genera of ancient and primitive groups that survive today are necessarily bradytelic, not merely *Latimeria* and *Lingula* but many vertebrates such as the lampreys, *Sphenodon* and the opossums, and many invertebrates besides the lamellibranchs that have been mentioned. Some insects are typically bradytelic. True may-flies (Ephemeroptera) and dragon-flies (Odonata) occur in the Permian, and one suborder of the dragon-flies, the Zygoptera, has changed little since the Upper Permian. Nevertheless, horotelic genera are far more numerous than the bradytelic. In successful groups such as the reptiles or the mammals the great majority of lines are horotelic. Horses, elephants, titanotheres and all other actively radiating lines of the mammals are typically horotelic.

We must ask how it comes about that bradytelic forms survive so long and evolve so slowly. There are several possibilities to be considered here. Bradytelic evolution might be due either to characters inherent in the animals or to unusual features in their interaction with the environment. Among characters of the animals that might result in slow evolution, we have, first and most obviously, a low mutation rate. If no mutations arose in a line of animals, it would be unable to evolve. But there is no evidence that mutations are absent or few in bradytelic lines; living bradytelic animals are not clearly less variable than other animals. A low mutation rate must be discarded as the cause of bradytely. Asexual reproduction is another character that might be expected to lead to slow evolution, for variation is less in asexual clones owing to the absence of recombination. Also, animals with long life-spans should evolve more slowly than others. But there is no evidence of association of bradytely with either asexual reproduction or with a long life-span. It is certainly not true that all long-lived animals are bradytelic—long-lived mammalian groups such as the elephants have evolved rapidly—and it is equally untrue that all bradytelic animals are long-lived—the bradytelic insects are not.

It is not possible to find inherent characters of the animal that might be the cause of bradytely, and Simpson comes to the conclusion that the true cause lies in the relations between the animal and its environment. Several features of these relations that would make for slow evolution may be suggested. We haves een (p. 185) that Wright came to the conclusion that large size of the interbreeding population would cause slow evolution, owing to the absence of any significant random modification where the population is large. A relatively unchanging environment will have the same effect, for, after the animal has become closely adapted to the conditions of the environment, there will be little stimulus to further change. It is also possible that animals might become adapted to a wide range of conditions rather than specialised to a narrow niche, and that, if this were so, they would not evolve new forms unless the conditions passed outside this wide range. In a relatively unchanging environment, wide tolerance of environmental conditions might result in the absence of any stimulus to change, and the animals might remain without evolutionary change for an indefinite period.

Simpson concludes that bradytelic animals are in general forms with large interbreeding populations, adapted to unspecialised habits of life in environments that are not subject to large and sudden changes of the conditions. It is not suggested that these conditions give a complete explanation of bradytely, nor that they are necessarily all present in every bradytelic line. But some typical examples of bradytely have the characters demanded by his theory. Both the littoral and abyssal regions of the sea are environments in which few changes likely to stimulate evolution occur. This is clearly true of the abyssal regions, and on the shore there are few sudden changes that might endanger the life of the fauna and cause active selection—the tidal rhythm is of much too short a period to do so, and seasonal rhythms of temperature and other conditions do not pass outside the viable range of the fauna. Both are stable environments, so far as conditions likely to be dangerous to the life of the fauna are concerned. We find on the shore bradytelic forms in many groups—most of the lamellibranchs mentioned above are shore forms; bradytely occurs among shore echinoderms (both starfishes and sea-urchins); *Amphioxus* and many other littoral animals are bradytelic. In the deep seas there are the crinoids. (The deep-sea fishes are mostly highly specialised—specialisation is possible and frequent in any environment.) Most of these bradytelic forms have external fertilisation and their interbreeding populations are likely to be large.

The tropical forest is another environment characterised by constancy of conditions and lack of sudden and dangerous environmental change. Here also many bradytelic forms are found—mammals such as the lemurs, opossums and others, birds such as the hoatzin of Guiana, *Peripatus* and other arthropods.

In contrast to these stable environments, the fresh-water shore is always subject to large and relatively sudden changes. The shore may dry owing to change of level of the water by evaporation, the water may freeze, or it may stagnate and become deoxygenated. These and other dangers will subject the fauna to occasional very active selection in which few individuals will survive. It is to be expected that these conditions will lead to rapid evolutionary change. We noted this when discussing rhythmical change in population numbers (p. 256). Probably for this reason most of the animals that have successfully invaded the land have come up the fresh-water and not the marine shore. Pulmonates, insects, oligochætes and vertebrates have all reached the land by this route. The fresh-water shore is not an environment in which animals are likely to remain bradytelic.

It may be said in criticism of Simpson's theory that there are bradytelic forms, especially among terrestrial animals, that have not the characters that he believes to lead to bradytely. Many certainly have small interbreeding populations and do not seem to be adapted to wide ranges of conditions. Many are rare—

for instance, *Sphenodon*, the monotremes, and *Peripatus*—and
are found only in restricted habitats. Simpson suggests that
these are relics of previously large populations and that they
are now near extinction. Some perhaps have been unable to
adjust their lives to recent changes caused either by the end of
the Pleistocene glaciation or by extension of man's interference.
It may also be noted that Wright finds a very small (as well as
a large) interbreeding population likely to lead to slow evolution
(p. 185).

On the whole it seems probable that Simpson's explanation
of bradytely is in large measure true. In animals with wide
tolerance of conditions living in relatively unchanging environments, after their early adaptation to the conditions of the
environment, almost any mutational change will be disadvantageous, so long as the environment remains unchanged.
Even if advantageous change were offered, the rate of evolution
in their large populations would be slow. Such animals are
likely to survive with little change until they meet competition
from more efficient forms belonging to groups that have been
evolved later. In that competition they will very probably go to
the wall and sooner or later become extinct.

Bradytely is the probable course by which animals reach a
condition of almost if not wholly complete evolutionary stag-
nation. It is in this condition that forms survive long after the
groups to which they belong have become otherwise extinct,
long after later forms with more complex and apparently more
efficient organisation have been evolved. If our interpretation
of bradytely is correct we have an explanation of this condition that is satisfactory and complete except in one respect.
We have not shown how it can come about that an animal
avoids the temptation to narrow specialisation that seems
inherent in evolution, and remains adapted to a broad range
of conditions. On that point little can be said. We know well
enough, from observation, that some animals have this character—man is as good an example as any—but why some animals
and not others have it is unexplained. Broad adaptation is
certainly likely to be of selective value to the animal that
possesses it, and sometimes perhaps of more value than close
adaptation to specialised conditions. This may more often be
true in environments where specialised niches are not frequent,

and perhaps also of animals which are strongly locomotory and range over wide areas; such animals cannot adapt to small niches. But not all bradytelic animals live in such environments, and few are strongly locomotory.

Leaving the slow evolution of bradytely, we may now pass to consider evolution rates at the other extreme of the range. Here we have to discuss how it is possible for some animals to evolve to the specific stage of structural differentiation within a few thousand years, whereas the normal period for this grade of differentiation in horotelic evolution is measured in hundreds of thousands of years. The most rapid evolutionary rates are called by Simpson ([275,] p. 134) *tachytelic*.

It must here be emphasised again that the "species" we are discussing are the systematic species of morphology and palæontology, and not biological species. In biological species we found (p. 127) that the extent of the specific difference was by no means always a clear-cut grade of structural differentiation. Some related biological species show smaller structural differences than others, and in some there are only very small differences in structure (p. 128). But the morphological differences that the systematists have thought large enough to discriminate systematic species have seemed to them equivalent, at least within a restricted group of animals. It is this grade of structural differentiation that some animals are able to evolve within a few thousand years and others only in several hundred thousand years. If the structural difference between systematic species is constant, the period in which a species is evolved may be taken as a rough measure of the rate of the evolution.

The examples of rapid evolution that have been quoted in this chapter—the char in the lakes of northern Europe and the cichlid fishes of the lakes of Africa—have both occurred in recent years, at a time when conditions have undergone great and rapid changes as the result of the retreat of the ice after the last glaciation. This is as true of the lakes of Africa as of those of Europe, for in tropical regions rainfall has been greatly reduced since the last Pluvial Period—contemporary with the last extension of the ice—and the changes in aquatic environments have been great as a result of this.

Change in the habits of an animal or in the conditions in

which it is living is always likely to lead to rapid evolutionary change. We noted the change in the structure of the apple capsid that has occurred since it took to feeding on apple. Huxley ([178], p. 187) quotes some other examples of rapid change in living animals. For instance, Jameson [183] found that the mice of an island in Ireland which had been isolated not more than 100–125 years had become lighter in adaptation to the colour of the sandy soil. There was here definite evolution, though not to the specific stage, in a single century. Mayr ([209], p. 220) quotes other examples of rapid change following change in habitat, and Dobzhansky ([80], p. 158) several examples, most of them in physiological characters.

It is probable that change in the habits of an animal or in its environment is a general cause of tachytelic evolution. After such changes the selective value of many characters will be altered. Some which were previously excluded by selection will be favoured; others, previously favoured, will be excluded. The characters of the population will move rapidly to a new optimum under the changed selection (p. 182). Also, if a change is large and sudden, it is probable that the population that survives the change will be a small fraction of that before it. In discussing rhythms in population numbers (p. 255), we concluded that occasional reduction of the population number may be expected to lead to rapid evolution, both during the decrease in numbers and during the later increase to a new maximum.

Many, if not all, the examples of tachytelic evolution that are found in palæontology may be accounted for in this way. The change from browsing to grazing in the horses was associated with change in environment, and it was suggested in our discussion (p. 287 and Fig. 56) that when part of the browsing population had varied so far from their original habit that they came under selection towards the grazing peak, they would rapidly evolve grazing adaptations. This would be an example of the rapid evolution following change of habit that we are here discussing. Whenever in adaptive radiation a line branches from the line from which it has arisen and occupies a new niche—and such branching is frequent in any group undergoing adaptive radiation—selection will take a new direction, and we should expect the early stages of the differentiation of the new line to be rapid. This may be one reason why we are so seldom able to trace the immediate origin of one group from another in palæontology. (We noted (p. 45) in discussing the fossil evidence of mammalian evolution that we are seldom able to do so.) But the rapidity of evolution at these stages will not be the only reason for their absence from the fossil record. A new line will usually arise in a single population and in a restricted environment, and the chance of its being preserved will be further reduced. Only when a new line has become successful and has spread widely, are we likely to find it among the fossils.

We may conclude that rapid evolution is probable after any change in the habits of a population or in its environment. Where the increase in rate is considerable we call the evolution tachytelic. This rapid evolution will be more frequent the oftener changes occur, and therefore more frequent in unstable than in stable environments. Undoubtedly there are many other conditions that will conduce to rapid evolution. For instance, as we saw (p. 185), the rate of evolution will be greater where the interbreeding population is of moderate size, neither too great nor too small, and still greater if the species is divided into partially isolated populations of moderate size (p. 190).

If these conclusions are correct, tachytelic evolution must be looked upon as no more than an extreme form of horotelic evolution; it occurs in conditions in which the factors favouring rapid evolution are especially effective. These factors are not peculiar to the circumstances in which tachytelic evolution occurs; they occur, though less effectively, in all environments. Thus, tachytelic evolution differs from horotelic in the rate of the evolutionary change but not in the kind of evolution taking place. We cannot separate a distinct class of tachytelic lines as we were able to separate a class of bradytelic lines. Any line may become tachytelic when the conditions are favourable for rapid evolution. Episodes of tachytelic evolution may occur in the history of any group of animals.

It is not profitable to attempt more exact definition of evolutionary rates. The absolute rate of evolution varies in all animals, not only from species to species and group to group, but also during the history of each group. There is no exact tachytelic or horotelic rate of evolution. These terms both cover a large range of evolutionary rates.

CONCLUSION

WE have been concerned chiefly with evolution in bisexual animals, and almost solely with the more general problems of evolution in these animals. Even there our discussions have not been complete. One subject that has hardly been mentioned is the possible rôle of Lamarckian inheritance, the question whether some such hereditary mechanism is required for a complete theory of evolution. Another is the action upon evolving animals of the accidents of world geography—the results, for instance, of isolation upon the evolution of the marsupials in Australia, the Xenarthra and other groups in South America, and of later invasion of these faunas by animals from other parts of the world. In any complete examination of the theory of evolution these subjects and many others would undoubtedly deserve a place. We have not had space for them.

The theory to which our discussions have led has been founded on that of Darwin. His theory has continually developed since he stated it, and the form now held differs in many ways from that which he put forward, and from the forms held in the first two decades of this century. It is not necessary to state our theory again here, but it may be worth while to state shortly in what ways the theory has been modified in the last thirty years.

1. MICRO-EVOLUTION

In the present-day theory, evolution is regarded as a process of change in the whole life of the animal. We do not think of evolution as primarily a process of elaboration of the structural (and perhaps also the physiological) organisation of the body, as earlier zoologists did; we think of it as a change in the animal's whole life, in its ecology, habits and behaviour as well as in the organisation of its body. It was always realised that evolution is very largely the result of changed interactions between the animal and its environment—Darwin realised this when he

340

saw the importance of natural selection. The change in outlook is one of emphasis. We now see, much more clearly than formerly, that in studying evolution no part of an animal's living activities can be considered separately; that change in any feature of an animal's life implies change in all its other features; and that, if the animal is to survive, its life and activities must at all times be so correlated with the environmental conditions that the animal remains a viable whole. Evolution demands simultaneous study of all aspects of the animal's natural history. It can be completely understood only if we know all the circumstances of the animal's life.

Since this is the nature of the evolutionary process, it is not surprising that the large advances of the last thirty years in animal ecology have greatly altered our views of evolution. Many systematists, as well as naturalists, have come to realise the biological species as a fact of nature, and the evolutionary importance of the species when it is defined as the natural group within which interbreeding normally occurs, provided there is opportunity for it. Equally important is appreciation of the organisation of the species into local, partially isolated populations of varying size—the demes—within which evolution is largely independent so long as the isolation is maintained.

If this is the organisation of animal species in nature, we need to know, before we can discuss their evolution, how this organisation will react to selection. Mathematical study of selection has given us much clearer ideas of the course that change is likely to take in populations organised in this way. Belief in selection as an effective agent in nature has been confirmed by experiments on natural populations and observations of them, though direct evidence for its effectiveness may still be weak; and mathematical analysis has also shown that selection may be effective even though the selective advantage is small. We have also learnt from mathematical studies much concerning the relative speeds at which evolution is likely to progress in populations of different sizes and under different conditions, and of many other questions, such as the course of events likely to follow meeting of interbreeding but differentiated forms. But perhaps the most general conclusion to which these studies have led is that evolution in nature must always take the form of continuous change in the interbreeding population as a whole; change cannot proceed independently in any smaller unit if the population consists of animals with bisexual reproduction. The older conception of the lineage as the evolving unit within a population, the conception that a population consists of a large number of family lines evolving more or less independently within it, must be discarded as unrealistic so long as the reproduction is bisexual. Only if reproduction is parthenogenetic or asexual can distinct clones evolve separately within a population. Another important result of mathematical study of selection is that non-adaptive characters may be evolved. This also is recent.

The study of animal populations in nature is by no means complete. One subject of which we know little is the extent and prevalence of close inbreeding in natural populations. Further knowledge of this would greatly clarify our views of micro-evolution. Another is the extent of variation in the conditions of natural environments and the nature of their variations. Such variations must clearly alter the selective advantages of characters from time to time, but we know little of the effects of these changes. In many other directions further knowledge of ecology would help our understanding of micro-evolution.

Behind the recent changes in our views of micro-evolution lie the changed conceptions of the genotype that have resulted from the work of the last thirty years in genetics. There is no doubt that the palæontologists and morphologists were right when they said at the beginning of the century that the "saltations" then the subject of Mendelian genetics could not be the chief raw material of evolution. It was demonstrably clear that gradual and directional evolution, consisting of small but cumulative changes, and often continuing in the same direction for long periods, could not be built up from these large and random saltations. Later advances in genetics have shown that the interactions of the genes in the phenotype are so complex and various that the genotype must be thought of as acting as a unit, and not the genes as acting independently; and that minute micro-mutations, which occur in all genotypes in numbers far exceeding the saltations, are a very large source of the raw material of evolution. We now see that gradual changes are to be expected if the heredity is Mendelian. Also, the supply of micro-mutation is likely to be sufficient for change in any direction demanded by selection, though perhaps not at all rates. Under the influence of long-continued selection in a constant direction, change may well be directional.

Another early objection to "saltations" as the material of evolution was that they were often degenerative and therefore could not be used in progressive evolution. This objection, also, has been answered by the recent changes in genetic theory. It is certainly true that many macro-mutations (though not all) are degenerative, but micro-mutations do not typically lead to degenerative change. Evolution based on genetic change may well be progressive.

Still one other early objection must be mentioned, for it also no longer has weight. Saltations are unrelated to each other in direction, and it was said that these unco-ordinated changes could not account for the immensely elaborate and detailed co-ordination of the parts in the animal body. The objection seems valid against the saltations of early genetics, but not against evolution based largely on micro-mutation. The supply of micro-mutation is sufficient to allow change in any direction favoured by selection, and simultaneous change in many organs. Co-ordination among the changes will be cared for by selection. The need for co-ordination may well make evolution slower, for much variation that might otherwise be valuable may be excluded if changes in other organs required for co-ordination are not at the same time available. But, so far as we can see, any co-ordination, however complex, may sooner or later be evolved. It is clear that our present views of genetic change give a suitable background for the evolution of co-ordination among the parts of the body.

Lastly, one difficulty may be mentioned that arose in genetic theory itself and not in correlation of the theory with the facts of palæontology and morphology. This was the contradiction between the largely dominant nature of natural genotypes and the recessiveness of the majority of macro-mutations. Though we now regard evolution as largely based on micro-mutation, we know that macro-mutations play their part in it, and it appeared that only the relatively rare dominant macro-mutations could do so. Here Fisher's theory of the evolution of dominance, if it is accepted, removes the contradiction. If it is not acceptable, we must still conclude that it is very largely only dominant macro-mutations that reach the genotype in nature. The problem is still open.

We may conclude that recent genetic work has shown that our knowledge of the genotype and of the changes that occur in it is in no way at variance with the facts of micro-evolution as we observe them. The apparent contradiction between the facts of morphology and palæontology and those of genetics has been resolved.

2. MACRO- AND MEGA-EVOLUTION

Simultaneously with these modifications of the theory of micro-evolution, there has been almost equally great alteration in our outlook on the larger evolutionary changes.

All evolution takes place on a background of micro-evolution, and in discussing macro- and mega-evolution we have chiefly to compare the effects of the same processes in long-continued action with their effects when there is less time for their action. In the long periods of palæontological time, types of change that do not appear in micro-evolution are able to become evident.

The alterations of the last thirty years in our views of the larger evolutionary changes may be summarised as follows:

Recognition of the system of allometry (p. 39) in the animal body has allowed us to understand the means by which many of the changes of adaptive radiation are brought about. It was always realised that an animal's body is adapted to life only at its own level of size, but the existence of allometric correlation between the relative size of an organ and the size of the body as a whole has only recently been made clear.

Allometry is the mechanism of many changes in the patterns of the organs as the body alters in size, but it does not account for many of the types of structural change that occur in evolution. Clear distinction between allometric change and the various kinds of aristogenesis (p. 43), which includes all changes of the organisation of the body except the allometric changes, is recent. In aristogenesis are included both alterations of the systems of pattern already present in the body, and the evolution of new pattern where no previous differentiations were present to be modified into the new pattern. It is present in all evolution, though it plays a greater part in the larger evolutionary changes. Evolutionary progress on a large scale is not possible without evolution of new pattern.

Continued study of the evolution of the life-history of animals has led to rejection of Haeckel's doctrine of recapitulation as the normal process by which the life-history evolves. Evolution of the life-history takes place by change at all its stages, and is not to any significant extent due to addition of stages at its end. Nevertheless, evolutionary change is usually greater in the adult than in earlier stages of the life-history. This is largely because the secondary effects of mutation may extend through all parts of the life-history later than the primary action, so that adult stages may be modified by mutations that act primarily on development as well as any that primarily modify the adult organisation. On the other hand, developmental stages cannot be modified by mutations that primarily affect the adult.

Realisation of the importance of pre-adaptation has made it possible to understand something of the means by which evolving animals are able to escape from a life to which they had become specialised and to pass to a different life. Study of evolutionary trends has shown that there is no need for any new evolutionary principles to explain them, and no need to postulate orthogenesis, except in so far as restriction of the supply of mutation may produce orthogenetic tendencies. Many of these trends are not evidence for orthogenesis of any kind; they result from orthoselection, long-continued selection acting continually in the same direction. By study of the rates of evolution it has been possible to interpret the great variability of its rates, and to separate a class of (bradytelic) species which evolve very slowly, probably because they are adapted to tolerate wide ranges of conditions in stable environments.

Almost everywhere the changes of macro- and mega-evolution are of kinds that we know to be produced by mutation. This is true of allometric change, of the changes in the life-history, and of all types of aristogenesis except, perhaps, the introduction of new pattern. It is only in this last type of change, the appearance in the course of evolution of novelties in the organisation of the body where there was no previous differentiation to be modified into them, that the parallel between evolutionary change and the effects of mutation is incomplete. It is

12*

possible that this gap in the parallel will be filled by further work.

At all times since the Darwinian theory was proposed, some zoologists have felt difficulty in accepting it unreservedly. Various arguments on which these difficulties have been based have been put forward from time to time. Before closing our discussions we may consider whether any of these arguments are unanswerable on our present form of the theory, and sufficiently cogent to raise doubts of the theory's validity.

We need not further consider the arguments that were valid against a theory based on the earlier conceptions of Mendelian heredity but are no longer valid. These we have just discussed (p. 342). There are now no sound objections to the belief that evolution as we observe it in nature may be based on a system of hereditary change of a kind that the modern genetic theory proposes.

Many objections have been raised against belief in natural selection as an effective agent in controlling evolutionary change.

Here an objection should be mentioned that has no real weight, although it has been raised at all times since Darwin wrote. It is said that natural selection is a destructive process, capable only of removing the inefficient, and not a process that could be responsible for any progress in the evolution of new organisation. These statements are certainly true, but the answer to them as an objection to the Darwinian theory is easy. Darwin did not look upon selection as the source of new organisation in evolution. He relied on hereditary variation for the raw material of evolution and looked upon natural selection as merely a sieve or filter to choose and preserve the favourable from among the variations. In addition, it may be pointed out that it is not true that selection is unable to produce anything new. In the selection of a population of the efficient from a mixed population of the efficient and inefficient, something new, an improved population, is produced.

Another objection sometimes raised is that the interactions of animals are not *all* competitive, and that in their interactions with the environment animals do not *always* act antagonistically to each other. It is pointed out that where there is no competition there can be no selection. This also is true enough. But it is not a requirement of the theory that selection should act continuously and in all circumstances. We saw earlier (p. 193) that not all mortality in animals is selective, and that it is enough for proof of the efficiency of selection that a significant fraction of the mortality should be. We came to the conclusion that there is enough evidence to allow us to believe that in nature a sufficient fraction is, in fact, selective, and that selection is therefore effective. It is no valid objection to the theory of natural selection to say that competition and antagonism are not universal.

There are many objections directed against more special aspects of the problems of evolution. Of these we can consider only a few.

It is often maintained that the Darwinian theory offers no explanation of the evolution of many organs in their early stages. This objection seems at first sight to apply most obviously to the evolution of complex organs, as, for example, the vertebrate eye. It is said that until the eye had reached considerable complexity it would not have been able to function as an organ of sight, and therefore would have had no selective value. This objection is based on too narrow a view of the functions that organs such as the eye have served in evolution; those who hold it fail to realise that function and structure have evolved simultaneously. In the case of visual organs we can get some idea of their early evolution from comparative study of the invertebrates ([37], ch. XVII). In their simplest forms visual organs were not organs of sight as we understand the term. Their earliest function was to appreciate only the presence or absence of light, and this could be done by a simple pigment spot. The possession of even this simple sense would undoubtedly have been of selective value, which would have led to further evolution of the organ. As the visual organ evolved greater complexity, it was able to give information of other features of the stimulation—the direction from which the light came, movement of the light source, the colour of the light, and, finally, the distribution of lighted objects in the environment by image-formation. It had then become an organ of sight in the full sense. It is by no means impossible to understand how the organ could have evolved gradually through all these stages, with structure and function evolving together and throughout under the control of selection.

Evolution of many other organs has been thought to give rise to similar difficulties, but always the difficulties arise from the unreal assumption that the organ's first rudiments served the same function as the fully evolved organ. The horns of the titanotheres, when they had reached large size, may have been used in sexual combat, and it may be said that the very small thickenings of the frontal bones, which we saw (p. 94) to have been their first rudiments, could not have been of any use as weapons of offence. That is true, but if in the early unhorned titanothere the head was used in butting an opponent—as it is in some other mammals—even a slight thickening of the frontals would have strengthened the skull and been valuable. The same argument will apply to the antlers of the stag and the horns of other ungulates. It will apply, *mutatis mutandis*, to many secondary sexual characters that are used in display. To take an example of another type, among mammals the tail is used for climbing (monkeys), to carry the young (some opposums), for swimming (whales, porpoises, etc.) and as an organ of offence or defence (glyptodonts). If we did not know the previous history of the tail, it might be said that at a small size it would not be useful for any of these purposes. It might therefore have been said that the tail could not have been evolved by natural selection. We do know the history, and that argument is not used in this case. It is realised that the tail in these various mammals has taken on new functions for which it was not originally evolved. Habits, though conservative, occasionally change in evolution, and the functions of organs change with them. We should never assume that the function of an organ has been the same throughout its evolution.

The facts of mimicry and protective resemblance are often thought to be difficult to interpret on the Darwinian theory of evolution. It is said that their evolution could not have been gradual, for imperfect resemblances would not deceive, and would therefore have no selective value. Here the solution lies not in change of function but in the nature of animal behaviour. Recent work has shown that animals are often deceived by resemblances in only one or at most a few characters of objects, even though in other characters the objects are entirely unlike.[38, 190, 261-3] Frogs may accept as food *any* small, *slowly moving* object near them; a new-born lamb will follow *any slowly receding* object, behaving towards it as it does towards its mother; a robin will act aggressively towards a patch of red feathers on a stick as it does towards another robin in its territory. Very partial resemblances, which would not deceive us, do, in fact, deceive animals. It is not hard to believe that a resemblance in one or a few characters might arise in evolution, perhaps by chance, and that more elaborate resemblances might be built up by the action of natural selection from these simple beginnings.

Lastly, we may consider the objection that pre-formation of an organ during development, that is to say its development at a stage of the life-history earlier than that at which it first functions, would not be favoured by selection, for it would have no selective value at that stage. This objection is answered when it is realised that the stages of the life-history cannot be considered separately in discussions of their evolution. Many organs cannot function until they have reached considerable complexity of organisation. Their development to this grade of complexity before functioning starts is necessary if the organ is to function later. The vertebrate heart, for example, must have become complex in structure before it can function, and, since development is gradual, its formation must start at earlier stages of the life-history. At the time when it starts to develop, the heart may have no selective value, but it is necessary for achievement of the life-history as a whole that it should develop at that time; the later stages could not be carried through if it did not. We know that development of an organ may be accelerated or retarded in time in the life-history (by heterochrony, p. 316). It is clear that acceleration of the development of the heart, so that it had reached sufficient complexity to function when its functioning was needed, would certainly have selective value, and would be evolved. These considerations are sufficient to account for pre-formation, even where—as occasionally happens—an organ is fully developed before it starts to function.

Most of these objections arise from failure in one way or

another to take a broad enough view of evolution, failure to realise that it is the whole life and activities of an animal that evolve together, and that all aspects of its evolution are interdependent. All these objections, and many others, can be answered, and, since this is so, they give no valid evidence against the truth of the present-day form of the Darwinian theory.

If the objections that can be brought against our theory of evolution fail, we must conclude that the theory is in all probability on the right lines. This does not mean that it is complete; it is by no means so. Nor would it be true to say that it is accepted by all contemporary zoologists that our present theory is in all respects sound in its outlook on the problems of evolution. It is probably healthy that this should be so, for progress results from disagreement and discussion— there is little spur to further investigation when all are agreed. Each zoologist will have his own reasons for dissatisfaction, but perhaps one of the commonest is that the theory of evolution that results from modern work is too mechanical, that, at least when dealing with the higher animals, it takes too little account of their higher functions and especially of their behaviour and powers of choice. Animals choose their environments; they modify their behaviour to some extent, and so are able to exert some control over the action of the environment upon them, and ultimately over their evolution. It seems to some zoologists that recent work treats animals far too much as if they were entirely at the mercy of the environment, that it deals with them too much as chemical and physical systems and too little as living and behaving organisms. These objections may be vague, but they are a real criticism, and indicate a direction in which future work may advance the theory. They show us some of the gaps in our theory; they do not give any good reason for discarding it. There can be no doubt that wider knowledge of animal behaviour would greatly help our interpretation of evolution.

The incompleteness of the theory is another point at which it is open to criticism. No one can look at the immensely complicated organisation of an insect or a vertebrate without doubting that our relatively simple theories can completely explain the origin of such complexity. The belief is unavoidable that there is much in evolution of which we have no knowledge. If it is the whole life and activities of an animal that evolves, our interpretation cannot be complete until we have complete knowledge of the animal's life, and we are very far from that knowledge of any animal. One feels this insufficiency very forcibly when we consider the course of evolution in the life-history. The life-history evolves at least in part by change in the organisation that controls its general course in the individual. This is most obviously true of many of the changes in the time-relations of the life-history. But we have hardly any knowledge of this control. We know that organs may cause the differentiation of neighbouring organs by evocation, and that genes may modify the progress of differentiation in the life-history by their action on enzymes. But we have no general knowledge of the organisation upon which they act, the system that causes the appearance of a set pattern in the development of each species and controls the growth of the parts so that the body keeps to the specific form. That organisation is at present outside our knowledge, and it is therefore inevitable that our theory of its evolution is incomplete. We are never able to give more than a summarised and superficial account of the phenomena of life in an animal. Evolution is a general and fundamental biological phenomenon, and our account of it is necessarily superficial. But if we are right in thinking that the modern theory of evolution gives a consistent account of the range of fact, already wide, provided by our present knowledge of many biological sciences, we may at least conclude that the theory is sound so far as it goes. However much it needs modification in the future, it is not likely that it will be shown to be wholly false.

BIBLIOGRAPHY

1. ABEL, O. (1912). *Grundzüge der Palæontologie der Wirbelthiere*, Stuttgart.
2. ALLEE, W. C. (1931). *Animal Aggregations, a Study in General Sociology*, Chicago.
3. —— (1932). *Animal Life and Social Growth*, Baltimore.
4. —— (n.d.). *The Social Life of Animals*, London.
5. ALPATOV, W. W. (1929). Quart. Rev. Biol., **4**, 1.
6. ARKELL, W. J. and MOY THOMAS, J. A. (1940). In *The New Systematics*, edtd J. S. Huxley, London.
7. ARMSTRONG, E. A. (1947). *Bird Display and Behaviour*, London.

8. BAGG, H. J., and LITTLE, C. C. (1924). Amer. J. Anat., **33**, 119.
9. BAGG, H. J. (1929). Amer. J. Anat., **43**, 167.
10. BAILEY, J. L. (1941). Amer. Nat., **75**, 213.
11. BAKER, J. R. (1928). Brit. J. exp. Biol., **6**, 56.
12. BALFOUR BROWNE, F. (1944). J. roy. micr. Soc., **63**, 55.
13. —— (1944). J. roy. micr. Soc., **64**, 68.
14. BALKASHINA, E. L. (1929). Arch. EntwMech. Org., **115**, 448.
15. BARCROFT, J. (1934). *The Architecture of Physiological Function*, Cambridge.
16. BATES, M. (1940). Ann. ent. Soc. Amer., **33**, 343.
17. BATESON, G. (1936). *Naven*, Cambridge.
18. BATHER, F. A. (1927). Quart. J. geol. Soc. Lond., **83**, lii.
19. —— (1927). C. R. 10th Intern. Congr. Zool., 95.
20. BEADLE, G. W. (1939), Ann. Rev. Physiol., **1**, 41.
21. BEECHER, C. E. (1901). *Studies in Evolution*, New York.
22. BISCHOFF, H. (1927). *Biologie der Hymenopteren*, Berlin.
23. BONNEVIE, K. (1934). J. exp. Zool., **67**, 443.
24. BOYDEN, A. E. (1943). Physiol. Zool., **15**, 109.
25. —— (1943). Amer. Nat., **77**, 234.
26. BRIDGES, C. B. (1918). J. exp. Zool., **28**, 337.
27. —— (1936). Science, **83**, 210.
28. —— (1935). J. Hered., **26**, 60.
29. —— (1938). J. Hered., **29**, 11.
30. —— and DOBZHANSKY, T. (1933). Arch. EntwMech. Org., **127**, 575.

31. BROOM, R. (1932). *The Mammal-like Reptiles of South Africa*, London.
32. BULLOUGH, W. S. (1947). Nature, **160**, 9.

33. CARR-SAUNDERS, A. M. (1936). *World Population . . .*, Oxford.
34. CARRUTHERS, R. G. (1910). Quart. J. geol. Soc. Lond., **66**, 523.
35. CARTER, G. S. (1934). J. Linn. Soc. Lond. (Zool), **39**, 147.
36. —— (1931). Biol. Rev., **6**, 1.
37. —— (1940). *A General Zoology of the Invertebrates*, London.
38. —— (1946). Sci. Prog., **34**, 547.
39. —— and BEADLE, L. C. (1930). J. Linn. Soc. Lond. (Zool.), **37**, 205.
40. CASTLE, W. E. (1929). J. exp. Zool., **53**, 421.
41. —— (1932). Science, **76**, 365.
42. —— and GREGORY, P. W. (1929). J. Morph., **48**, 81.
43. CHAPMAN, F. M. (1931). Bull. Amer. Mus. Nat. Hist., **63**, 1.
44. CHAPMAN, R. N. (1931). *Animal Ecology with special reference to Insects*, New York.
45. CLIFT, S. G., and TRUEMAN, A. E. (1939). Quart. J. geol. Soc. Lond., **85**, 77.
46. COOPER, J. OMER (1931). Nature, **127**, 237.
47. CRAMPTON, H. E. (1925). Amer. Nat., **59**, 5.
48. —— (1924). Science, **59**, 558.
49. —— (1925). Publ. Carneg. Instn. no. 228.
50. —— (1932) Publ. Carneg. Instn. no. 410.
51. CRANE, J. (1941). Zoologica, N.Y., **26**, 145.
52. CREW, F. A. E. (1925). *Animal Genetics*, Edinburgh.
53. CROMBIE, A. C. (1943). Proc. zool. Soc. Lond., A **113**, 77.
54. —— (1944). Brit. J. exp. Biol., **20**, 135.
55. —— (1945–6). Proc. roy. Soc., B **132**, 362; **133**, 76.
56. —— (1947). J. Anim. Ecol., **16**, 44.
57. CROUSE, H. V. (1939). Amer. Nat., **73**, 476.
58. CROW, J. F. (1946). Amer. Nat., **80**, 663.
59. CUÉNOT, L. (1932). *La genèse des espèces animales*, Paris.
60. CUMLEY, R. W. (1938). Genetics, **23**, 146.
61. CUSHING, J. E. (1941). Condor, **43**, 233.

62. DANSER, B. H. (1929). Genetica, **11**, 399.
63. DARLING, F. FRASER (1937). *A Herd of Red Deer*, London.
64. —— (1947). *Natural History in the Highlands and Islands*, London.
65. DARLINGTON, C. D. (1942). Nature, **149**, 66.
66. DARWIN, C. (1906). *The Origin of Species . . .*, 6th edn, London.

67. DAVENPORT, C. B. (1903). Decenn. Publ. Univ. Chicago, **10**, 57.
68. DAVIES, J. H., and TRUEMAN, A. E. (1937). Quart. J. geol. Soc. Lond., **83**, 210.
69. DE BEER, G. R. (1940). In *The New Systematics*, edtd J. S. Huxley, Oxford.
70. —— (1940). *Embryos and Ancestors*, Oxford.
71. DE VRIES, H. (1901). *Die Mutationstheorie . . .*, Leipzig.
72. DICE, L. R. (1939). Contrbns. Lab. vert. Genet. Univ. Mich., nos. 9, 12.
73. —— (1940). Amer. Nat., **74**, 212, 289.
74. DIVER, C. (1929). Nature, **124**, 183.
75. —— (1939). J. Conch., **21**, 91.
76. —— (1940). In *The New Systematics*, edtd J. S. Huxley, Oxford.
77. DOBZHANSKY, T. (1927). Z. indukt. Abstamm. VererbLehre, **43**, 350.
78. —— (1930). Z. indukt. Abstamm. VererbLehre, **54**, 427.
79. —— (1936). Biol. Rev., **11**, 364.
80. —— (1937). *Genetics and the Origin of Species*, New York.
81. —— (1937). Amer. Nat., **71**, 404.
82. —— (1937). Scientia, Bologna, p. 280.
83. —— (1939). Genetics, **24**, 391.
84. —— (1939). Proc. 8th Intern. Congr. Genet., 104.
85. —— (1939). Biol. Rev., **14**, 339.
86. —— (1940). Amer. Nat., **74**, 312.
87. —— (1944). Amer. Nat., **78**, 193.
88. —— and TAN, C. C. (1936). Z. indukt. Abstamm. VererbLehre, **72**, 88.
89. DOLLO, L. (1893). Bull. Soc. belge Géol. Pal. Hydr., **7**, 164.
90. DONCASTER, L. (1914). *The Determination of Sex*, Cambridge.
91. DUBININ, N. P., et al. (1944). Biol. Zh. Mosk., **3**, 166.

92. ELTON, C. S. (1924). Brit. J. exp. Biol., **2**, 119.
93. —— (1927). *Animal Ecology*, London.
94. —— (1930). *Animal Ecology and Evolution*, Oxford.
95. —— (1938). In *Evolution, Essays presented to E. S. Goodrich*, Oxford.
96. —— and NICHOLSON, M. (1942). J. Anim. Ecol., **11**, 215.

97. FANKHAUSER, G. (1945). Quart. Rev. Biol., **20**, 20.
98. FENTON, C. L. (1931). *Studies in the Evolution of the genus Spirifer*, Publ. Wagner Inst. Sci., **2**, 1.
99. —— (1935). Amer. Nat., **69**, 139.
100. FISHER, J. (1941). *Watching Birds*, Harmondsworth.

101. FISHER, R. A. (1928). Amer. Nat., **62**, 115.
102. —— (1928). Amer. Nat., **62**, 571.
103. —— (1929). Amer. Nat., **63**, 553.
104. —— (1930). *The Genetical Theory of Natural Selection, Oxford.*
105. —— (1931). Biol. Rev., **6**, 345.
106. —— (1941). Ann. Eug. Cambr., **11**, 53.
107. —— and FORD, E. B. (1947). Heredity, **1**, 143.
108. FLANDERS, S. E. (1946). Quart. Rev. Biol., **21**, 135.
109. FORD, E. B. (1940). In *The New Systematics*, edtd J. S. Huxley, Oxford.
110. —— (1940). Ann. Eug. Cambr., **10**, 227.
111. —— (1945). Biol. Rev., **20**, 73.
112. —— (1945). *Butterflies*, New Naturalist Series, London.
113. FORD, H. D., and E. B. (1930). Trans. ent. Soc. Lond., **78**, 345.
114. FORD, E. B., and HUXLEY, J. S. (1927). Brit. J. exp. Biol., **5**, 112.
115. FOX, H. M. (1924). Proc. Cambr. Philos. Soc. Biol. Sci., **1**, 71.
116. —— (1924). Proc. roy. Soc., B **95**, 523.
117. —— (1948). Proc. roy. Soc., B **135**, 195.
118. FRYER, J. C. F. (1913). Philos. Trans., B **204**, 227.
119. —— (1928). Trans. Intern. Congr. Entom., Ithaca, **2**, 229.

120. GALTON, F. (1869). *Hereditary Genius*, London.
121. GARSTANG, W. (1928). Quart. J. micr. Sci., **72**, 51.
122. GAUSE, G. F. (1934). Arch. Protistenk., **84**, 207.
123. —— (1934). *The Struggle for Existence*, Baltimore.
124. —— (1934). Biol. Zbl., **54**, 536.
125. —— (1947). Trans. Conn. Acad. Arts Sci., **37**, 17.
126. —— and WITT, A. (1935). Amer. Nat., **69**, 596.
127. GEMEROY, D. G. (1943). Zoologica, N.Y., **28**, 109.
128. GEORGE, W. (1947). Sci. Progr., **35**, 447.
129. GEROULD, J. H. (1923). Genetics, **8**, 495.
130. —— (1941). Genetics, **26**, 152.
131. GILMOUR, J. S. L. (1940). In *The New Systematics*, edtd J. S. Huxley, London.
132. —— and GREGOR, J. W. (1939). Nature, **144**, 333.
133. GOLDSCHMIDT, R. (1916). Amer. Nat., **50**, 705.
134. —— (1920). *Mechanismus und Physiologie der Geschlechtsbestimmungs*, Berlin.
135. —— (1920). Z. indukt. Abstamm. VererbLehre, **25**, 89.
136. —— (1924). Arch. EntwMech. Org., **101**, 92.
137. —— (1929). Biol. Zbl., **49**, 437.
138. —— (1935). Z. indukt. Abstamm. VererbLehre, **69**, 70.
139. —— (1937). Univ. Calif. Publ. Zool., **41**, 277.
140. —— (1938). *Physiological Genetics*, New York.

356   BIBLIOGRAPHY

141. GOLDSCHMIDT, R. (1939). Amer. Nat., **73**, 547.
142. —— (1940). *The Material Basis of Evolution*, New Haven and London.
143. GORDON, C. (1939). Brit. J. exp. Biol., **16**, 278.
144. GREGORY, W. K. (1936). Biol. Rev., **11**, 311.
145. —— (1936). Amer. Nat., **70**, 517.
146. —— and CONRAD, G. M. (1936). Amer. Nat., **70**, 193.
147. GRÜNEBERG, H. (1947). *Animal Genetics and Medicine*, London.
148. GUNTHER, M., and PENROSE, L. S. (1935). J. Genet., **31**, 413.

149. HAECKEL, E. (1866). *Generelle Morphologie der Organismen*, Berlin.
150. —— (1918). *The Evolution of Man*, transltd J. McCabe, London.
151. HALDANE, J. B. S. (1927). *Possible Worlds*, London.
152. —— (1927). Biol. Rev., **2**, 199.
153. —— (1930). Amer. Nat., **64**, 87.
154. —— (1932). *The Causes of Evolution*, London, Appendix.
155. —— (1933). Amer. Nat., **67**, 5.
156. —— (1941). *New Paths in Genetics*, London.
157. HARLAND, S. C. (1932). Bibliograph. Genet., **9**, 107.
158. —— (1932). J. Genet., **25**, 261.
159. —— (1933). J. Genet., **28**, 315.
160. —— (1935). J. Genet., **31**, 21.
161. —— (1936). Biol. Rev., **11**, 83.
162. HEITZ, E., and BAUER, H. (1933). Z. Zellf., **17**, 67.
163. HERSH, A. H. (1929). Amer. Nat., **63**, 378.
164. —— (1934). Amer. Nat., **68**, 537.
165. HERTER, K. (1934). Arch. Naturgesch., **3**, 313.
166. HINGSTON, R. W. G. (1933). *Animal Colour and Adornment*, London.
167. HOGBEN, L. T. (1940). In *The New Systematics*, edtd J. S. Huxley, Oxford.
168. HOWARD, H. ELIOT (1929). *An Introduction to Bird Behaviour*, Cambridge.
169. HOVANITZ, W. (1943). Biol. Bull., **85**, 44.
170. HUBBS, C. L. (1940). Amer. Nat., **74**, 198.
171. —— (1943). Ann. N.Y. Acad. Sci., **44**, 109.
172. —— and L. C. (1932). Pap. Mich. Acad. Sci., **15**, 427.
173. —— and MILLER, R. R. (1940). Pap. Mich. Acad. Sci., **28**, 343.
174. HUXLEY, J. S. (1923). J. Linn. Soc. Lond. (Zool.), **35**, 253.
175. —— (1930). Proc. 7th Intern. Congr. Ornith., 107.
176. —— (1932). *Problems of Relative Growth*, London.
177. —— (editor) (1940). *The New Systematics*, Oxford and London.

178. HUXLEY, J. S. (1942). *Evolution, the Modern Synthesis*, London.
179. HYATT, A. (1867). Mem. Boston Soc. nat. Hist., **1**, 193.
180. —— (1900). In *Textbook of Palæontology*, by K. v. Zittel, English edition.

181. IMMS, A. D. (1930). *A General Textbook of Entomology*, London.
182. —— (1931). *Recent Advances in Entomology*, London.

183. JAMESON, H. L. (1898). J. Linn. Soc. Lond. (Zool.), **26**, 465.
184. JOHANNSEN, W. (1903). *Über Erblichkeit in Populationen und in Reinen Linien*, Jena.

185. KERR, J. GRAHAM (1926). *Evolution*, London.
186. KOSTITZIN, V. A. (1937). *Mathematical Biology*, London.
187. KRAMER, G. and MERTENS, R. (1938). Arch. Naturgesch., **7**, 189.
188. KÜHN, A., and HENKE, K. (1936). Abh. Ges. Wiss. Göttingen, **15**, 1.

189. LACK, D. (1940). British Birds, **34**, 80.
190. —— (1943). *The Life of the Robin*, London.
191. —— (1946). J. Anim. Ecol., **15**, 123.
192. —— (1947). *Darwin's Finches*, Cambridge.
193. LEVIT, S. G. (1936). J. Genet., **33**, 411.
194. L'HERITIER, P., and TEISSIER, G. (1937). C. R. Soc. Biol. Paris, **124**, 880.
195. LITTLE, C. C., and BAGG, H. J. (1924). J. exp. Zool., **41**, 45.
196. LITTLE, C. C., and MCPHETERS, B. W. (1932). Genetics, **17**, 674.
197. LOEB, L. (1945). *The Biological Basis of Individuality*, Springfield, Ill.
198. LOEWY, A. (1903). Ergebn. Physiol., **2**, 130.
199. LOTKA, A. J. (1932). J. Wash. Acad. Sci., **22**, 461.
200. LULL, R. S. (1929). *Organic Evolution*, New York.
201. LUMER, H., ANDERSON, B. G., and HERSH, A. H. (1942). Amer. Nat., **76**, 364.
202. LUTZ, B. (1948). Evolution, **2**, 29.

203. MACKENZIE, K., and MULLER, H. J. (1940). Proc. roy. Soc., B **129**, 491.
204. MATHER, K. (1941). J. Genet., **41**, 159.
205. —— (1943). J. Genet., **43**, 309.
206. —— (1943). Biol. Rev., **18**, 32.
207. —— and DOBZHANSKY, T. (1939). Amer. Nat., **73**, 5.
208. MAYR, E. (1940). Amer. Nat., **74**, 249.

209. MAYR, E. (1942). *Systematics and the Origin of Species,* New York.

201. MEISE, W. (1928). J. Orn., **76**, 1.

211. MILLER, A. H. (1942). Amer. Nat., **76**, 25.

212. —— (1947). Evolution, **1**, 186.

213. MOHR, O. L. (1932). Proc. 6th Intern. Congr. Genet., **1**, 190.

214. MOLONY, H. J. C. (1937). *Evolution out of doors,* London.

215. MORGAN, T. H. (1911). Science, **34**, 384.

216. —— (1924). Sci. Monthly, **18**, 273.

217. MULLER, H. J. (1918). Genetics, **3**, 422.

218. —— (1928). Genetics, **13**, 279.

219. —— (1939). Biol. Rev., **14**, 261.

220. —— (1940). In *The New Systematics,* edtd J. S. Huxley, Oxford.

221. —— and MOTT SMITH, L. M. (1930). Proc. nat. Acad. Sci. Wash., **16**, 277.

222. MULLER, H. J., PROKOFIEVA, A., and RUFFEL, D. (1935). Nature, **135**, 253.

223. MULLER, H. J., et al. (1935). Amer. Nat., **69**, 72.

224. NEEDHAM, J. (1938). Biol. Rev., **13**, 225.

225. —— (1942). *Biochemistry and Morphogenesis,* Cambridge.

226. NELSON, J. A., STURTEVANT, A. H., and LINEBURG, B. (1924). Bull. U. S. Dept. Agric., no. 1222.

227. NICHOLSON, A. J., and BAILEY, V. A. (1935). Proc. zool. Soc. Lond., p. 551.

228. NOBLE, G. K., and JAECKLE, M. E. (1928). J. Morph., **45**, 259.

229. NOMURA, E. (1926). Sci. Rep. Tohoku Univ., **2**, 63.

230. NOPCSA, F. (1923). Proc. zool. Soc. Lond., p. 1045.

231. NORMAN, J. R. (1938). *A History of Fishes,* London.

232. OCHS, G. (1927). Koleopt. Rdsch., **13**, 34.

233. ONSLOW, H. (1917). Proc. roy. Soc., B **89**, 36.

234. OSBORN, H. F. (1929). *Titanotheres of Ancient Wyoming, Dakota and Nebraska,* U.S. Dept. Int. Geol. Surv. Monogr., no. 55.

235. —— (1934). Amer. Nat., **68**, 193.

236. PAINTER, T. S., and MULLER, H. J. (1929). J. Hered., **20**, 287.

237. PAINTER, T. S. (1934). Genetics, **19**, 175.

238. —— (1935). Genetics, **20**, 301.

239. PLAGENS, G. M. (1933). J. Morph., **55**, 151.

240. PLUNKETT, C. R. (1933). Amer. Nat., **67**, 84.

241. POPHAM, E. J. (1941). Proc. zool. Soc. Lond., **111A**, 135.

242. POPHAM, E. J. (1943). Proc. zool. Soc. Lond., **112A**, 105.
243. —— (1944). Proc. zool. Soc. Lond., **114A**, 74.
244. —— (1948). Proc. zool. Soc. Lond., **117**, 768.
245. POULTON, E. B. (1903). Proc. roy. ent. Soc. Lond., lxxvii.
246. PUNNETT, R. C. (1911). *Mendelism*, London and New York.

247. QUAYLE, H. J. (1938). Hilgardia, **11**, 183.

248. RAJEWSKY, B. N., and TIMOFÉEFF-RESSOVSKY, N. W. (1939). Z. indukt. Abstamm. VererbLehre, **77**, 488.
249. RAPAPORT, J. A. (1947). Amer. Nat., **81**, 30.
250. RAYMOND, P. E. (1939). *Prehistoric Life*, Harvard and Oxford.
251. REEVE, E. C., and MURRAY, P. D. F. (1942). Nature, **150**, 402.
252. REGAN, C. TATE (1925). Rep. Brit. Ass. Adv. Sci., 75.
253. RENSCH, B. (1933). Verh. dtsch. zool. Ges., p. 19.
254. —— (1934). *Kurze Anweisung für zool.-syst. Studien*, Leipzig.
255. ROBB, R. C. (1935). J. Genet., **31**, 39.
256. ROBSON, G. C., and RICHARDS, O. W. (1936). *The Variation of Animals in Nature*, London.
257. ROHM, R. B. (1947). Amer. Nat., **81**, 5.
258. ROOT, R. W. (1931). Biol. Bull., **61**, 427.
259. ROWE, A. W. (1899). Quart. J. geol. Soc. Lond., **55**, 494.
260. RUBTZOV, I. A. (1935). Bull. ent. Res., **26**, 499.
261. RUSSELL, E. S. (1916). *Form and Function*, London.
262. —— (1940–1). Proc. Linn. Soc. Lond., p. 250.
263 —— (1941–2). Proc. Linn. Soc Lond., p. 195.
264. —— (1942–3). Proc. Linn. Soc. Lond., p. 186.

265. SALT, G., et al. (1948). J. Anim. Ecol., **17**, 139.
266. SANDERSON, I. T. (1938). *Living Treasure*, London.
267. SCHULTZ, J. (1929). Genetics, **14**, 366.
268. SCHWANWITSCH, B. N. (1928). Z. Morph. Ökol. Tiere, **10**, 433.
269. —— (1929). Z. Morph. Ökol. Tiere, **14**, 36.
270. SCOTT, T. and A. (1912–3). *British Parasitic Copepoda*, London.
271. SCOTT, W. B. (1937). *A History of the Land Mammals in the Western Hemisphere*, New York.
272. SEGERSTRÅLE, S. G. (1947). J. mar. biol. Assn., U.K., **27**, 219.
273. SHULL, A. F. (1936). *Evolution*, New York and London.
274. SIMPSON, G. G. (1937). Bull. geol. Soc. Amer., **48**, 303.
275. —— (1944). *Tempo and Mode in Evolution*, New York.
276. SMITH, G. (1906). Fauna u. Flora des Golfes v. Neapel, no. 29.
277. SMITH, W. WRIGHT (1947). Presid. Address, R. S. Edin., in Year Book of the Society.
278. SPATH, L. F. (1933). Biol. Rev., **8**, 418.

279. SPENCER, W. P. Quoted by H. J. Muller in *The New Systematics*, edtd J. S. Huxley, 1940.
280. —— (1935). Amer. Nat., **69**, 223.
281. SPOONER, G. M. (1941). J. mar. biol. Assn., U.K., **24**, 444.
282. —— (1947). J. mar. biol. Assn., U.K., **27**, 1.
283. STALKER, H. D. (1942). Genetics, **27**, 238.
284. STERN, C. (1929, 31). Biol. Zbl., **49**, 261, **51**, 547.
285. —— (1937). Amer. Nat., **70**, 123.
286. STRONG, L. C. (1947). Amer. Nat., **81**, 50.
287. STURTEVANT, A. H. (1923). Science, **58**, 269.
288. —— (1929). Publ. Carneg. Instn. (Zool.), no. 399.
289. —— (1938). Quart. Rev. Biol., **13**, 333.
290. —— and MATHER, K. (1938). Amer. Nat., **72**, 447.
291. —— and NOVITZKI, E. (1941). Proc. nat. Acad. Sci. Wash., **27**, 392.
292. SUFFERT, F. (1929). Arch. EntwMech., **120**, 299.
293. SUMNER, F. B. (1934). Amer. Nat., **68**, 137.
294. SUOMALAINEN, E. J. (1940). Hereditas, **26**, 51.
295. SWINNERTON, H. H. (1932). Biol. Rev., **7**, 321.
296. —— (1939). Quart. J. geol. Soc. Lond., **95**, xxxiii.
297. —— (1940). Quart. J. geol. Soc. Lond., **96**, lxxvii.
298. SWINTON, W. E. (1940). *The Dinosaurs*, London.

299. TAN, C. C., and LI, J. C. (1934). Amer. Nat., **68**, 252.
300. THOMPSON, D'A. W. (1942). *Growth and Form*, Cambridge.
301. THORPE, W. H. (1930). Biol. Rev., **5**, 177.
302. —— (1940). In *The New Systematics*, edtd J. S. Huxley, London.
303. TICEHURST, C. B. (1938). *A Systematic Review of the Genus Phylloscopus*, British Museum, London.
304. TIMOFÉEFF-RESSOVSKY, N. W. (1934). Z. indukt. Abstamm. VererbLehre, **66**, 319.
305. —— (1937). *Experimentelle Mutationsforschung in der Vererbungslehre*, Dresden u. Leipzig.
306. —— (1940). In *The New Systematics*, edtd J. S. Huxley, London.
307. TOWER, W. L. (1910). Biol. Bull., **18**, 285.
308. TRUEMAN, A. E. (1922). Geol. Mag. Lond., **59**, 258.
309. —— (1924). Geol. Mag. Lond., **61**, 360.
310. —— (1930). Biol. Rev., **5**, 296.

311. VALENTINE, J. M. (1943). J. Wash. Acad. Sci., **33**, 353.
312. VANDEL, A. (1927). C. R. Soc. Biol. Paris, **97**, 106.
313. VAVILOV, N. I. (1922). J. Genet., **12**, 47.

314. VAVILOV, N. I. (1940). In *The New Systematics*, edtd J. S. Huxley, London.
315. VILLEE, C. A. (1942). Amer. Nat., **76**, 494.
316. VOLTERRA, V. (1926). Mem. Accad. Nuovi Lincei, **2**, 31.

317. WAAGEN, W. (1868). Geogr. Palæont. Beitr., **2**, 179.
318. WADDINGTON, C. H. (1935). *How Animals Develop*, London.
319. —— (1939). *An Introduction to Modern Genetics*, London.
320. —— (1939). Growth, suppl. **1**, 37.
321. WATSON, D. M. S. (1940). Trans. roy. Soc. Edinb., **60**, 195.
322. WELCH, D. A. A. (1938). Bull. Bishop Mus. Honolulu, no. 152.
323. WHITE, M. J. D. (1945). *Animal Cytology and Evolution*, Cambridge.
324. —— (1946). Amer. Nat., **80**, 610.
325. WHITING, P. W. (1945). Quart. Rev. Biol., **20**, 231.
326. WIGGLESWORTH, V. B. (1939). *The Principles of Insect Physiology*, London.
327. WILLIAMS, C. B. (1930). *The Migrations of Butterflies*, Edinburgh.
328. WILLMER, E. N. (1934). Brit. J. exp. Biol., **11**, 283.
329. WOOD, T. B., and BANTA, A. M. (1926). Anat. Rec., **34**, 135.
330. WORTHINGTON, E. B. (1935). Int. Rev. Hydrobiol., **35**, 304.
331. —— (1940). In *The New Systematics*, edtd J. S. Huxley, London.
332. WRIGHT, S. (1929). Amer. Nat., **63**, 274, 556.
333. —— (1931). Genetics, **16**, 97.
334. —— (1934). Amer. Nat., **68**, 24.
335. —— (1940). Amer. Nat., **74**, 232.
336. —— (1940). In *The New Systematics*, edtd J. S. Huxley, London.
337. —— (1941). Physiol. Rev., **21**, 487.
338. —— (1943). Genetics, **28**, 114.

339. ZEUNER, F. (1943). Trans. zool. Soc. Lond., **25**, 107.
340. —— (1946). *Dating the Past*, London.

INDEX